The Elements Rage

The Elements Rage

Frank W. Lane

Chilton Books
A Division of Chilton Company
Publishers
Philadelphia and New York

To Valerie Jiles
A token of friendship

by the same author

Animal Wonder World
(1951)

Animal Wonderland
(1962)

Kingdom of the Octopus
(1960)

Nature Parade
(1954)

Frank Lane's name is synonymous with exciting reading. Born in London in 1908, Mr. Lane has written books which are now classics in eight languages. He has contributed hundreds of articles to both American and foreign magazines and is the author of *Kingdom of the Octopus, Nature Parade,* and *Animal Wonder World*. Well known as a photographer as well, he lives with his wife and three children in Middlesex, England.

Preface

This is a book about extreme natural violence. No one could write such a book if he recorded only his own experiences. He would be dead long before he had witnessed a minute fraction of the incidents recorded here.

I have therefore used the writings of a multitude of people, both scientists and laymen, and I also have had an extensive correspondence with experts in more than a dozen countries. Most of these were busy professional scientists, yet to very few did I appeal in vain. I have also used the work of numerous photographers who, sometimes at the risk of their lives, have obtained permanent records of Nature's violence and the effects left on the earth.

To these scientists, authors and photographers I am deeply indebted; they alone made this book possible.

Unlike the last book I wrote,[1] which dealt with one class of one phylum of the animal kingdom, this book ranges over the sciences of meteorology, astronomy and geology, and has references to history, physics, and mathematics. Much of the subject matter is highly technical. I have had to take the scientist's technicalities—and sometimes his jargon—and translate them into the language of Everyman.

Coping with technicalities has been the hardest part of my task, especially as there is considerable disagreement among experts. The popularizer who has to steer his way between contending specialists realizes that it is *impossible* to please everyone. I considerably revised the draft of one chapter as the result of technical criticism, only to be told by a later reader that the revision was wrong and that the original was right!

The specialist may feel that I have sometimes oversimplified. I have tried to give a *general* picture, and I believe too many qualifications take all the life out of writing. To quote that great popularizer in another field, Sir Winston Churchill: "The reserve of modern assertions is sometimes

---

[1] *Kingdom of the Octopus* (Sheridan House, New York, 1960).

pushed to extremes, in which the fear of being contradicted leads the writer to strip himself of almost all sense and meaning."[2]

This book is not a detailed treatise and much of it concerns facts and observations which, although often dismissed by specialists as irrelevancies, are of considerable general interest. I hope this material will help to sugar the pill of the inevitable technicalities.

I have deliberately refrained from much theorizing. Sometimes there is no generally accepted theory to account for phenomena—as for the origin of tornadoes—sometimes the theories are too involved and recondite for the scope of a popular book. Readers wanting more information should consult the technical works and papers listed in the bibliography.

Authorities and references are given for virtually every statement, except for accepted facts and some general remarks, and thus readers can check the provenance of quotations, and so on, for themselves. Dates are given after names only when it is necessary to distinguish between different publications of the same author. All dates are given in the bibliography.

Some details about the book—so far published in six countries—may be of interest. It was first published in 1945, when men were so engrossed with their own destruction that they had little time for the vast impersonal forces of Nature. Since then man has achieved the extreme violence of the H-bomb and discovered the extreme natural violence of the quasars. Both are typical of the immense advances which have been made in science during the past quarter of a century, not least in the subjects treated of in this book. The time seemed opportune, therefore, for a new edition, revised, doubled in length, and with a new chapter on floods.

Research, writing and checking have been spread over some six years —three for the first edition, three for this new edition. During that time I exchanged over 3,000 letters with people in more than 20 countries. Altogether more than 80 people have read the manuscript in whole or in part.

In fairness to the host of helpers who have given so generously of their time and knowledge, I must stress that ultimate responsibility for everything in this book is mine. I have not accepted every suggestion and criticism, however, and some material has been added after the critical readings.

F.W.L.

Pinner, Middlesex, England

---

[2] A History of the English-Speaking Peoples (Bantam Books, New York, 1963).

Acknowledgments

The bibliography of about a thousand entries indicates the extent of my indebtedness to published sources. In addition, many people have helped by criticism and comment. Each chapter has been read by at least three experts in the subject, and also by a dozen or so other scientists and laymen. I have also had help with specialized aspects—a man may be strong on seismology, but weak on geography.

To list everybody who has helped would be tedious, but it would be churlish not to thank publicly any of those who have given so generously of their time and knowledge. I particularly wish to thank the following:

Professor Louis J. Battan (Tornadoes and Waterspouts); Professor K. Berger (Lightning); Miss Cicely M. Botley (Hail, Lightning, and Meteoroids); Dr. Francis K. Davis (all chapters); Dr. Marcel de Quervain (Avalanches); Dr. Gordon E. Dunn (Hurricanes); Professor Tetsuya Fujita (Tornadoes and Waterspouts); Professor Angelos G. Galanopoulos (Earthquakes and Volcanoes); Dr. John Glasspoole (all meteorological chapters); Dr. R. H. Golde (Lightning); Dr. William Gray (Hurricanes); Mr. E. L. Hawke (all meteorological chapters); Mr. Peter Haynes (physics references); Dr. Max H. Hey (Meteoroids); Dr. D. C. House (Hail, Tornadoes, and Waterspouts); Dr. C. L. Jordan (Hurricanes and Waterspouts); Dr. T. R. Kaiser (Meteoroids); Professor Leonard B. Loeb (Lightning); Dr. David M. Ludlum (Hurricanes); Dr. William C. Macklin (Hail); Professor D. J. Malan (Lightning); Dr. Brian Mason (Meteoroids); Mr. Patrick Moore (Meteoroids); Dr. Syun'itiro Omote (Earthquakes); Dr. E. R. Oxburgh (Earthquakes and Volcanoes); Mr. J. L. Paulhus (Floods); Dr. Herbert Riehl (Hurricanes); Professor Leon E. Salanave (Lightning); Dr. Koichiro Takahashi (Hurricanes); Professor Haroun Tazieff (Volcanoes); Dr. Sigurdur Thorarinsson (Volcanoes); Professor Gilbert E. White (Floods); Mr. Peter G. Wood (geographical references). Dr. John Harpum read all the chapters and also compiled the Energy Scale in Appendix C. Dr. Francis Davis, of Philadelphia, also read the entire manuscript and was of considerable assistance.

[xi]

I thank the editors of the *National Geographic* and *Flying Review International* for permission to quote from articles they published. I also thank Mr. T. Ifor Rees and the *Geographical Magazine,* London, for permission to quote from an article by him, and the *Reader's Digest* for an article by Colin Fletcher which appeared in the British edition of the *Reader's Digest* for July 1963, and Professor B. J. Mason for an extract from a broadcast talk reprinted in *The Listener.*

I also wish to thank the following publishers and authors for permission to quote from the books mentioned:

George Allen & Unwin, Ltd., London, *Great Earthquakes* by Charles Davidson

Atlantic—Little, Brown & Company, Boston. From *History of U.S. Naval Operations in World War II,* Volume XIII, *The Liberation of the Philippines,* by Samuel Eliot Morison. Copyright, (c), 1959 by Samuel Eliot Morison.

General Electric Company (USA) *The Story of Lightning* by Karl B. McEachron

Harvard University Press, Cambridge, Mass., *Between the Planets* by Fletcher G. Watson

Her Majesty's Stationery Office, London, *Observer's Handbook*

Holt, Rinehart & Winston Inc., New York, *The Destruction of Dresden* by David Irving

J. B. Lippincott Company, Philadelphia, *Johnstown, The Day The Dam Broke* by Richard O'Connor

W. W. Norton & Co., Inc., New York, *Ur of the Chaldees* by Sir Leonard Woolley

Oklahoma Press, Norman, Oklahoma, *Tornadoes of the United States* and *Hailstorms of the United States* by Snowden D. Flora

Princeton University Press, Princeton, New Jersey, *Earthquakes* by Nicholas H. Heck

Raleigh Press, Exmouth, *Lynmouth Flood Disaster* by E. R. Delderfield.

Mrs. J. Rasmussen (Mrs. J. Kingdon-Ward) and A. D. Peters & Co., *My Hill So Strong* by Mrs. J. Kingdon-Ward

The Williams and Wilkins Co., Baltimore, *Meteors* by Charles P. Olivier

The result of all the help I have received can be seen in the bibliography: so far as I know, the most extensive on natural violence in any general book so far published. For each subject I have also given references to collected bibliographies. The onerous task of setting out titles and other publishing details in correct form has been done by Mr. Ronald Hassell,

F.L.A.

An author is often so immersed in his subject matter that he is blind to literary and other faults which are obvious to his readers. The best way to overcome this occupational hazard is to ask a few friendly critics to act as "diabolizers," as Sir Edward Marsh called those whose common-sense criticisms make authors' manuscripts more readable. He diabolized for such eminent craftsmen as Sir Winston Churchill, Sir Harold Nicolson, and Mr. Somerset Maugham. Those who have diabolized for me are Dr. Gerald Curzon, Mr. Peter Haynes, and Mrs. Cecily Morrison. Despite all the attention my work received, my publishers detected some inaccuracies.

To my secretary, Mrs. Kathleen Dennis, I owe much. She has typed over 1,000 letters; typed the manuscript and then retyped—and sometimes re-retyped—many pages; and assisted in choosing the 70 photographs used in this book from over 600 obtained from many sources throughout the world. Her cheerfulness and enthusiasm have helped to lighten a long and arduous task.

Finally, I desire to thank my wife, Barbara. Authors, especially when in the throes of composition, are not the easiest people to live with. In addition to coping with my vagaries, she has borne more than her fair share of family responsibilities, thus freeing me to spend more time on this book.

I have had to consult a large number of technical books and journals, many of which are held only in specialist libraries. In particular I desire to mention the Library of the Royal Meteorological Society, of which I am a Fellow, with appreciation of the assistance given by Mr. R. S. Read. I have also made use of the vast resources of the British Museum Library.

Like many other British authors, I owe much to the magnificent service of the public library system. The counter of Ruislip Library—with its pleasant and helpful staff—has proved the open sesame to the 75 million volumes which line the shelves of our public libraries; the books held in many private and university libraries; and to the runs of technical journals held in the National Lending Library for Science and Technology. During the years I have been working on this book I have received scores of volumes and journals—often on extended loan. Once, when a volume could not be traced in any British library, it was obtained for me from Moscow.

Contents

Illustrations

The Elements Rage

chapter 1

Hurricanes ⟩⟩

Wind is air in motion. In any study of wind, therefore, it is desirable to have a clear idea of what air is. It is a mixture of gases. At sea level perfectly dry air consists of about 78 per cent nitrogen, 21 per cent oxygen, 0.9 per cent argon, and minute quantities of several other gases. It is slightly sticky, with a tendency to adhere to solid bodies.

Air is surprisingly heavy, a cubic yard of it—a large bathtubful—weighs two pounds. The air in a tank 30 × 25 × 20 feet (15,000 cubic feet—about the size of a six-room house) weighs about half a ton. And we live on the floor of an immense ocean of air, vastly greater in volume than all the seas of the world.

The first tenuous beginnings of the atmosphere are at least 500 miles above the earth. But 75 per cent of the air is within about seven miles of the earth (the troposphere). The total weight of the earth's atmosphere is estimated to be 5,600 trillion tons, equal to a mass of granite roughly 1,250 miles long, 1,000 miles wide and 1 mile thick. So there is about a *ton* of air on every square foot of earth's 197 million square miles. This means that the average man has above his head about half a ton of air every moment of his life, and when he lies down there is about five tons of it above his body. *That* is atmospheric pressure. It is not felt because the air and fluids inside the body press outward with the same force. In view of such facts it is somewhat misleading to say "as light as air." It is the very heaviness of air which accounts for the tremendous force it exerts when it is moving at high speed.

The primary force in the circulation of the air, and therefore in the manufacture of wind, is the sun. Roughly, the air is heated in the tropics, rises and flows toward the polar regions, eventually falling toward the earth. It then flows back to the tropics. But the rotation of the earth and other influences are constantly at work, and it is these which occasionally cause millions of tons of air to sweep wildly across the face of the earth.

Wind speed varies with height above ground: in Britain the standard exposure for an anemometer is at a height of 33 feet in an open situation. This is called the effective height. It is estimated that a wind which has a

[1]

speed of 40 m.p.h. at 33 feet will blow at 50 m.p.h. at 100 feet, but at only 30 m.p.h. at 6 feet above the ground.

Meteorologists have evolved several scales for indicating wind speed. The most widely used is the Beaufort scale, invented by Admiral Sir Francis Beaufort in 1805. It was designed to help mariners in the handling of ships and rigging sail. In the original table no reference was made to actual speeds; the British Meteorological Office added these in 1906. Modifications and additions—from force 11 onwards—were made in 1944. There are several versions of the scale—that given in the British *Observer's Handbook* (1962), with modifications later made by the Meteorological Office, is given in Appendix A.

The scale defines any wind which exceeds 72 m.p.h. as a hurricane-force wind, "that which no canvas could withstand" according to Beaufort.[1] Actually, there are a number of winds exceeding 72 m.p.h. which do not occur in hurricanes. Some of the most famous of these are in Europe and occur when the wind sweeps down through breaks in mountain ranges— the föhn, the mistral, and the bora. The air in these winds rarely exceeds 100 m.p.h., although gusts sometimes reach about 125 m.p.h. But although they cause damage it is not as bad as that of hurricanes (see W. Undt, G. Band, and Friedrich Defant).

A hurricane is a special type of windstorm, the most destructive of all. Although not so violent as a tornado, hurricanes cover a much wider area and last much longer—some cover half a million square miles and last three weeks. The total destruction is therefore greater. Incidentally, a hurricane sometimes generates tornadoes on the fringes of its path; they occurred with hurricanes Cleo, Dora, and Hilda in 1964. Lightning frequently occurs also.

The word *hurricane*[2] is apparently derived from the Spanish *huracan,* which, in turn, is thought to have originated from the Caribbean Indian word for "big wind." The same wind is also called typhoon and cyclone (mostly in Asia), tropical cyclone, baguio (Philippines), and willy-willy (Australia). There are no records of fully developed hurricanes in the South Atlantic or Southeast Pacific.

Christopher Columbus is generally regarded as the first European to encounter a hurricane. This is not so. The storm off the Azores when he was returning from his first voyage is not now regarded as a hurricane (Charles F. Brooks). But in June 1494, during his second voyage, two ships were left in harbor at Isabella, Santo Domingo (now the Dominican Republic), while Columbus was sailing south of Cuba. A hurricane swept down and it appears that these two ships either sank or were driven ashore. Columbus

---

[1] In the United States a hurricane-force wind is defined as one equal to or greater than 73 m.p.h.

[2] There are some 40 variant spellings, including harrycain, jimmycane, hurleblast, and furicano.

Wind and wave batter Miami Beach, Florida, during a hurricane in September, 1947.   *American Red Cross*

himself suffered his first hurricane at Isabella during October 1495. There were at least seven ships in the harbor, but only Columbus's *Niña* survived.

The above information was given to me by José Carlos Millás, who has made a special study of early West Indian hurricanes. He adds: "The first description of a hurricane by one who suffered it is found in the *Naufragios de Alvar Nuñez Cabeza de Vaca*, Zamora, Spain, 1542. I have translated his description in my second Report. Hurricane of 1527, October 30–31 (Gregorian calendar), at Trinidad, Cuba."

Since the end of the Second World War, and particularly after the devastating hurricanes of 1954 and 1955, more intensive study has been devoted to hurricanes than to any other problem in American meteorology. In 1956 the National Hurricane Research Project was set up and has been responsible for an immense amount of detailed investigation into these awesome storms.

Such great interest is understandable. Hurricanes have caused more damage in the United States than any other type of natural catastrophe. In the first sixty years of this century they took 17,000 American lives and caused property damage of five thousand million dollars. And there is the statistical probability that about once every 12 years there will be a hurricane which, because of its violence, size and the regions it strikes, will take 100 lives and do damage of a thousand million dollars. In other lands the loss of life is usually much greater. The frequency of hurricanes is, on the average, eight a year in the Atlantic, twenty-eight in the Pacific. The main areas which spawn Atlantic hurricanes are the Gulf of Mexico, the Caribbean, and the Southwest Atlantic.

Hurricanes form over warm ocean waters (generally when the sea temperature is 80° F. or above) within about 5 to 30 degrees north and south of the Equator. Somehow thousands of millions of tons of warm moist air rise and the Coriolis force (deflecting effect of the earth's rotation —1,000 m.p.h. at the Equator) makes the whole mass whirl. At the Equator itself there is insufficient deflection, hence hurricanes do not form there. In the Northern Hemisphere the winds in a hurricane always revolve in a counterclockwise direction; in the Southern Hemisphere they rotate clockwise. This is because the Coriolis force acts to the right of the direction of motion of winds in the north; to the left in the south.

What starts the hurricane-forming process? Even today, with all the intensive research, there is no generally accepted answer. If there were it would be a great aid to forecasting, and possibly to hurricane control. Virtually every day the general weather situation is favorable for a hurricane somewhere in the tropics yet—fortunately—only a few form each year. And in 1914 there was not one Atlantic hurricane. It is obvious, therefore, that there is a rare and elusive factor (or factors) which fires the meteorological engine to produce one of these storms.

William Gray, an American authority on hurricanes, tells me:

A multitude of meteorological variables interact together to determine the degree to which the broader-scale (≈ 1,000 miles) atmosphere can force and maintain the necessary water vapor convergence to produce a hurricane. A less favorable climatology (*i.e.,* early summer, cooler ocean temperatures, etc.) will place a more stringent requirement of larger mass convergence. Given a favorable climatology, the crux of the problem rests with understanding precisely how the meteorological parameters combine to force a convergence of water vapor in a restricted area. At the present time, these conditions are not clearly understood. Much speculation and confusion has arisen as to which meteorological parameters are most important, etc.[3]

Hurricane formation theory is a technical subject and can best be studied in the works of such specialists as Herbert Riehl (1954) and Dunn and Miller.

The course of a hurricane is influenced by neighboring areas of pressure; high pressure acting as a barrier. Atlantic hurricanes generally travel in a northwesterly direction.

True hurricanes never form in European waters. The reasons appear to be the lower moisture content of the atmosphere, the lower temperature of the sea surface, and the stronger winds of the middle latitudes. Despite these considerations, however, Tor Bergeron says: "Disturbances sometimes occur showing such a rare intensity and small horizontal extent that they may be regarded as a kind of extra-tropical hurricane." (See p. 11.)

What fuels the vast energies of a hurricane? As the warm moist air rises, it expands against the reduced pressures aloft. Moisture condenses from the rising air, a process which releases heat into the surrounding atmosphere. Dunn and Miller say:

> Essentially the hurricane is a heat engine, which implies the existence of a heat source and a cold source. The interior of a hurricane is warmer than its environment. This warm core of the hurricane is the heat source. Air flows into the storm at low levels (moving from lower to higher temperatures) and ascends from near the surface of the ocean to the upper atmosphere, where it is removed from the region of the cyclone [*i.e.* hurricane]. It then mixes with the surrounding atmosphere and gradually sinks. In this type of circulation, ascent takes place at higher temperatures than does descent. This results in the production of kinetic energy, *i.e.,* wind. *This transformation of heat to kinetic energy can take place only when temperatures increase toward the cyclone center.*

The movement of hurricanes over the earth's surface is erratic; they have even been known to make a complete loop. Most Atlantic hurricanes follow curving routes from southeast to west or northwest. If they reach the areas of prevailing westerly winds they recurve northward, occasionally hitting the eastern seaboard of the United States on the turn. New England has experienced at least fourteen severe hurricanes during the past 350 years. Incidentally, California has occasionally been hit by a Pacific hurri-

---

[3] A parameter is a quantity which is constant in a particular situation, but which varies in different situations.

cane. The last, in September 1939, cost 45 lives and caused damage of about two million dollars, mainly in Los Angeles and Santa Barbara.

The heat released in a large hurricane of some 30,000 cubic miles is equivalent to that from a conflagration continuously burning two or more million tons of coal. In one day a large hurricane releases as much energy as a 13,000 megaton nuclear bomb. Some hurricanes take a week to reach such intensity, others mature in a day or so. And during this time another may be at full blast a thousand miles away.

The rate at which a hurricane moves varies considerably, depending on conditions and area; sometimes one remains almost stationary. The average speed of movement for an Atlantic hurricane is about 12 m.p.h., although speeds less than half this have been recorded. The speed usually increases when the hurricane moves northward out of tropical waters. The famous hurricane of September 1938 traveled through New England at about a mile a minute.

The average life of an Atlantic hurricane is about nine days, during which it travels some 3,000 miles. Some, however, last three weeks and travel 10,000 miles. The great San Ciriaco hurricane of 1899 is believed to have lasted from about August 3 to September 7. Beginning in the Cape Verde region it passed over Puerto Rico and the Bahamas, was observed off Cape Hatteras, and finally died near the Azores.

On land one of the first signs of an approaching hurricane is the storm swell. Far out at sea the winds furrow the ocean into giant windrows. Traveling at 30 m.p.h. or more, these waves spread out and traverse great distances, carrying their warning of impending disaster to mariner and shoreman alike. Sometimes the storm swell breaks upon the shore 400 or 500 miles ahead of the hurricane.

These swells have a slower beat than ordinary waves: roughly four to the minute instead of seven or more. They pound against the shore with a roar that is sometimes heard for several miles inland. In the New England hurricane of September 1938, the trembling of the earth as the seas fell on the shore was recorded on seismographs in Alaska, 3,000 miles away. So, when slow heavy waves start crashing on the beach—'ware hurricane!

The shape of a hurricane is like a gigantic phonograph record, or a monstrous mobile doughnut with a small center. The winds spiral several miles high, and often cover a circle 500 miles or more in diameter, although hurricane-force winds do not occur over the whole of the area. The great Atlantic hurricane of September 1944 was some 800 miles wide, but the fiercest winds occurred within an area only some 200 miles in diameter. But the outer, gale-force winds of hurricanes cause considerable damage. The famous Labor Day storm of 1935 had fierce winds in an area only some 40 miles in diameter, but it was one of the most violent hurricanes on record, killing 408 people in Florida.

A hurricane generally begins to break up when it passes over land, although it may still cause considerable damage for hundreds of miles before it finally disperses. Over the sea interaction between atmosphere and water reheats the air which has been cooled by the falling rain. But such reheating —which recharges the hurricane—cannot take place when it moves over land. This is why, with its fuel supply cut, a hurricane generally dies over land.

Hurricane Hazel of October 1954 swept with undiminished fury up the eastern part of the United States, leaving an 800-mile trail of destruction from North Carolina to Canada. Unusual meteorological conditions over land were the cause—"a major convulsion in the broad-scale circulation pattern" (Dunn and Miller). But some meteorologists consider that Hazel was not a true hurricane in its later stages.

Confusion is sometimes caused to those who read about hurricanes because the rotary and progressive movements of the winds are not differentiated. But if the hurricane is compared to a spinning top this difficulty is resolved. The swift spinning of the top is the equivalent of the hurricane's spiraling winds; the changing position of the top relative to the ground is comparable to the progression of the hurricane across the sea.

The winds composing a hurricane whirl at very high speeds. At the extreme edge they are light to moderate but as they move inward the speed increases, and those blowing round the center whirl violently. The winds are faster over the sea, where there is a minimum of surface friction, than over the land.

What is the maximum speed? During the Galveston hurricane of September 1900 an anemometer disintegrated after recording about 100 m.p.h. winds. Speeds of over 150 m.p.h. have been measured for continuous periods of five minutes. During the great New England hurricane on September 21, 1938, an anemometer at Blue Hill Observatory near Boston recorded 121 m.p.h. for five minutes and 186 m.p.h. for a shorter period.[4] It must be remembered, however, that the accuracy of anemometers decreases with increasing wind speed. Incidentally, the windiest place in the world is Commonwealth Bay, Antarctica, where gales sometimes blow at 200 m.p.h.

The highest instrumental wind speed was recorded on April 24, 1934, on 6,000-ft. Mt. Washington, New Hampshire. According to the U. S. Weather Bureau, the wind blew at 231 m.p.h. for 1.17 seconds, but C. F. Marvin, who made a special study of the record, considers that the true

---

[4] Faster continuous speeds occur in the jet stream, which sometimes blows 20,000 to 35,000 ft. above the earth. Maximum speed is about 300 m.p.h. This "Gulf Stream of the air," as it has been called, is of great importance to high-flying airplanes.

speed was 221 or 225 m.p.h., according to which calibration system was used. No hurricane was involved. Ivan R. Tannehill, an American authority on hurricanes, says: "There is good reason to believe that the gusts of the hurricane represent air movements for brief intervals that may reach as high as 250 miles an hour in the most violent storms." Structural engineers, estimating from wind effects on buildings, consider that 250 m.p.h. has been reached in some hurricanes.

When a hurricane is fully formed its maelstrom of winds moves in a vast spiral round the center of the storm—hence "cyclone" (one of the popular names for a hurricane) meaning "coil of the snake." The "eye," as it is called, is one of the characteristics of a hurricane—the hole in the phonograph record—but it is not always in the center of the hurricane. It is an oasis of comparatively calm air and sometimes sunshine, although the sea is whipped into high choppy waves. The temperature is considerably higher than in the surrounding vortex.

The eye of a hurricane averages some 14 miles in diameter, although there are wide variations. Dunn and Miller say that the smallest diameter known was four miles: the formative stage of a hurricane off the Florida coast on July 27, 1936. A 25-mile-diameter eye occurred in another Florida hurricane in September 1928. Even greater diameters have been reported, but in some hurricanes an eye does not appear to form at all. The eye is but a short interlude between the two halves of the storm, just a breathing space to the battered victims of the hurricane. After it has passed, the winds blow again, but from the opposite direction. To find the eye, the observer stands (if he can!) with his back to the wind: the eye is then on his left.

When the eye of hurricane Janet passed over Swan Island in the Caribbean on September 27, 1955, it took about 10 minutes for the wind to subside from 200 m.p.h. to 30 m.p.h.

When the eye passes over a ship near land, flocks of birds—and occasionally butterflies and other flying insects—sometimes land on the deck and rigging. Some ships have been covered with such aerial visitors. The pilots of weather planes observing hurricane Carla in September 1961 reported that the eye was so filled with birds that they dared not fly through it (*Ibis*, October 1962). Why? The winds are so violent that any living thing caught in them is powerless, and is carried willy-nilly wherever they blow. As the winds spiral towards the center anything caught in them will eventually reach the calm eye and, once there, will be unable to break out and must remain until the hurricane subsides. When, therefore, the eye passes over a ship it is natural that any living creatures should land on the vessel to rest from their life-and-death struggle with the elements. Incidentally, birds sometimes travel great distances in the eye. Tropical birds have been found in New England after a hurricane—a distance of 2,000 miles.

What is it like in the eye of a hurricane? One of the best descriptions is that given by R. H. Simpson who flew into the eye of hurricane Marge on August 15, 1951, on a reconnaissance flight.

> The plane flew through bursts of torrential rain and several turbulent bumps. Then, suddenly, we were in dazzling sunlight and bright blue sky.
>
> Around us was an awesome display. Marge's eye was a clear space 40 miles in diameter surrounded by a coliseum of clouds whose walls on one side rose vertically and on the other were banked like galleries in a great opera house. The upper rim, about 35,000 ft. high, was rounded off smoothly against a background of blue sky. Below us was a floor of low clouds rising to a dome 8,000 ft. above sea level in the center. There were breaks in it which gave us glimpses of the surface of the ocean. In the vortex around the eye the sea was a scene of unimaginably violent, churning water.

An idea of the great stresses experienced in such flights—particularly if the hurricane is exceptionally violent—is evident from the report of Victor Klobucher, the weather officer aboard the reconnaissance plane sent to observe the September 1944 hurricane which ravaged the eastern seaboard from North Carolina to New England. He says that the turbulence was so great that the plane went out of control and several times he feared it would crash or be torn apart in the air. When it returned to base about 150 rivets had been sheared off one of the wings (quoted by H. C. Sumner). Jordan, however, tells me: "The turbulence encountered on most flights into hurricanes, especially at levels above 5,000 feet, is quite mild compared to that indicated in the preceding quotation. During the penetration of hurricanes, crew members on U. S. Weather Bureau and U. S. Navy aircraft have found that in nearly all cases they have been able to move about the aircraft quite freely as required in their observational duties."

Why are such flights made? Because they obtain information—vital to the weather forecasters and hurricane experts—which cannot adequately be obtained in any other way. Tannehill (1954) has written a book about this work and the brave men who pilot the planes.

Variations of barometric pressure are noticed as a hurricane approaches and recedes. Sometimes there is a rise, indicating a pressure greater than usual, which is about 29.92 inches. As the hurricane comes closer, the barometric pressure begins to fall, and is lowest in the eye. Extreme readings are: on land, 26.35 inches, at Long Key, Florida on September 2, 1935; at sea, 25.91 inches during hurricane Ida in the western North Pacific on September 24, 1958 (U. S. Weather Bureau).

Such differences may seem very little, but for every inch drop in pressure about 70 pounds is lifted off every square foot of surface. Thus a drop in barometric pressure from 29.92 to 27.92 inches, removes a load of some two million tons from each square mile. It is this drastic reduction which

A U. S. Navy plane flies above hurricane Gracie. The eye is just above the plane's tail. These "hurricane hunters" provide valuable information and warnings about hurricanes long before they strike land. Although sometimes hazardous, the flights are not as dangerous as they appear.   *U. S. Navy*

accounts for such widely different hurricane phenomena as refrigerators bursting and fishes' eyes popping out of their heads (Dunn and Miller).

Fortunately, winds of hurricane force rarely blow in Great Britain. But they do sometimes: in the first 60 years of this century 20 gusts of 100 m.p.h. or over were registered by anemometers. Although higher speeds have been recorded unofficially, the highest official wind speed for Great Britain is 122 m.p.h., reached in a gust at a height of 43 ft. above ground on Lowther Hill, Scotland, on February 12, 1962. On February 16, 1962 a freak windstorm, with gusts up to 96 m.p.h., pounded Sheffield, Yorkshire for about eight hours. The wind then dropped to 40–50 m.p.h. but continued for many hours. Enormous damage was done to property. Over 90,000 houses were damaged, 48 wrecked beyond repair. 170 schools were damaged, 89 seriously, and 5,500 trees were destroyed (Henry Smith). The British Standard Code for buildings envisages a maximum wind speed (for inland areas up to 800 ft. above sea level) of 63 m.p.h., based on the average speed for one minute.

Although tropical hurricanes do not scourge the British Isles, violent storms with continuous high-speed winds have, on three occasions during the past six centuries left their scar on British history. The most recent, that of January-February, 1953 is dealt with on page 147.

"St. Mary's Wind" of 1362 was so named because it occurred on this saint's day—January 15. It is reported by Irish, Scottish and English chroniclers. The wind did an enormous amount of damage. To quote a contemporary scribe, writing in the *Chronicon Angliae:* "A vehement wind burst forth with such strength that its blowing violently threw down high houses, tall buildings, towers, bell turrets, trees and other strong and durable things and likewise it raged in such manner that the remains which are still extant are weaker even until now." (Translation in C. E. Britton)

The greatest British windstorm raged across England and Wales from the Wash to the English Channel in November 1703. To quote Macaulay: "The only tempest which in our latitude has equalled the rage of a tropical hurricane." Some meteorologists believe that this storm was a West Indian hurricane that had crossed the Atlantic and somehow became rejuvenated in its old age.[5] There were strong southwest winds from about November 10, then during the night of November 26 the storm reached its utmost fury, with winds reaching an estimated 120 m.p.h. There was little rain but a roaring that would sound in men's ears so long as they lived.

Here is an enumeration of the worst of the damage; details can be obtained from Daniel Defoe, George M. Trevelyan, and Carr Laughton and V. Heddon.

On the Welsh coast the storm drove a great tide up the River Severn which, with the accompanying winds, left the port of Bristol in ruins. For days afterwards boats were rowing through the surrounding countryside rescuing people from house roofs and treetops.

Hitting the mainland, the storm left a trail of fallen chimneys and church spires, and ruined houses. Boats were blown out of rivers, carriages flung off the highways, over hedges and into fields. Trees fell by the tens of thousands—four thousand in the New Forest alone. Four hundred windmills —fair game this—were wrecked. Lead was stripped off hundreds of church and cathedral roofs, wrapped "like a parchment roll" and carried away. The damage in London alone was put at £1,000,000. A hundred citizens were reported killed in the ruins of their houses. The next morning London looked like a city that had been bombarded.

Wind and wave took a heavy toll at sea. The newly built Eddystone Lighthouse off Plymouth, Devon, was flung down and all inside, including its builder, were killed. Vessels of all sizes were wrecked, sunk or damaged, how many no one knows. A report from Deal, Kent, said: "We find missing

---

[5] This may be true, for hurricane Carrie, which formed near the North African coast early in September 1957, blew itself out over Cornwall at the end of the month.

of our Merchant Men upwards of 70 sail." Some ships on the east coast which ran before the storm were carried across the North Sea, ending their enforced voyage on the Norwegian coast.

The storm was particularly hard for the Royal Navy. Fifteen warships were lost, and one admiral and 1,500 seamen were drowned. England was at war with France and could ill afford such loss, which would have been even greater save for "the skill and courage of the crews of innumerable vessels, fighting the greatest naval battle of the war against no mortal foe." (Trevelyan)

In other lands hurricanes are all too frequent visitors. In the peak years of 1916 and 1950, eleven hurricanes were reported in the Atlantic, Caribbean, and the Gulf of Mexico. In 1950 and 1961 there were four hurricanes blowing at the same time. But in 1914 not a single hurricane was recorded. The annual average is about eight. But not all hurricanes reach land, and an average of less than one a year is severely destructive.

To encounter a hurricane at sea is a terrifying experience. Here is a description, by Weston Martyr, an ocean-going yachtsman, of what it feels like to be caught in an Atlantic hurricane:

> Do you know that you cannot breathe with a hurricane blowing full in your face? You cannot see, either; the impact on your eyeballs of spray and rain flying at over 100 miles an hour makes seeing quite impossible. You hear nothing except the scream and booming of the wind, which drowns even the thunder of the breaking seas. And you cannot move except by dint of terrific exertions. To stand up on deck is to get blown away like a dead leaf. You cannot even crawl; you have to climb about, twisting your arms and legs around anything solid within reach.

I don't wonder that Martyr says he would rather face an intense artillery bombardment (which he has) than ride out a hurricane aboard a sailing yacht. A. E. Dingle did just this, and his book, *A Modern Sinbad,* contains the day-to-day log of his epic 1,200-mile voyage (alone except for his dog) in a small boat through a hurricane off Bermuda in 1918.

Others who have survived a hurricane at sea say that it is impossible to speak, because the wind blows your mouth out of shape. Sometimes the clothes are ripped off men's backs as they struggle across exposed parts of the deck. And many a man has been washed overboard when caught by wind-whipped giant waves, which rise 20, 30 and occasionally 40 feet above the normal sea. When the *Aquitania* was caught in a hurricane in September 1922, ten ports on the B deck were smashed—50 feet above the water line. An official on the *Mauretania* said that heavy seas easily break the inch-thick glass of the portholes. The plate glass used to screen the bridges of ships has sometimes been shattered during a hurricane, and the splinters have penetrated wooden bulkheads like glass daggers.

A merchant ship lashed by hurricane Carol's maelstrom of wind and wave.   *U. S. Navy*

No one knows the maximum all-time height of an ocean wave. Waves have reached at least 60 feet and there are reports of waves reaching 98 and even 112 feet from trough to crest (H. Arakawa and K. Suda, and N. D. and A. R. McWhirter). These giant waves are generally the result of two wave systems clashing, resulting in a great explosion of surface water. Even greater heights are reached by waves caused by seismic disturbances (see p. 232).

The most dangerous Atlantic hurricane of historic times caused more destruction to ships than a major sea battle.[6] The "Great Hurricane," as it was called, of October 1780, is thus described by Elise Reclus:

Starting from Barbados, where neither trees nor dwellings were left standing, it caused an English fleet anchored off St. Lucia to disappear, and com-

---

[6] Although 1,200 vessels are said to have been sunk in the hurricane of August 1873 which swept up the east coast of North America from Bermuda to Nova Scotia.

pletely ravaged this island, where 6,000 persons were crushed under the ruins. After this, the whirlwind, tending toward Martinique, enveloped a convoy of French transports, and sunk more than 40 ships carrying 4,000 soldiers; on land the towns of St. Pierre and other places were completely razed by the wind, and 9,000 persons perished there. More to the north, Dominique, St. Eustatius, St. Vincent, and Porto Rico were likewise devastated, and most of the vessels which were on the path of the cyclone foundered with all their crews. Beyond Porto Rico the tempest bent to the north-east, toward the Bermudas, and though its violence had gradually diminished, it sunk several English warships returning to Europe.

The most strongly built ship can be seriously damaged by a hurricane. When the *Phemius* ran into a hurricane in November 1932, her funnel was carried away, she became unmanageable, and was swept along like drift-wood. Hatches were blown overboard, derricks and boats wrecked, upper and lower bridges stove in. The maximum wind speed was estimated at 200 m.p.h. Eventually the *Phemius* was taken in tow by another vessel. (Tannehill, 1956 b)

A similar experience befell the *Coamo* during the hurricane which wrecked the city of Santo Domingo in September 1930. She encountered the storm when seven miles from the city. When the wind rose to 125 m.p.h. the ship became unmanageable even with the engines running at full speed ahead. Just before she entered the hurricane's eye the wind increased to 160 m.p.h., then it abated but the sea remained wild and dangerous. The barometer fell rapidly and passed off the scale at 27.75 inches. Then the needle jumped up and down and the internal pressure on the eardrums was so great that one of the passengers later said: "I thought my ears would burst; I had a distinct taste of blood in my mouth."

The ship passed out of the eye and met the tremendous winds whirling round its edge. Capt. T. G. Evans wrote in his log (as quoted by C. E. P. Brooks) :

> The terrible wind and driving rain and spray made it impossible to see the foremast from the pilot-house. It was impossible to give any estimate of the velocity. It could not possibly blow any harder. The windows in the pilot-house were blown in like paper, and it was hard to hang on and dodge the flying glass. Skylights on boat deck, ventilators and boat covers, also the antenna were blown away. Ship unmanageable and heading S.E. by E. The engines were going full speed ahead. Ship labouring and pounding heavily, having a list of from 15 to 20 degrees to port and at times reaching an angle of from 40 to 45 degrees. The wind so terrible and powerful that the ship had no chance to right herself.

Even a modern battle fleet is in hazard when a hurricane strikes. This was tragically demonstrated when Task Force 38 of the United States Third Fleet encountered a typhoon off the Philippines on December 17–18, 1944. The typhoon, to quote Samuel Eliot Morison, was "young, small and tight." But Hanson W. Baldwin, military correspondent of the New York *Times,* who calls it "one of the most famous typhoons in history," says that in 500 years of naval history there had been no wind like it.

Owing to various factors the typhoon caught Task Force 38 unawares and in the middle of refueling. This, of course, meant that many ships were low in ballast and in no condition to fight the storm. A few captains prudently filled their empty oil tanks with sea water. It was, in fact, a standing order for destroyers to do this when encountering rough weather, but this is an extremely hazardous operation under typhoon conditions.

When the typhoon struck, the fleet of some 90 ships was spread over 3,000 square miles of Pacific Ocean. At the height of the storm some of the ships were unmanageable; they were unable to head into or down wind and took it abeam. The wisest captains followed the ancient dictum of the seas: "You can't fight a typhoon", and hove to.

A vivid description of the fleet during the height of the storm on the afternoon of December 18 is given by Morison:

> Except in the case of the battleships, all semblance of formation had been lost. Every ship was laboring heavily; hardly any two were in visual contact; many lay dead, rolling in the trough of the sea; planes were crashing and burning on the light carriers. From the islands of the carriers and the pilot houses of destroyers sailors peered out on such a scene as they had never witnessed before, and hoped never to see again. The weather was so thick and dirty that sea and sky seemed fused in one aqueous element. At times the rain was so heavy that visibility was limited to three feet, and the wind so powerful that to venture out on the flight deck a sailor had to wriggle on his belly. Occasionally the storm-wrack parted for a moment, revealing escort carriers crazily rising up on their fantails or plunging bow under, destroyers rolling drunkenly in hundred-degree arcs or beaten down on one side. The big carriers lost no planes, but the extent of their rolls may be gauged by the fact that *Hancock's* flight deck, 57 feet above her waterline, scooped up green water.

The destroyers suffered most. The *Hull* was pounded until her deck was swept clean of nearly everything movable. Then a gust estimated at nearly 130 m.p.h.[7] pinned her down on her beam ends. The raging sea poured into her funnels and she sank. The few survivors had their life jackets torn from their backs by wind and sea.

---

[7] The highest wind speed recorded during the typhoon was 124 knots—142 m.p.h. The barometer fell to 27.30 inches.

The heavy destroyer *Spence,* very low in fuel—only 15 per cent of capacity—was in no condition to fight a typhoon. On the morning of December 18 she began to roll heavily to port. Water poured in through ventilators and the rudder jammed. Then at 11:10 A.M. she rolled deeply, recovered, rolled again—and sank. The fuel tanks of *Monaghan* were three-quarters full, but like *Spence,* she also rolled over and sank.

In this typhoon the fleet lost three destroyers, 146 aircraft, and 790 men. Eighteen ships suffered major damage and many others needed repairs. War plans had to be altered while the fleet recovered.

After such happenings as this it is hardly surprising to learn that since the war the U. S. Navy has studied the possibility of "steering" typhoons toward an enemy fleet!

Following the Court of Inquiry's report on this typhoon, Fleet Admiral Chester W. Nimitz issued a long Fleet Letter. Had the advice given in his last three sentences been followed by everyone responsible for the safety of the Fleet there would have been fewer casualties. Those sentences are:

> The time for taking all measures for a ship's safety is while still able to do so. Nothing is more dangerous than for a seaman to be grudging in taking precautions lest they turn out to have been unnecessary. Safety at sea for a thousand years has depended on exactly the opposite philosophy.

Less than six months later, the Third Fleet was again in hazard with a typhoon and suffered damage, although not so severe as in December. The typhoon struck on June 5, 1945, when the Fleet was engaged in the battle for Okinawa, in the Northwest Pacific and movement of ships was therefore restricted.

As a result of these two typhoons various improvements were made in ship design, storm forecasting was improved, and more attention given to seamanship.

It is not surprising that when a hurricane's colossal energy turns inland it causes enormous destruction: sometimes thousands are killed and material damage may run into many millions of dollars. In some of the most severe hurricanes 50,000 people have been killed. Not surprisingly, the Roman Catholic Church once decreed that *Ad repellendam tempestatis* should be intoned during the hurricane season.

The destruction wrought by a hurricane is caused in three main ways: by wind, by rain and by waves, especially storm surges. In islands and coastal areas, of course, all three combine to destroy.

The fierce gusts deliver blows of 25 to 50 pounds—sometimes more—per square foot. Such winds develop both positive and negative forces: pushing from the front, pulling (suction) from the rear and on top (es-

Even modern warships are humbled by the elements. Twice in the second world war the U. S. Pacific Fleet was struck by violent typhoons, losing ships and men. In the typhoon of June, 1945, near Okinawa, the cruiser USS *Pittsburgh* lost her bows.   *U. S. Navy*

pecially on flat roofs). Conditions, of course, vary greatly with the speed and direction of the wind, and the shape, location and structure of the building, but sometimes the local pressures tending to lift a roof are several times greater than the direct pressure of the wind (C. W. Newberry and A. F. E. Wise). Another factor is that, to quote Riehl (1962): "The resistance capacity of many structures appears to become exhausted rapidly when the winds exceed 75 to 85 m.p.h."

Rough Guide to Relation Between Wind Speed and Pressure
(Shape, angle, surface and other factors modify the effect on structures)

Wind speed m.p.h.	Pressure per square foot (pounds)
50	6
100	26
125	40
150	58
200	102
225	130
250	160
300	230

Hurricanes

During the Galveston, Texas, hurricane of September 1900, roofs were ripped off and as they whirled through the streets along with other objects carried by the wind, they acted as battering rams to knock down other structures to leeward.

A hurricane's winds have been known to pick up pieces of shingle, hurl them through the air like bullets, and embed them in the trunks of hardwood trees.

During a violent hurricane which passed over Florida on September 2, 1935, a beam of wood 18 feet long and 6 by 8 inches in cross section was blown 300 yards, then smashed through a house, wrecking it like an artillery shell (J. E. Duane).

During the hurricane of September 2, 1935, two heavy land turtles (*Testudo*)—one weighed 165 pounds—were swept 20 miles across the Gulf of Florida. C. H. Townsend, of the New York Zoological Society, considers that they must have drawn their heads and legs tightly under their hard protective shells and have been rolled continuously across the tempestuous seas. They must have traveled at about 20 m.p.h. because at a lesser speed they would have sunk.

It sounds fantastic, yet it is true, that some towns have been blown away by hurricanes. The old city of Santo Domingo (later Ciudad Trujillo, now Santo Domingo) which admittedly was composed of flimsily constructed dwellings, was destroyed in the hurricane of September 3, 1930. And during the night of September 27, 1955, hurricane Janet blew down Chetumal, Mexico, a township of 2,500 inhabitants. When morning came, only four battered buildings were left upright.

It was wind which gave New Englanders their first experience of a major hurricane in 70 years.[8] Before it was done this wind—and accompanying rain and flood—battered the towns of New England badly. The hurricane was the famed "Long Island Express" of September 21, 1938, named from the speed—about 60 m.p.h.—with which it swept up the eastern seaboard. At 600-ft. Blue Hill Observatory, Massachusetts, wind for a five-minute period was timed at 121 m.p.h., and a gust at 183 m.p.h.

The anemometer on the 1,200-ft. Empire State Building registered gusts of 120 m.p.h. All over eastern New York State the wind caused havoc. Steel towers and radio masts were toppled to the ground, and thousands of wooden houses blew over or were crushed like matchboxes under pressures of 50 and more pounds to the square foot.

In Vermont and New Hampshire the wind played tenpins with forest

---

[8] Since then, however, severe hurricanes have hit the area four times, the last in 1954, and there have been minor storms in 1955 and 1962. Suggestions that these visitations are related to nuclear explosions are discounted by professional meteorologists.

timber. Wherever the shape of the terrain served to intensify wind speeds, there were tremendous blow-downs, trees lying in swaths. This great hurricane also moved oyster beds at the bottom of the ocean; "picked" four million bushels of apples; tossed ocean-going vessels into the streets of Bridgeport and New London; sent carloads of onions floating down the Connecticut River; and smashed enough plate-glass windows "to cover 17 football fields" (George Ainlay, and F. Barrows Colton, 1939). Incidentally, the wind carried sea salt 120 miles inland to whiten windows in Vermont.

An aerial reconnaissance of part of the devastated area was made by Rudy Arnold, who says:

> Acres of trees were scattered about like matchsticks. Automobiles were lying on their sides, half buried in sand. Houses [mostly wooden] were flattened out as though they had been crushed under steam rollers. . . . At one spot, nearly 15 houses were whirled together as though they had been in the grip of a giant eggbeater. At another place, a yacht was resting on a front lawn with a five-foot hedge between it and the sea. Near Madison, Connecticut there was the strangest sight of all—a two-story house which had been blown half a mile and had come to rest upside down without a single windowpane broken!

The toll of this New England hurricane was around 350 million dollars: 26,000 cars, 20,000 miles of electric lines, and 275 million trees were destroyed or damaged. Hurricane-felled trees knocked down lines to some 600,000 New England telephones. At one time so many wires were down that telegrams from Boston to New York City were being sent via London! About 600 lives were lost; the figure would have been higher but for the heroic and alert rescue services.

When I visited New England in 1951, the scars of the hurricane were still visible. I saw the ruins of houses, and skeleton trees which had been stripped of their bark by the rasping effect of wind-whipped sand. The same hurricane had sandblasted all the paint from cars, and scrubbed painted houses down to the plain wood.

During the terrible Labor Day hurricane of September 2, 1935, in Florida, some people were literally sandblasted to death. When found, they had no clothes except belts and shoes—and the skin had been rasped from their bodies. One weird effect was that at the height of the storm the air appeared to be filled with millions of fireflies; minute electrostatic discharges generated by the wind-blown sand (Dunn and Miller). This hurricane was the most violent in the Western Hemisphere this century. Peak winds were estimated to have reached 200 m.p.h., and on Long Key the barometer touched an all-time American low (except in tornadoes) of 26.35 inches.

Later in 1951 I nearly experienced a hurricane myself. I was in Hous-

ton, Texas, at the time a hurricane was sweeping across the Gulf of Mexico. In the middle of August this hurricane blew across the Caribbean Sea and headed for Jamaica. The Jamaicans were warned that their old enemy was on its way. They prepared what defenses they could. In Kingston, the capital, iron shutters protected shop fronts, hotels and large buildings battened down like ships on a rough sea, and police guards lined the streets.

At 9:45 on Friday night, August 17, 1951, the worst hurricane in Jamaica's storm-troubled history swept across the island. Kingston, on the southeast coast, was hit by the full force of winds which had been gathering momentum over a thousand miles of open sea. For five dreadful hours the night was turned into a maelstrom of wind, sea and rain which swept away all but the most impregnable defenses.

Seventeen inches of rain fell in five hours. Near-horizontal sheets of water driven by 125-m.p.h. winds poured over the island. In Kingston harbor, six steamships were driven ashore, and in the town breadfruit, coconuts, avocados, and other tropical produce rained into the streets. The town's Palisadoes Airport was wrecked: its steel hangars crumpling like tin. In Port Royal wind, traveling at 130 m.p.h., blew down a prison wall and 76 convicts escaped into the wild night.

By morning wind and rain were gone. The sun shone from a clear sky—but this hurricane had killed some 150 people, injured 2,000 more. More than 20,000 buildings were destroyed or badly damaged. The total loss was estimated at 56 million dollars.

The hurricane moved on westward, passed over Yucatan on August 19, and then blew across the Gulf of Mexico, hitting the mainland between Vera Cruz and Tampico. Here, in a final rampage, it killed 50 people before dying away.

As a hurricane's spiraling winds pass over the ocean they suck up enormous quantities of water vapor, which is later released in the form of torrential rain, sometimes in so-called cloudbursts.[9] The water comes down in rain bands that spiral toward the eye. Between these bands rainfall is comparatively light, and at the circumference there is frequently no rain at all. Where a mountain mass stands in the way of a hurricane especially heavy rains occur on the windward side. In temperate latitudes a rainfall of an inch in 24 hours is considered heavy; a hurricane sometimes pours down

---

[9] The underwater nuclear bomb used in Test Baker in the Pacific on July 25, 1946, lifted ten million tons of water. Large hurricanes lift a quarter of a million tons of water vapor *a second*—over 2,000 times Test Baker's feat every 24 hours.

←— Wood through wood! During a hurricane on Puerto Rico on September 13, 1928, a ten-foot pine board measuring three by one inches was shot through this Royal Palm tree.   *U. S. Weather Bureau*

20 inches in 24 hours! Exceptionally, however, there are hurricanes which have only a little rainfall.

The average annual rainfall for Paris is about 22 inches, for London 24 inches, and for New York City 42 inches. These figures provide a comparison for some of the record hurricane rainfalls. During the second greatest rainfall for the continental United States, 22.22 inches fell in 24 hours in North Carolina. The flood which resulted from this downpour was the greatest ever known in the southern Appalachians. The greatest 24-hour rainfall in the United States was 23.22 inches at New Smyrna, Florida, on October 10–11, 1924. In 24 hours on September 13–14, 1928, at Adjuntas, Puerto Rico, 29.60 inches fell. Ivan Ray Tannehill (1956a) says that at the end of the hurricane of September 7–11, 1921, 23.11 inches of rain fell at Taylor, Texas, in 24 hours—but at nearby Thrall 36.4 inches collected in an open barrel in 18 hours! This amount was exceeded during typhoon Gloria: when it passed over Taiwan (Formosa) 49.13 inches fell in 24 hours on September 10–11, 1963, at Paishih. But even this amount is far below the world record rainfall for 24 hours. On March 15–16, 1952, 73.62 inches fell at Cilaos on the island of La Réunion in the Indian Ocean (J. L. H. Paulhus).

In considering these figures it needs to be borne in mind that when wind is blowing at speeds of 50 m.p.h. or more, rain travels almost horizontally and a lot hits the sides of the containers used for measuring rainfall. There are also eddies around the gauges. No one, of course, can tell for certain, but some meteorologists consider that in a hurricane a rain-gauge reading of five inches really means that some eight inches or more actually fell (Dunn and Miller). Of course, rain may also "bounce" up from the ground and fall into the gauge. Incidentally, the world record rainfall for four days is 137.95 inches which fell on March 14–18, 1952, at Cilaos on the island of La Réunion (J. L. H. Paulhus).

In the most violent hurricanes the intense rain is driven by 150-m.p.h. winds in a blinding horizontal sheet that sweeps roads and thoroughfares clear of every living thing.

The weight of rain poured down is measured in millions of tons. It was estimated that in the 1900 Galveston hurricane, two thousand million tons of rain a day came down. During the hurricane in August 1899 the total weight of rainfall on Puerto Rico alone was estimated to be 2,600 million tons. In the great Florida hurricane of 1947 it was computed that on September 17, 12,000 million tons of rain fell (Bergeron). Great floods are often an aftermath of severe hurricanes.

The suction power and driving force of the hurricane's winds sometimes cause the sea to rise far above normal levels. The French call the phenomenon *raz de marée*, "rise of the sea." It is often referred to as "tidal waves," but the phenomenon has nothing to do with tides in the ordinary sense of the word. Riehl (1962) says: "The storm wave appears so quickly and is carried with tremendous force so far inland that often there is no time for the coastal inhabitants to rescue themselves or their belongings."

The explanation and theory of the storm surge—or rather surges, for there is more than one rise—are complicated and will not be considered here. The subject is dealt with in some of the technical works listed in the bibliography, such as those by Riehl (1954), Dunn and Miller, and D. Lee Harris.

Waves are the sea's battering rams and, when whipped by 100-m.p.h. winds and with all the weight of the sea behind them, their destructive power is enormous. Waves, fortunately, do not hit at this speed but some do break against sea works—harbors, piers, breakwaters, etc.—at 30 m.p.h. or more. In even a moderate storm there are sometimes 600 waves an hour crashing against sea works, each wave striking with a one-ton blow for every foot-length of the obstruction.

Waves do not only have a battering effect; in addition, the rapid subsidence of the mass of water sometimes produces a partial vacuum which, in turn, causes sudden pressure to be exerted from within. That is why, very rarely, a lighthouse door is broken *outward,* after the fall of a monstrous wave.

Marine engineers measure the force of a wave by spring dynamometers fixed into sea walls which, when struck by a wave, record the pressure in pounds per square foot. The same instruments are also used to measure the suction force of a wave, and the force exerted when wave water falls from a height.

Thomas Stevenson, father of Robert Louis, made many measurements on the storm-tossed coasts of his native Scotland. On the Island of Tiree, off the west coast, the *average* reading in the summer was 611 pounds per square foot, in the winter 2,086 pounds. But sometimes monster waves registered pressures greatly in excess of these figures. During a strong gale with a heavy sea, a wave estimated to be 20 feet high registered 6,083 pounds per square foot. Even this was not a record, for at Dunbar on the southeast coast, there was a reading of 7,840 pounds—3½ tons to the square foot.

Even this figure, however, is far from the record. French engineers have made careful tests, using refined techniques, of waves striking on sea walls at Dieppe and Le Havre. Reporting on these experiments, R. R. Minikin says: "The highest intensity of pressure so far [1963] recorded is no less than 6.6 tons per square foot at a point just above the base of the wall."

Stevenson recorded at Dunbar that a wave which exerted a battering force of 700 pounds per square foot had a recoil (suction) effect of 2,240 pounds—eloquent testimony to the immense force of the back draft of some waves.

Some other figures are of interest. Downward-facing dynamometers, projecting from the wall 23 feet above the sea showed that the vertical force exerted by one wave was 2,352 pounds on every square foot—yet the greatest horizontal force exerted by any wave during this series of tests was only 28 pounds.

When heavy waves crash against vertical obstacles, water sometimes shoots upward at 200 m.p.h., reaching 200 feet, with spray flying 20 to 30 feet higher. Tons of water fall with such force that 12-inch timbers are broken like the proverbial matchsticks. Not surprisingly, Gaillard says that falling water has suddenly exerted a total force of seven tons over an area of six square feet.

Sometimes waves entrap air against sea walls. The surrounding water compresses it until there is a minor explosion as the air bursts free. The force of such an explosion may be imagined from the fact that the granite facing on part of the Admiralty pier at Dover, Kent, is frequently blown out by the compressed air of breaking waves (Minikin).

Because of the varying pressures and stresses set up by wave action "no other force of equal intensity so severely tries every part of the structure against which it is exerted, and so unerringly detects each weak place or faulty detail of construction." This is a quotation from *Wave Action* by Lieut. Col. David D. Gaillard of the U. S. Army Corps of Engineers. He made a detailed study of wave action on sea works and published the results in 1904.

The lighthouse on Tillamook Rock, Oregon, is often struck by heavy seas. During every severe storm fragments of rock are torn loose. In December 1894 one rock weighing 135 pounds was flung over 100 feet high to crash into, and partially wreck, the lightkeeper's house. And wave-flung water, probably armed with rock fragments, broke 13 panes of glass in the lantern, which was 140 feet above sea level. The late Rachel Carson said that glass in the Dunnet Head lighthouse, Scotland, has often been broken by wave-swept stones—and this lighthouse stands on the summit of a 300-ft. cliff!

All these facts about wave action should be borne in mind when considering the story about the breakwater at Wick, on the northeast tip of Scotland, otherwise there will *not* be a "willing suspension of disbelief", and I shall be classed with the fiction writers to whose work that mental attitude rightly applies.

The seaward end of this breakwater was protected by a cap of rubble, stone, and cement welded together with 3½-in.-diameter iron rods. The total weight was 1,350 tons. Then came the great storm of 1872 and, as resident engineer, D. M'Donald watched from a nearby cliff, this great mass, under the impact of successive mountainous seas, slewed round until it broke away as a unit and rested at right angles to its original position.

The Elements Rage   [24]

One wave did this. While the British trawler, *Thornella,* was on a fishing trip in northern waters in January, 1953, she ran into heavy seas. The captain said: "A wave swept up from the bows and crashed against the bridge with terrifying force. The front caved in."   *Donald I. Innes*

This is remarkable enough, but subsequently another cap was installed with a total weight of about 2,600 tons, and then, during another violent storm in 1877, this also was carried away.

Fantastic as such happenings may appear to those unacquainted with the tremendous force of waves, marine engineering literature contains many similar examples. Miniken says:

> Boulders up to 15 tons weight have been washed over parapets of sea walls 10 to 12 feet above sea level. Concrete blocks of 20 tons weight laid as wave breakers on the weather side of the breakwater at Ymuiden [Holland] have not only been pushed bodily over the bottom but one was washed over the 12-ft.-high breakwater into the harbour. An iron casting 18 inches diameter and 1½ inches thick and embedded in concrete 30 feet above sea level has been sheared from its base: a mass of concrete weighing 70,000 tons has been washed whole from its foundations into the harbour.

So much for waves in general. Hurricane waves are the fiercest of all—apart from those caused by seismic disturbances, but these have nothing to do with meteorology.

In hurricanes, waves dash against the shore at anything up to 40 m.p.h. and 20 feet high, surge over all but the highest and most strongly built

Hurricanes

sea walls, and sweep miles inland to swell the rain floods. Thus, to the havoc caused by the hurricane's wind and rainfall is added that of inundation. On the rare occasions when a storm wave coincides with a seasonal high tide the destruction is sometimes catastrophic. The weight and force of the water wash out the foundations of buildings so that they collapse, turn turtle or float away—and sometimes all three! According to Tannehill (1956), inundation is responsible for more than three-quarters of the deaths from hurricanes. And Ervin A. Volbrecht, of the Weather Bureau Office at Galveston, tells me: "The real killer during a hurricane is the storm surge."

The most deadly hurricane in North America this century sent immense waves surging into Galveston Island, Texas, in the Gulf of Mexico in mid-September of 1900, destroying 3,600 houses and killing 6,000 people, about one-sixth of the population.[10] I. M. Cline, the U. S. Weather Bureau's observer there, said that the water rose four feet in as many *seconds* (quoted by Tannehill, 1956b).

This terrible disaster had one good result: Galveston was made the best hurricane-protected city in the world. Today, between Galveston and the sea, there is an immense barrier nearly 11 miles long. There is a riprap (loosely piled barrier of granite) 20 to 40 feet wide and 3 feet high at the foot of the sea wall which is founded on 30-ft. timber piles and covered with concrete. It is 16 feet wide at the base and rises 17 to 19 feet in a backward sloping concave curve. Before Galveston was founded, the island was protected by sand dunes rising to 15 feet. When these were removed by the settlers the town was at the mercy of the first hurricane to strike. Hence the disaster of 1900.

On August 16, 1915, a hurricane hit the Texas coast and violent seas with wave crests reaching 21 feet tested Galveston's defenses. Water flooded over the wall and some 275 people died.

The wall was then strengthened so that it had a maximum height of 19.2 feet. This was as well, for, on September 11, 1961, Carla, the worst Texas hurricane of the century, raged against Galveston. Fortunately, the hurricane center was 100 miles away, so the town was spared Carla's wildest fury, in which winds reached 175 m.p.h. Despite this, Galveston was flooded from water which swept round the wall and entered the city from inside the defenses, (Albert B. Davis, Jr.). Two people died; seven others were killed by a tornado associated with Carla.

It is obvious that the Galveston engineers have not been overcautious. Look what happened to the sea forts at Guadeloupe in the tremendous hurricane which struck the island on August 4, 1666. Mountainous seas

---

[10] "The worst recorded disaster ever to strike the North American continent." John E. Weems.

A wall of water flies high in the air as a wave crashes against a promenade.   *U. S. Coast and Geodetic Survey*

pounded at the fortifications until all the batteries, with their *six-foot*-thick walls, were destroyed and the 14-pounder guns were washed away.

In the hurricane of October 1846, the lighthouses at Key West and Sands Key, Florida, were swept into the sea. During the West Indian hurricane of September 1888 whole towns along the Cuban coast were swept out of existence by gigantic seas (Tannehill, 1956b). And in the hurricane of August 1893, a vast wave submerged the islands between Charleston, South Carolina, and Savannah, Georgia, killing 1,000 people.

Admiral Sir George Rodney said of the hurricane that swept over Barbados in early October 1780:

> The strongest buildings and the whole of the houses, most of which were of stone, and remarkable for their solidity, gave way to the fury of the wind [sea?], and were torn up to their foundations; all the forts destroyed, and many of the heavy cannon carried upwards of 100 feet from the forts. Had I not been an eye-witness, nothing could have induced me to have believed it.

This October hurricane is still referred to as "The Great Hurricane." It first hit land at Barbados, raged onto St. Vincent and Martinique, crossed the eastern Caribbean and wheeled north near Turks Island. It then passed south of Bermuda, where it drove 50 vessels ashore. It finally died away in mid-Atlantic.

There has been preserved a firsthand account of this hurricane's passage over Barbados, written by the Governor, Major-General Cunninghame. Here it is, slightly abbreviated.

The evening preceding the hurricane, the 9th of October, was remarkably calm, but the sky surprisingly red and fiery; during the night much rain fell. On the morning of the 10th, much rain and wind from the N.W. By ten o'clock it increased very much; by one the ships in the bay drove; by four o'clock the *Albemarle* frigate (the only man of war then there) parted her anchors and went to sea, as did all the other vessels, about 25 in number. Soon after, by six o'clock, the wind had torn up and blown down many trees, and foreboded a most violent tempest.

At the Government House every precaution was taken to guard against what might happen; the doors and windows were barricaded up, but it availed little. By ten o'clock the wind forced itself a passage through the house from the N.N.W. and the tempest increasing every minute, the family took to the center of the building, imagining from the prodigious strength of the walls, they being three feet thick, and from its circular form, it would have withstood the wind's utmost rage: however, by half after eleven o'clock, they were obliged to retreat to the cellar, the wind having forced its way into every part, and torn off most of the roof. . . .

Anxiously did they wait the break of day, flattering themselves, that with the light they would see a cessation of the storm; yet when it appeared, little was the tempest abated, and the day served but to exhibit the most melancholy prospect imaginable; nothing can compare with the terrible devastation that presented itself on all sides; not a building standing; the trees, if not torn up by their roots, deprived of their leaves and branches; and the most luxuriant spring changed in this one night to the dreariest winter. In vain was it to look round for shelter; houses, that from their situation it was to have been imagined would have been in a degree protected, were all flat with the earth, and the miserable owners, if they were so fortunate as to escape with their lives, were left without a covering for themselves and family.

General Vaughan was early obliged to evacuate his house; in escaping he was very much bruised; his secretary was so unfortunate as to break his thigh.

Nothing has ever happened that has caused such universal desolation. Not one house in the island is exempt from damage. Very few buildings are left standing on the estates. The depopulation of the negroes, and cattle, particularly of the horned kind, is very great, which must, more especially in these times, be a cause of great distress to the planters.

It is as yet impossible to make any accurate calculation of the number of souls that have perished in this dreadful calamity; whites and blacks together, it is imagined to exceed some thousands, but fortunately few people of consequence are among the number. Many were buried in the ruins of the houses and buildings. Many fell victims to the violence of the storm and the inclemency of the weather, and great numbers were driven into the sea, and there perished. The troops have suffered inconsiderably, though both the barracks and the hospital were early blown down.

Alarming consequences were dreaded from the number of dead bodies that lay interred, and from the quantity the sea threw up; which however are happily subsided. What few public buildings there were, are fallen in the general wreck; the fortifications have suffered very considerably. The buildings were all demolished; for so violent was the storm here, when assisted by the sea, that a twelve-pound cannon was carried from the south to the north battery, a distance of 140 yards.

The loss to this country is immense, many years will be required to retrieve it. [*The Gentleman's Magazine* (London), 1780, pp. 621–623]

But all these disasters happened long ago, before the work of modern architects and builders. Well, consider hurricane Hazel of October 1954 and Garden City, South Carolina. Near the beach was a two-story concrete-block store, 80 by 40 feet. Hazel's waters pounded the lower floor until it disintegrated, then hurled the upper story, almost intact, 300 feet away.

It was here that Hazel leveled 20-ft. grass-covered sand dunes, then went on to smash homes and houses—complete with concrete-slab floors—until they just disappeared. Sometimes storm surges wash beaches completely clear of sand.

But nowhere was destruction so complete as at Long Beach, North Carolina. Dunn and Miller say:

Everything on the island was destroyed. Where 300 homes existed at daybreak, all had disappeared by noon—far worse than the destruction of a tornado. Well-built concrete-block buildings with concrete floors and paved driveways were carried away. No litter or debris remained—it had been swept clean. The homes had been built in a space of some 75 to 100 yards between the beach and the highway, but after the hurricane the beach reached the highway and beyond.

(I am told that houses on the Carolina beaches are now being set up on piles eight to ten feet above the sand, thus allowing the sea to pass under houses without destroying them.)

Three years after Hazel, hurricane Audrey struck. On June 27, 1957, it swept up the Gulf of Mexico and battered Louisiana with wind, rain and storm surges—above all storm surges. The little town of Creole was washed out of existence: one concrete building remained, four others floated away but came to rest within the city limits; of the remainder—nothing but debris.

East of Creole a well-made house drifted off its foundations, floated intact for several miles and then, ballasted with tons of mud, sank into marshland. It's still there, an incongruous country mansion in the middle of nowhere whose only residents are marshland wildlife, especially rats and cottonmouth moccasins.[11]

Audrey's waters carried some houses 30 miles. And typical of the bizarre macabre happenings when elements rage, coffins, encased in concrete tombs, were washed out of burial grounds and carried 15 to 20 miles (Dunn and Miller).

Most of this chapter has been about Atlantic hurricanes. Violent and destructive as these are, they are matched in both respects by their Eastern sisters—the Pacific typhoons.[12] When typhoon Vera ravaged central Japan in September 1959, wind, sea, and rain left over 5,000 dead, more than 40,000 injured or missing, and completely destroyed over 40,000 houses. Japan's railway system, its lines cut in 827 places, was crippled.

Owing largely to its funnel-like shape, the Bay of Bengal—particularly the Hooghly River area—has experienced the most destructive typhoons in history, chiefly from storm surges. Another factor is that thousands of flimsily built shelters are jammed together near the coast. On October 7, 1737, at the mouth of the Hooghly River near Calcutta, a violent typhoon and its accompanying 40-ft. storm surge destroyed 20,000 boats and other vessels and killed 300,000 people.

In 1942 another typhoon struck Bengal.[13] Stuart Emeny visited the area a few weeks later. He says that to picture the effect of the tremendous wave which swept over 5,000 square miles, one should try to imagine the sea first receding halfway across the English Channel, then recoiling and rushing back against the southeast coast in an irresistible flood that sweeps over the sea walls and rushes for several miles inland.

One of the few men who came through the Bengal floods alive said that he saw the sea recede for a dozen miles and then come hurtling back as a solid wall of water 30 feet high, driven by a 120-m.p.h. wind. He saw it smash over and through the 14-ft. sea wall which had been built to protect the coast after the disaster of 1864. In another place a massive brick dam was swept away by the overpowering force of the waves.

Why are such strongly built structures unable to withstand the waves? Some reasons have already been given, but apart from thousands of tons of

---

[11] One of the zoological hazards of sitting out a hurricane is that poisonous snakes compete with people for the available accommodations. During Carla's rampage in September 1961, there was a plague of rattlesnakes in Texas City.

[12] Sisters seems an appropriate relationship as both are called by girls' names (see p. 33). Pacific typhoons are often larger than Atlantic hurricanes, there are more of them, and they often occur in comparatively cool weather.

[13] Several devastating typhoons struck the area in the 1960's. One in May 1965 was estimated to have cost nearly 13,000 lives (*The Observer*, London, May 30, 1965).

fast-moving water, the debris which the waters carry along with them acts like a concentration of battering rams. Telegraph and telephone poles, heavy beams, tree trunks, pieces of masonry and large rocks smash continuously against any structure barring their path.

If caught in harbors, ships are sometimes pounded against piers, walls, and wharves until they disintegrate. The sea rise is sometimes sufficient to lift the anchors, and ships are dashed ashore. The combined action of tide, wave and current has gouged great rocks from the sea bottom. Reclus, writing of the hurricane at St. Thomas, West Indies, in August 1837, says: "The fortress which defends the entrance of the port was demolished as if it had been bombarded. Blocks of rock were torn from a depth of 30 or 40 feet beneath the sea and flung on shore." Nor was this an isolated occurrence. William Reid says that in the Bermuda hurricane of September 1839 rocks measuring 20 cubic feet were removed, "some of them bearing evidence of having been broken off from the beds on which they rested." And during the great hurricane of August 1915, the Trinity Shoals buoy off the Texas coast was moved nearly ten miles to the west. It had been anchored in 42 feet of water and, with its sinker and chain, weighed about 15 tons.

Today, the risk from hurricanes, especially along the American coast, is considerably less than it was. Much of the credit for this is due to Willis L. Moore, of the U. S. Weather Bureau. At the outbreak of the Spanish-American War in April 1898 he went to President William McKinley and pointed out that throughout history more ships had been sunk by weather than by war. After examining the evidence McKinley said: "I am more afraid of a West Indian hurricane than I am of the entire Spanish Navy. Get this [hurricane warning] service inaugurated at the earliest possible moment." A limited service had been in operation since 1873 but it did not include warnings to ships. A forecasting center was now established on Jamaica.

It is now virtually impossible for a hurricane to come within hundreds of miles of the United States without ample warning unless, of course, it forms near the coast. General weather observations are constantly received from reconnaissance planes, automatic weather stations, radio-equipped balloons, ships, radar stations, Weather Bureau offices, and from satellites.

The best-known hurricane joke—it may well be true—concerns a warning. A man bought a barometer, but when installed it pointed to "Hurricane," and continued so to point despite all the ritual knockings with which barometer owners assault their instruments. The man wrote a letter of complaint to the manufacturer and went out to post it. When he returned, a hurricane had blown his home away. I also like the heading of the Miami *Herald*'s weather report the day after a hurricane: "BLEW SKIES."

Although most hurricanes don't reach the continental United States, when one forms it is kept under constant watch, and every ship and coastal area likely to be affected is warned. Red black-centered flags are broken out

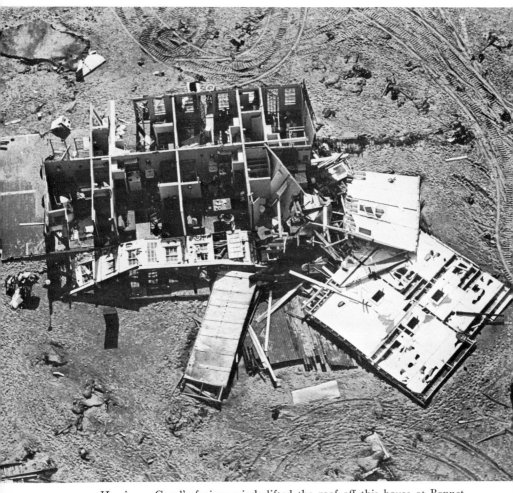

Hurricane Carol's furious winds lifted the roof off this house at Bonnet Shores, Rhode Island.   *Thomas D. Stevens*

when a hurricane is near, although most people today receive warnings from radio, television and the press.

No warning service is perfect,[14] and hurricanes are notorious for varying

---

[14] This was tragically demonstrated in Formosa on September 11, 1964, when the island's Weather Bureau said typhoon *Gloria* would not strike. But strike it did, killing some 330 people and causing property damage of 17½ million dollars. The director of the Weather Bureau was indicted for dereliction of duty but was not punished. He claimed that the broadcast he gave was the best he could in view of the information and limited facilities available to him (*Weather*, January 1965).

direction and speed, but the watchers and forecasters have caused a drastic reduction in the annual death roll—it is now some 3 per cent of what it was before the Second World War. When violent Carla of September 1961 was moving toward Texas, sheriffs broadcast: "Get out or drown." The result was the greatest mass exodus in American history—half a million people barricaded homes, packed essentials, and drove inland. It was well they did, Carla was later estimated to possess 90 times as much energy as a 50-megaton explosion.

The great improvement in the warning services was demonstrated in two hurricanes which devastated British Honduras. The hurricane of September 10, 1931 killed about 2,000. Then, as the sun rose on October 31, 1961, hurricane Hattie hit the country. It was much more violent than the 1931 storm; winds rose to between 150 and 160 m.p.h., and a storm surge over 10 feet high swept along the Belize waterfront, depositing mud on the third floor of some buildings. Three-quarters of the town was ruined but the death roll was less than one-seventh (about 275) that of the earlier hurricane. The difference was due entirely to the vast improvement in the warning services in 30 years (Gordon E. Dunn).

But while the number of deaths has been reduced, the amount of destruction has not. Diane in August 1955 was the first billion-dollar hurricane in history, the greatest natural catastrophe—judging from damage to property—in the history of the United States. This was largely because of the flooding caused by the heavy rainfall on ground already saturated from previous rain.

As is well-known, Atlantic hurricanes are now given girls' names—as the ancient Greeks similarly christened their Furies. For hundreds of years many hurricanes were named, a trifle unfairly, after the saint's day on which they occurred. Later, hurricanes were identified on a latitude and longitude basis, but this was cumbersome. Then, during the Second World War, meteorologists began using girls' names and found it was ideal, both in writing and speaking. This becomes obvious when it is remembered that a single hurricane (such as the devastating Diane of August 1955) may be referred to millions of times—by telephone, television, radio, telegrams, newspapers, and in conversation. When hurricane Ione, of September 1955, threatened the eastern United States, the weather numbers in New York City and Washington, D. C. were each called about 400,000 times.

Twenty-six (A to Z) names are selected in advance. The first hurricane of the year is then given the girl's name beginning with A, the second with B, and so on for other hurricanes throughout the year. A name is not used again for a ten-year period if it has been used for a very severe hurricane. As the record number of hurricanes in the general Atlantic area in any one season is 11, there is little likelihood of the names running out. The name is followed by the year, e.g., Diane, 1955. I am pleased to say that the only hurricane named after my wife, Barbara, which occurred in August 1953 and passed over part of North Carolina, was comparatively mild.

Pacific typhoons are also given girls' names, although the naming system is different—84 names are used and the list is started again when all these have been used.

Today, the National Hurricane Center in Miami, Florida (which incorporates the National Hurricane Research Laboratory), is the clearing-house for a vast mass of information. In addition to the "old" methods of studying hurricanes, they are now investigated by camera-carrying rockets that picture the complete cloud system and its immediate environment, and by satellites.

Can a hurricane be prevented from forming or, once formed, can it be destroyed? Several H-bombs might be effective, but this would be an example of cure being worse than complaint. Seeding hurricanes with dry ice or silver iodide has been tried on several occasions, but without definite evidence that the effect was beneficial (R. R. Braham). Volbrecht comments: "Deformation or dissipation experimentation must necessarily be slow and exacting. There is some evidence to support eye distortion during one seeding drop."

Another suggestion for taming hurricanes is control of the warm ocean waters. Without heat hurricanes cannot form: if, therefore, some of the cool water just below the surface could be deflected upward hurricanes might be prevented. With man's rapidly increasing investigation of the world beneath the sea this anti-hurricane notion may prove practical in a few years.

Dunn and Miller suggest that the only method of control may lie in the hurricane itself, its tremendous energy being used to start a chain reaction which will cause it to destroy itself. But, supposing this were possible, would it be wise to attempt it? Maybe a worse evil would result. Hurricanes appear to be important agents in the general circulation of the atmosphere and the maintenance of heat balance. If hurricanes were prevented altogether, who knows what consequences would follow? It can be highly dangerous to frustrate Nature's forces, as witness the catastrophic results of blocking a volcano's normal outlet (see p. 243).

Mankind's best hope against this meteorological fury may well be to control its direction. Dunn and Miller say:

> It is possible that if a certain portion of a hurricane were seeded, a concentration of energy could develop in one quadrant which might alter the course of the storm in that direction. Of course within a few hours the storm would resume its normal track, but the temporary diversion might take it far enough to one side of a heavily populated area to decrease significantly the damage and loss of life.

Edwin A. Koch, a New York architect, designed a "hurricane house"

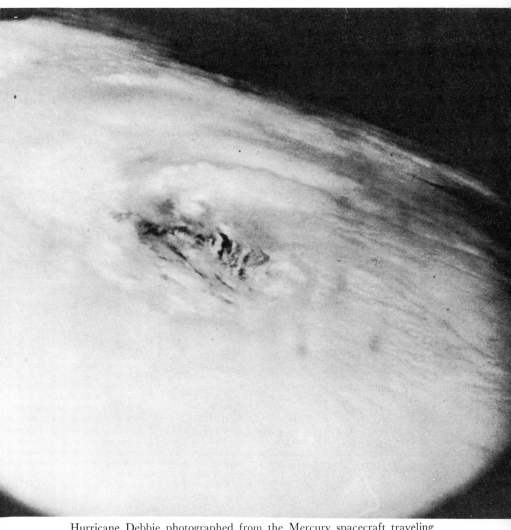

Hurricane Debbie photographed from the Mercury spacecraft traveling at 17,500 m.p.h. over one hundred miles above the earth. *National Aeronautics and Space Administration*

which he believed would be able to withstand the battering of the destructive winds. It was built in the form of a giant teardrop—a good streamlined shape—and rested on flanged wheels. By a simple mechanism it could be rotated in any direction. Should a hurricane approach, the house would be swung round so that the broad end faced the storm. When the winds struck, the broad surface would deflect them smoothly round its curving sides,

Hurricanes

WHEN A HURRICANE THREATENS

KEEP YOUR RADIO OR TV ON...AND LISTEN TO LATEST WEATHER BUREAU ADVICE TO SAVE YOUR *LIFE* AND POSSESSIONS

BEFORE THE WIND AND FLOOD	HAVE GAS TANK FILLED... CHECK BATTERY AND TIRES.	HAVE SUPPLY OF DRINKING WATER. STOCK UP ON FOODS THAT NEED NO COOKING OR REFRIGERATION.
HAVE ON HAND FLASHLIGHT, FIRST AID KIT, FIRE EXTINGUISHER, BATTERY-POWERED RADIO.	STORE ALL LOOSE OBJECTS: TOYS, TOOLS, TRASH CANS, AWNINGS, ETC. BOARD OR TAPE UP ALL WINDOWS.	GET AWAY FROM LOW AREAS THAT MAY BE SWEPT BY STORM TIDES OR FLOODS.

DURING THE STORM	STAY INDOORS... DON'T BE FOOLED IF THE CALM "EYE" PASSES DIRECTLY OVER... AND DON'T BE CAUGHT IN THE OPEN WHEN THE HURRICANE WINDS RESUME FROM THE *OPPOSITE* DIRECTION.	LISTEN TO YOUR RADIO OR TV FOR INFORMATION FROM THE WEATHER BUREAU, CIVIL DEFENSE, RED CROSS, AND OTHER AUTHORITIES.

AFTER THE STORM HAS PASSED	DO NOT DRIVE UNLESS NECESSARY. WATCH OUT FOR UNDERMINED PAVEMENT AND BROKEN POWER LINES.	REPORT DOWNED POWER WIRES, BROKEN WATER OR SEWER PIPES TO PROPER AUTHORITIES OR NEAREST POLICEMAN.
	USE EXTREME CAUTION TO PREVENT OUTBREAK OF FIRE, OR INJURIES FROM FALLING OBJECTS.	USE PHONE FOR EMERGENCIES ONLY. JAMMED SWITCHBOARDS PREVENT EMERGENCY CALLS FROM GOING THROUGH.

YOUR ABILITY TO MEET EMERGENCIES WILL INSPIRE AND HELP OTHERS

U.S. DEPARTMENT OF COMMERCE • WEATHER BUREAU

Hurricane warning.

throwing them harmlessly off at the pointed tip (*Popular Science Monthly*, October 1939).

Strange as it may sound in view of the immense destruction they cause, hurricanes have their blessings for mankind. Science has not yet found an economical way of obtaining large quantities of drinkable water from the seas. Hurricanes do just that, lifting and evaporating thousands of millions of tons of sea water and dropping it as salt-free rain. The heavy rains accompanying a hurricane revive crops and replenish supplies of storage water. This benefit is received over a wider area than is ravaged by the hurricane's winds. The hurricane of June 1945 relieved one of the worst droughts in the history of Florida. After some hurricanes fruit trees have flowered and borne fruit a second time. O. L. Fassig estimated that of the hurricanes which struck Puerto Rico during 1899–1928, 60 per cent were beneficial, 30 per cent were locally destructive but beneficial in other areas, and only 10 per cent were overwhelmingly destructive.

Sometimes hurricanes have affected the course of history. Toward the end of the Second World War, the Allies were made uncomfortably aware of the Japanese word *kamikaze*. Its meaning, "divine wind," refers to the violent storms—typhoons?—which, centuries ago, wrecked the vessels of invading armies (H. Arakawa). And the United States' Third Fleet had to contend, not only with kamikaze suicide pilots, but also with their meteorological namesake—except that for the Americans the wind was the reverse of divine.

Although not technically a hurricane, it was a very similar phenomenon which helped to save England from the Spanish Armada.

Hurricanes affected the rival fleets during the American War of Independence, 1775–1783, especially during 1780, one of the worst hurricane years on record. The logbooks of British, French, Spanish and Dutch ships show dramatically this other war against the elements (William Reid). The Savanna-La-Mar hurricane of the first week in October hit a British fleet some 500 miles east of Florida and damaged most of the ships. The same hurricane then struck another British fleet patrolling off the Virginia Capes, causing such havoc that an entire squadron had to put into port for repairs.

In the middle of the month an even worse disaster befell a great Spanish fleet of 64 warships and transports assembled in the Gulf of Mexico to reduce the British base at Pensacola, Florida. Solano's hurricane, named after the Spanish admiral, scattered the fleet over the central Gulf, dismasted some of the ships and severely damaged others. The attack was abandoned (Ludlum).

The most dramatic example of a hurricane changing history was in 1889. Early that year a German naval force shelled a native village at Apia, Samoa. During the shelling a United States flag, which had been run up to protect property, was torn down and burned, and American property was destroyed. Three American warships were ordered to Samoa, arriving there in March. They steamed into the harbor, where there were already three German warships and one British. The situation was tense, with the three nations on the brink of war. Then a hurricane struck. It swept down the bottleneck of the harbor and winds and waves surged round the seven warships. War was forgotten in the greater battle against the elements.

The force of the wind was so great that the comparatively feeble engines of the American and German ships were powerless to make headway against the storm, or even to hold their anchorage. All six sank. Six merchant ships which were also in the harbor foundered, and altogether about 150 sailors were drowned. The death toll would have been higher had not the hurricane made all the belligerents as one, and there were many acts of heroism in the international rescue work: Polynesians saved American and German sailors alike, sometimes at the risk of their own lives.

When the hurricane passed there were no ships immediately available to carry on the war; the hurricane had brought a compulsory armistice. Fortunately, before hostilities could break out again, the dispute was settled amicably, and the Treaty of Berlin in 1889 resulted in the freedom of Samoa being guaranteed for many years.

But this was not all. There had been another warship in the harbor when the hurricane struck—the British *Calliope,* one of the earliest vessels to be equipped with engines that made her largely independent of canvas. In the teeth of the hurricane the *Calliope* steamed from the inner harbor for the comparative safety of the open sea. It was a terrific struggle to make headway. It took her an hour to cover less than half a mile. But sound engines and good seamanship eventually brought the *Calliope* out of the harbor and she survived. As she passed one of the American vessels the crew, although in danger of imminent death themselves, stood and cheered in admiration of the gallant seamanship displayed.

This episode made a deep impression on naval experts throughout the world. The U. S. Navy at once laid plans for equipping the fleet with more powerful engines. Thus did a hurricane in the South Pacific change the course of history. (*Report of the Secretary of the* [U. S.] *Navy,* 1889.)

chapter 2

Tornadoes

A tornado is the most violent and devastating of all windstorms. Its behavior is often so fantastic as to border on the incredible. But extraordinary tornadic phenomena have been described by reliable observers—and sometimes photographed—and their reality is fully established. Tornadoes occur in all continents but are most frequent and violent in the United States.

It is not possible to describe the exact cause of tornadoes; W. J. Humphreys (1940) lists no fewer than 26 conditions for their occurrence. Even today their nature is not fully understood. It used to be thought that the one general condition without which no tornado could form was the meeting of two air masses of different degrees of temperature and humidity. But it is now known that tornadoes occur in air without these differences. Sir Graham Sutton, one-time Director-General of the British Meteorological Office, says:

> The mechanism of the tornado is still obscure, but its formation is clearly associated with marked instability in the lower layers of the atmosphere. In general, tornadoes are formed in conjunction either with strong cold fronts and squall lines or with thunderstorms. . . . The precise combination of conditions which produce the pendant vortex is not known.

Technically, tornadoes result from the working of well-known principles of fluid mechanics—Bernoulli's principle, the conservation of momentum, and probably the Coriolis force. Very roughly these same principles are involved in the formation of the little whirlpool at the drainage hole in a bath.

The violent whirling action of the winds—inward and upward—is the main characteristic of a tornado, and accounts for its popular name "twister." In the Northern Hemisphere the whirling is nearly always in a counterclockwise direction, because that is the direction imparted by the large masses of air from which the tornado comes. Such air masses take *their* direction from the earth's rotation.

[*39*]

The classic photograph of a tornado, taken near Jasper, Minnesota, on July 8, 1927.   *Lucille Handberg*

There appear to be two types of tornado: 1) those formed by local convection processes and which are relatively weak, and 2) those formed by the meeting of vast air masses, and which are extremely powerful. The conditions for the second type are found mainly in the United States, whose worst tornadoes are the most violent on earth.

Although tornadoes are generally reported as "loners," a dozen or so may form in a day. In the Northern Hemisphere the tornado season extends roughly from March to October. In North America tornadoes strike in all areas, including Alaska, and at every season, but most frequently in the mid-continent in April, May, and June. They normally occur in the afternoon, although they have been recorded as early as 4 A.M. and as late as 11 P.M. Tornadoes generally travel from southwest to northeast: statistics show that nearly 90 per cent come from a westerly direction, only 4 per cent from the east.

The one saving feature about a tornado is that it is the most localized of all storms, and its destructive path is generally short and narrow; although, when conditions are favorable, tornadoes form in "families" whose paths may cover an area several miles wide.

Statistics on the duration, width and length of path of tornadoes are complicated, because it is not always possible to know whether one or more funnels are referred to. Some tornado systems involve only one funnel, others may involve several. Extreme figures which have been given are:

Duration: a few seconds to four hours.
Width: nine feet to two miles.
Length of path: "a few feet" to nearly 400 miles (with some short breaks where the funnel momentarily lifted).

Averages, however, are very much nearer the lower figures given above. Louis J. Battan, in a study of tornado duration and length of path, considers that the average duration is about four minutes and the average path two miles. Average funnel width is about 1,000 feet.

There are several known instances in which people have stood within 150 feet of the funnel and have felt no violent wind. Sometimes the destruction in one place is complete, with every building, tree, and fence leveled to the ground, while a few feet away the lightest object is undisturbed (John P. Finley, and Laura V. Wolford).

The Great Plains, stretching from the Gulf of Mexico to Canada, have more tornadoes than anywhere else on earth. The area comprising Texas, Oklahoma, Kansas, and Missouri has been called "Tornado alley."

On yearly average—1916–1958—the states most frequently hit are: Texas, with 23; Kansas, 24, and Oklahoma, 20 (Wolford). In proportion to its size, Kansas is hit most frequently—about three times more than Texas. Hence its nickname, the "Cyclone State." Central Oklahoma, however, is more tornado-prone than any area of comparable size in the world. Incidentally, Washington, D. C., has been hit four times this century, by far the worst blow coming on November 17, 1927, when damage amounted to nearly 700,000 dollars—and the dollar was worth a good deal more then. There is no record of any damaging tornado ever hitting New York City.

The conditions preceding the birth of a violent tornado have been vividly described by many eyewitnesses. "It seemed as if the lightest garments that I could put on were a burden to me," . . . "The air at times came in puffs as from a heated furnace," are two typical comments.

John G. Albright says: "The temperatures preceding tornadoes are higher than usual, but soon after they fall very rapidly. The relative humidity is unusually high, making the air very oppressive and sultry for hours or even days before the tornado." Sometimes it is as though night had descended prematurely. Strange-colored clouds mill wildly about. Jet-black, greenish, purple, or clouds of "a strange lividness," often mingled with steamlike grays and whites, are typical descriptions of the colors of tornado-forming clouds.

Many observers tell of seeing two cloud masses meet, one moving from the southwest and the other from the northwest. "They came together with a terrific crash, as if thrown from the mouths of cannons" says one eye-witness. As the clouds meet they break up in a wild turmoil; sometimes they dart toward the earth, then shoot up high into the sky like gigantic rockets.

In the middle of this confused medley, portions of cloud begin to roll about each other in a well-developed whirl. This action develops until, in the midst of the turmoil, a funnel is formed. Occasionally, however, there is a windstorm with all the other characteristics of a tornado but without a funnel. And in some tornadoes clouds do not appear to merge into the funnel at all.

The funnel frequently looks like a gigantic elephant's trunk, sometimes a mile high, dangling from the heavens. Both shape and color vary according to atmospheric conditions and the viewpoint of the observer. Typical descriptions are: a thin dangling rope, a fairly wide and solid-looking funnel, balloonlike, and the tail of an enormous kite. The same tornado may change its shape from time to time. The axis of the funnel may be straight or contorted, vertical or considerably inclined.

The most frequent colour is gray, due to the condensation of the water vapor. In air with a fairly low moisture content it may be invisible. When the funnel touches the ground and begins its work of destruction, the color may be considerably modified by dust and debris. Snowden D. Flora (1953) says that a tornado in Utah passed over a snowfield and turned almost white.

The funnel undergoes two movements in addition to its characteristic whirling motion which is the cause of all the destruction. These are horizontal (forward movement) and vertical (up and down movement).

Once a tornado is fully formed, it roars across the countryside at speeds generally between 20 and 30 m.p.h., although speeds as low as 5 m.p.h. and as high as 65 m.p.h. have been reported. Sometimes a tornado remains almost stationary for a few minutes, although Flora (1929) says that a tornado at Hardtner, Kansas, on June 2, 1929, remained practically in the same place for nearly half an hour.

The tornado's funnel often rises from the earth and dips again a little farther on. Although it generally moves in a fairly straight line, it sways from side to side and frequently writhes and twists. It changes form and shape, and bounces up and down—gyrations which complicate the escape efforts of those caught in its path.

All this violent action is accompanied by tremendous noise. A tornado, like thunder, is heard many miles away. As it approaches, there is a peculiar whistling sound that rapidly changes to an intense roar, reaching a deafening crescendo as it strikes. The screeching of the whirling winds is then so loud that the noises caused by the fall of wrecked buildings, the crashing of trees, and the destruction of other objects is seldom heard. The bellowing of a million mad bulls; the roar of ten thousand freight trains; like that of a million cannons; the buzzing of a million bees (when the tornado is high in the air), and, more recently, the roar of jet airplanes—these are some of the phrases used by those who have experienced a tornado.

A tornado's awesome effect is frequently heightened by an accompanying thunderstorm, with deluges of rain and hail. Sometimes very heavy stones fall, weighing a pound or more. Flora says that during a tornado at Kiowa, Kansas, on June 2, 1929: "Where the sun could still be seen shining over the top of the tornado cloud, slugs of ice, disk-shaped, and 2½ inches wide and almost an inch thick, fell in the sunlight like gleaming meteors out of a black cloud that backed it from the east."

Lightning sometimes plays about the funnel. George Raveling, an observer of the U. S. Weather Bureau, says of one tornado: "From the sides of the boiling, dust-laden cloud a fiery stream poured out like water through a sieve, breaking into spheres of irregular shape as they descended." A less restrained observer wrote: "The tornado came wriggling, jumping, whirling like a great green snake, darting out a score of glistening fangs." After this it is not surprising to learn that strange sulphurous odors (ozone?) are sometimes emitted by tornadoes. This most probably comes from the lightning (see J. C. Jensen, and H. A. Hazen).

One of the most impressive displays of lightning was seen at the time of the great St. Louis, Missouri, tornado of May 27, 1896. A Weather Bureau official reported:

> The electrical display during the storm was of exceeding brilliancy. It was first observed at 5:00 P.M., an hour before the tornado occurred. This continued with short intermissions until 5:45 P.M., when it became almost continuous and extended more into the west and north. At 6:00 P.M., when the tornado occurred, the whole west and northwest sky was in a continuous blaze of light. Intensely vivid flashes of forked lightning were frequent, being outlined in green, blue, purple, and bright yellow colors against the dull yellow background of the never ceasing sheet lightning [quoted by H. T. Harrison].

Some investigators, such as Bernard Vonnegut, have suggested that atmospheric electricity may be the cause of tornadoes. This theory has been criticized by E. M. Wilkins, but violent lightning is certainly a frequent accompaniment of tornadoes, strokes sometimes occurring at a rate of 10 to 20 per second, a rate much in excess of that in ordinary storms. A steady electrical discharge has also been observed in some tornado funnels. To the ancient Greeks and Romans such a tornado was known as a *prester* (S. K. Heninger, Jr.).

In view of the awesome accompaniments of a tornado it is understandable that, in a less sophisticated age, the sight and sound of a twister made men think that the end of the world and the Day of Judgment were at hand. And many a tornado *has* been the end of the world for some people. Consider this account taken, not from a novel or popular work, but from a scientific textbook—Snowden D. Flora's *Tornadoes of the United States.* He is writing of the tremendous tornado which struck Irving, Kansas, on May 30, 1879:

> There appeared in the west a cloud of inky blackness and enormous dimensions. It presented a square front of blackness almost two miles wide, with the front almost perpendicular. Many people actually believed that Judgment Day had come and offered up fervent prayers and loud appeals for preservation.
>
> With a roar "like that of a thousand cannons," the cloud covered the little town. In an instant everything was swept from the earth in ruin, and death was experienced in its most dreadful forms. In the twinkling of an eye, according to persons who experienced it, all was gone. Life, property, and happiness were crushed and annihilated. The power of the storm was sufficient to accomplish in a few moments what disease and accident had not done in years.
>
> Persons who lived through the storm to tell the tale said that the air was filled with fumes like sulphurous smoke, the sky had a reddish tinge bordering on purple, and the ground was rocked as if by an earthquake. What seemed to them vast waterspouts reached the ground in several places, swinging to and fro in the gale like elephants' trunks, seizing and taking up into the whirling vortexes everything that stood in their way.

The forces in a tornado are colossal in the true meaning of the word. Estimates have been made of the actual power involved. Vonnegut calculates that for a tornado with a diameter of about 350 feet—a small one—its power is about 10^{18} ergs per second, or 10^8 kilowatts, which is in excess of the capacity of all the generating stations in the United States.[1]

The air composing a tornado whirls at tremendous speed, especially near the center of the funnel. The maximum speed has never been measured directly, because no instrument has so far proved capable of withstanding the terrific buffeting. The highest wind speed ever recorded by an anemometer was a gust of about 225 m.p.h. (see p. 7). But this was not in a tornado,

---

[1] 10^{18} is 1 followed by 18 zeros, 10^8 is 1 followed by 8 zeroes. An erg is a unit of energy—see Appendix 3.

← As the tornado of April 2, 1957, approaches Dallas it shows its awesome power by throwing debris high into the air.   *U. S. Weather Bureau*

and it is almost certain that far greater speeds are reached in large tornadoes. They blow anemometers away!

Finley says: "Theoretical velocities of over 2,000 m.p.h., based upon certain assumed atmospheric conditions, have been deduced. Such velocities are mathematically possible, but not meteorologically probable." Several estimates have been attempted from the effects produced.

When Elias Loomis investigated a tornado in Ohio on February 4, 1842, he found small pieces of board with blunt ends driven into turf land to a depth of 18 inches. He procured a number of similar boards, loaded them into a six-pounder gun, and fired them into a hillside. By comparing the depth of penetration, and the force involved, with the penetration achieved by the tornado, he concluded that the winds must have had a velocity of 682 m.p.h.—the speed of a revolver bullet!

From some of the effects produced by the great St. Louis tornado of May 27, 1896, Frank H. Bigelow estimated that speeds in excess of 250 meters per second, i.e., above 560 m.p.h., must have been reached. But E. van Everdingen points out that "all calculations of the force of the wind from the pressure of the wind, estimated from its destructive effect, yield too high values, because it is certain that other forces of the same order of magnitude must have been present at the same time. These are the differences in atmospheric pressure."

But it is now possible to obtain electronic readings of wind speed. The U. S. Weather Bureau has a tornado speedometer, based on the Doppler principle. Radar echoes from a moving target, in this instance the wind, are shifted in frequency determined by the target speed. The speedometer detects this shift and thus makes a direct measurement of the target's (i.e., wind's) speed. American police use a radar unit based on the same principle to check the speed of cars. On June 10, 1958, Doppler radar recorded a speed of 206 m.p.h. in a tornado at El Dorado, Kansas (Robert L. Smith and David W. Holmes). The speed varies considerably during the life of a tornado, and 206 m.p.h. is slow, as tornado wind speeds go.

The destruction wrought by tornadoes is due to three effects: pressure, updraft, and vacuum.

PRESSURE

The pressure exerted by wind increases approximately as the square of the velocity. (This relationship applies until the velocity of sound, about 750 m.p.h., is reached, when other factors complicate the relation between speed and pressure.) Thus a 500-m.p.h. wind would exert not five times but about 25 times the pressure of a 100-m.p.h. wind. But the shape of objects considerably affects the practical effect of the pressure, which in a great tornado is in excess of 250 pounds per square foot.

The furious winds turn normally harmless objects into dangerous missiles. Sand and gravel are whipped along with such force that they enter human bodies like shotgun pellets.

After the St. Louis tornado of 1896 some wheat straws were found embedded over an inch deep in a tree trunk. Even more remarkable was an incident which occurred during a tornado at Scottsbluff, Nebraska, on May 30, 1951. An egg was found with its shell uncracked—but with a neat hole through which a bean had been forced an inch deep into the yolk (Flora). It has even been claimed that after one tornado a *flower* was found in a plank of wood!

Willis L. Moore, then chief of the U. S. Weather Bureau, visited St. Louis the day after the 1896 tornado and spent much time examining the wreckage. Here is a paragraph from his report.

> The writer saw a two by four pine scantling [narrow piece of timber] shot through five-eighths [inch] of solid iron on the Eads Bridge, the pine stick protruding several feet through the iron side of the roadway, exemplifying the old principle of shooting a candle through a board. He saw a six by eight piece of timber driven four feet almost straight down into the hard compact soil, a gardener's spade shot six inches into the tough body of a tree, a chip driven through the limb of a tree, and wheat straws forced into the body of a tree to the depth of over half an inch. Such was the fearful velocity of the wind as it gyrated about the small center of the tornado—a velocity exceeding that of any rifle bullet.

UPDRAFT[2]

One of the most powerful effects of a tornado's winds is the creation within the funnel of an updraft of tremendous force. Estimates of its speed in large tornadoes is as high as 200 m.p.h. It is possible that there are updrafts much in excess of even this speed. Edward M. Brooks (in T. F. Malone) says that in June 1938 at Abilene, Texas, a tornado created a cumulonimbus cloud that shot up 35,000 feet in 60 seconds—a speed of some 400 m.p.h.!

The updraft is generally the cause of the first destruction; as the funnel commences to drop from the sky, small objects are sucked up from the earth.

Writing of the approach of a tornado, Talman says: "Around the top of the distant cloud observers tell of seeing black objects go wheeling through the air like flocks of birds. These are some of the multitudinous things that the monster has swept up from the face of the earth—trees, branches, parts of houses, living beings, or whatever else may happen to be in its path."

---

[2] The late C. E. P. Brooks commented: "Perhaps you have put too much emphasis on updraft. A good deal of the suction effect is probably due to the release of pressure on air in the ground."

Wood through steel! After the great tornado which ripped across St. Louis, Missouri, on May 27, 1896, this wooden plank was found embedded in a steel bridge.   *U. S. Weather Bureau*

Another man said that when he saw cornstalks and bed quilts coming down from the sky he knew it was time to look around for a tornado!

A Russian tornado was responsible for the Soviet equivalent of a "pennies from heaven" episode. On June 17, 1940, in the Gorky *Oblast* (region), silver kopecks fell on a village, and about 1,000 were collected. They had been minted in the latter part of the 16th century. What had happened? N. Kolobkov, who relates the incident, says: "Somewhere, the heavy rain had scoured away the soil and laid bare an old treasure of coins that were picked up by the tornado." Incidentally, Moscow has been hit by damaging tornadoes at least twice in this century: on the afternoons of June 29, 1904, and September 2, 1945.

When fully formed, the suction power of the updraft performs feats which, to those unacquainted with tornadic phenomena, seem incredible. Tornadoes have been known to carry large iron bridges from their foundations and drop them in a heap of crumpled battered metal. In one incident a 200-pound steel beam, 13½ feet long, was fastened down at each end with two half-inch bolts. The tornado hurled this beam an eighth of a mile, then drove it endwise through the heart of a cottonwood tree 15 inches in diameter at the point where it struck, 20 feet above the ground. On June 12, 1957, a tornado struck a steel airport hangar in Dallas County, Texas, and pulled the concrete piers from the ground (Wolford).

Flora says that the extremely violent tornado that struck Irving, Kansas, on May 30, 1879, lifted a large iron bridge from its piers and twisted it into an iron scrap heap. It also sucked up the water, exposing the river bed, and sprayed the water above the tops of the tallest trees.

W. J. Humphreys (1937), of the U. S. Weather Bureau, says that a man once walked into one of their offices and asked: "What I want to know is: Can the thing happen that I saw happen?" The man may be forgiven for doubting his own eyesight, for he thought he had seen a tornado pick up a railway engine from one track, turn it round in midair and set it down on a neighboring parallel track facing the other way! Humphreys commented: "What our observer saw happen could have happened." And the following encounters between trains and tornadoes, reported by Flora, support him.

On June 22, 1919, near Fergus Falls, Minnesota, a violent tornado struck the Oriental Limited as it was traveling at about 35 m.p.h. Seven of the eleven coaches were thrown from the rails, and the baggage car was wrenched away from the other cars and set down 30 feet away at right angles to the track. The tornado, presumably by a combination of vacuum and updraft, also tore out part of the track where the train had passed.

On May 27, 1931, again in Minnesota—near Moorhead—a tornado struck the Empire Builder when it was traveling at about 60 m.p.h. Five 70-ton coaches were lifted from the track, one being carried 80 feet and then laid in a ditch. It was later proved that one of the coaches had been lifted directly upward several inches from the track—the connecting coupling was found still closed.

Here are some of the miscellaneous objects which have been levitated by "this giant vacuum cleaner of the skies" as Humphreys calls the tornado. Each incident is recorded by a reliable authority.

An 800-pound ice chest was transported over three miles. The spire of a church, complete with weathercock, was carried 15 miles through the air. A wooden house was blown two miles, and the roof of another 12 miles. Some legal documents were carried 50 miles and dropped on the top of a mountain, and an insurance policy was taken for a 75-mile ride.

Glider pilots who have had the temerity to fly into regions of violent wind currents have sometimes had the wings torn off their machines. The most strongly built modern aircraft would have little chance if caught in the winds of a "prairie twister." It is possible that some unexplained disappearances of airplanes, when no trace of machine or load has been found, may be due to their having been caught in the furious winds of tornadoes. Robert N. Buck, an airline pilot, says that the wreckage of an aircraft torn apart by wind was spread over an area of seven square miles.

Tornadoes

Many times animals have been whisked from the ground and carried through the air. One tornado dipped into a corral, lifted out a cow and deposited her, not seriously injured, several hundred feet away. A bull was similarly levitated, carried 40 yards and then set down unhurt but, not surprisingly, bellowing frantically. A horse that was snatched from the ground was flung 200 yards and torn in two. But there are records of horses being carried half a mile (Wenstrom) and two miles (Ward) and being set down alive.

The Great Plains were also the favorite resort of the vast herds of bison, numbering tens of millions, which roamed North America before the coming of the white man. There is no parallel on earth today of the appalling scenes which must, at times, have been witnessed by the Plains Indians when the long dark funnel swept across the closely packed ranks of these great animals. Some of them weighed over a ton. Bison would have been hurled to the ground as the tornado cut a swath of dead and dying animals which might be miles long and hundreds of yards wide. Some bison would be lifted skyward, carried for a distance, then smashed to the ground. I know of only one observation which gives a glimpse of such fantastic happenings. Ely Moore says that two bison were found completely stripped of hair and with every bone broken.

Sir Graham Sutton says there is a Kansas story "of a herd of cows emulating the nursery rhyme and taking off for the moon looking like gigantic birds in the sky.' " I wrote to the U. S. Weather Bureau district office at Kansas City about this legend. Donald C. House, the meteorologist in charge, replied: "We have been unable to verify the legend you refer to in your letter, but we believe that it is within the realm of the possible." He added that if a herd of cows did thus become airborne they would probably refer to it as "the herd shot round the world."

Human beings are certainly carried aloft by tornadoes. During a tornado at El Dorado, Kansas, on June 10, 1958, a woman was sucked—or blown— through a window and carried 60 feet. When she landed she found beside her a phonograph record titled "Stormy Weather"—broken. On April 9, 1947, near Higgins, Texas, a man opened his front door just as a tornado struck. It picked him up and carried him 200 feet over the treetops. And at Lanark, Illinois, on April 18, 1955, a car containing two people was carried 100 feet, then dropped right side up without injuring the occupants (Wolford).

Finley tells of a man who was picked up by a tornado and, while traveling skyward, stretched out his hand which came in contact with the tail or mane of a horse (his indefiniteness may be pardoned in the circumstances). He grasped it firmly but during his aerial excursion he became separated from the horse, and when he eventually landed he was grasping a handful of horse's hair in one hand and his hat in the other. . . .

The Elements Rage   [50]

Many readers will disbelieve this story. But there is nothing intrinsically impossible in it, and it is recorded in all seriousness by one of America's foremost authorities. Burr says that five men and eight oxen were whirled into the air by a "cyclone" in South Africa. A man in Oklahoma told me that a woman and her baby had been snatched up, carried some way through the air and set down alive. He also said that a horse had been picked up and set down astride a barn.

It will no doubt be wondered why any living thing can go through such experiences and not be dashed to death. The explanation is that they frequently descend through an ascending air current (see also p. 119). If, of course, they fell from the height to which the tornado carried them—in extreme cases it may be a mile—through still air they would suffer severe injury or instant death. But the upward current of air allows them to be lowered gently to earth, as though descending by parachute.

This also accounts for the occasional "gentleness" of the twister. A house has been ripped apart, but the kitchen cupboard, filled with dishes, has been carried off and set down without one broken dish. Mirrors have traveled miles and then dropped undamaged. A 50-pound basket of books was transported two miles and then lodged in a tree with the contents intact. Another tornado picked up a jar of pickles, carried it 25 miles and then lowered it unharmed in a ditch. And pots of flowers have flown through the air for a mile or so and then fallen to the ground undamaged.

VACUUM

People who have had a tornado sweep over them and have lived to tell their tale speak of a bursting sensation in their ears and chest. This feeling is due to the partial vacuum formed in the tornado's funnel by the centrifugal force of the whirl. The exact fall in atmospheric pressure is not known; obviously it differs with various tornadoes. Normal pressure at sea level gives a barometer reading of 29.92 inches, or 14.7 pounds to the square inch.

Few barometers are likely to withstand the shock of a big tornado. Nevertheless, there are a few records of barometer readings taken at the time a tornado passed, or passed near by, which show a drastic drop in pressure. It is almost certain that the actual drop is greater than that shown on instruments. Inside buildings pressure changes take some seconds to register and the tornado is gone before the barometer shows the lowest figure. T. S. Outram records the experience of two men who watched a barometer as a tornado passed and saw the needle sink momentarily to 23.0 inches, giving a drop of about $3\frac{1}{2}$ pounds per square inch from normal pressure.

If, allowing for the difference between land and sea level, possible exaggeration, and instrumental error, it is assumed the pressure dropped only two pounds per square inch, this is still an enormous figure. Expressed in terms of the air in a small building 20 by 10 by 10 feet, it means that the

Homes torn apart by the tornado which devastated parts of Massachusetts on June 9, 1953, killing ninety people, injuring 1,288. *Worcester Telegram-Gazette*

drop in air pressure outside causes a sudden upward force on the ceiling of about 26 tons and an outward force on each of the walls of about 13 tons. The two movements of the air, upward and outward, seem necessary to explain some of the incidents which occur in tornadoes. Moreover, the structure against which the forces are applied has probably been battered already by the tornado's violent winds.

These forces would be released if the reduction in air pressure in the center of the tornado's funnel was no more than 15 per cent of normal. Milham says, however, that from the explosive effects produced it has been estimated that in some tornadoes pressure drops to perhaps 50 per cent of normal. It is difficult to visualize what an enormous figure this is. It is necessary to remember these figures if undue scepticim is to be avoided when considering some of the believe-it-or-not results of the vacuum effect of tornadoes.

When anything containing air is encompassed by the tornado's funnel, the reduction in the surrounding pressure causes the internal air to burst outward with explosive violence. When the funnel encompasses a house, air

The Elements Rage [52]

often cannot escape quickly enough and frequently houses literally explode—destroyed by the outrush of the entrapped air.

The passing of the funnel rips the surface off highways and digs holes in the ground; pulls corks out of bottles; splits kegs wide open; explodes chests, scattering their contents far and wide; peels bark off trees; explodes automobile tires; strips harness off horses—and clothes off human beings, sometimes leaving them completely naked. The sudden reduction of outside pressure could cause a man literally to burst, but I have not read or heard of such a macabre happening.

Finley says that after one tornado dead sheep were found shorn of their wool to the bare skin. Chickens are frequently denuded of feathers and often survive the depluming. Hazen says: "In some cases roosters have been seen walking around, days after the tornado, crowing, and without a feather on their backs." A woman in Oklahoma told me that she had known a tornado to deplume a chicken and drive the feathers into trees.

Why the feathers are plucked is not known for certain. It has been suggested that it is the result of the vacuum, but James P. Espy put a chicken in the receiver of an air pump and then rapidly exhausted the air. But the rooster retained its feathers. Perhaps, however, the vacuum formation was too slow. Flora suggests that the hollow quills may suddenly expand, or explode, in the funnel's vacuum. He says that after a tornado near Lansing, Michigan, on June 1, 1943, thirty nude chickens were found in the poultry house. They were all sitting stiffly to attention—dead. G. W. Reynolds in his study of the problem concluded that the feathers were blown off rather than sucked out.

Moore, in his report on the 1896 St. Louis tornado, gives a vivid example of the immense suction power of its funnel. He saw bricks in a plastered wall "neatly cleaned of all plaster by the expansion of the air inside the brick, as the air pressure from the outside was reduced."

Some remarkable incidents were witnessed during the great tornado which struck Worcester, Massachusetts, on June 9, 1953. A man carrying a crate of eggs said they started "popping out but they weren't falling to the ground." And two mothers said that they saw a child floating away but pulled it down—like a balloon on a string. There is a resemblance between some of the phenomena of the tornado's vacuum effect and those of the spaceman's weightlessness.

During some tornadoes soft materials, such as clothes, become saturated with mud. The existence of the mud is explained by the deluge of rain which frequently accompanies a tornado. But what accounts for the remarkable penetration? W. M. Davis suggests that it is due to the inrush of air following the passing of the partial vacuum in the funnel. He says that clothes which have thus become impregnated by mud cannot be cleansed by repeated washings. According to Finley heavy bed quilts have been "so filled with mud that when dry they were as stiff and hard as boards."

Pressure, updraft, and vacuum have been dealt with separately, but obviously all three effects are present in any tornado, and some results are probably caused by a combination of all three. Anything in the direct path of a tornado experiences a fourfold attack: pressure from the first winds, vacuum and updraft from the funnel, and then pressure again from the second winds (the back wall of the tornado).

Tornado damage has many similarities to the freakish destruction caused by conventional bomb blast. As that sometimes skips a house, while destroying or damaging those on either side, so a tornado funnel often jumps over one place to descend and destroy a few yards farther on. This action, plus the other effects of the winds, helps to account for some of the strange incidents recounted in tornado lore. There is nothing intrinsically impossible in these stories—highly improbable though they must appear to those unacquainted with tornadoes.

Humphreys (1937) says that in a small town in Oklahoma one building only was untouched by the tornado of May 2, 1920—the unoccupied one-story wooden town jail—yet 30 feet away a *concrete* store was utterly wrecked. A tornado sometimes runs along a wire fence, pulling up the supporting posts and rolling up the wire as if it were knitting yarn. The resulting ball may be 50 feet in diameter. During the great tornado on June 30, 1912, at Regina, Saskatchewan, a telephone pole was seen traveling vertically down a street.

Tornadoes frequently lift water. Even deep wells with 20 feet or so of water are sometimes drained. Finley (1890) says that in one well two buckets of milk were hanging. It was common practice in Finley's day to do this in order to cool the milk. A tornado came along, hoisted the two buckets and departed with them for parts unknown! When the tornado of June 23, 1944, passed over a river in West Virginia, the river was momentarily sucked dry where the funnel passed, leaving the bed exposed.

Often the tornado's destructive funnel skims over the ground, 20 or 30 feet high, and sometimes it shears off the upper stories of buildings leaving the lower parts practically unscathed. When a large tornado struck Louisville, Kentucky, on March 27, 1890, it appears that the funnel never actually touched the ground but raced across the town at some 80 m.p.h. demolishing the upper stories of buildings. But few houses were wrecked and many single-story buildings were untouched. Yet 76 people were killed, many injured, and much property destroyed. Had this tornado swept across the town at ground level the devastation would have been catastrophic.

There is a rending action in a tornado's winds. They appear to have very unequal motions in a small space. Bedding and clothing are often torn to rags. During a tornado in South Africa sheets of corrugated iron were swept from two strongly-constructed sheds, crumpled like paper, and carried for miles.[3]

Tornadoes have several effects on trees. Owing to the whirling winds trees often fall on opposite sides of the path and also at opposite angles. Sometimes a tornado just plucks off the tops of trees, at other times it twists them clean out of the ground. A violent tornado carries trees aloft and they sail through the air like huge misshapen birds. A tornado on June 18, 1927, at Elfros, Saskatchewan, cleared a strip of bush country, seven miles long by 200 yards wide. Thousands of trees were piled on either side of the strip, some heaps being 50 feet high (A. B. Lowe and G. A. McKay).

The sucking rending violence of a tornado's winds harries and scours the earth itself as the funnel passes over. A very powerful tornado plows the earth in deep furrows; at other times it digs circular holes in the ground. William Cobb, a Kansas farmer, said that a tornado which crossed Kiowa County on June 22, 1928, plowed a furrow across a pasture of buffalo grass a mile long and up to five feet deep (quoted by Alonzo A. Justice). Lowe and McKay say that a tornado at Killarney, in western Canada, dug up a farmer's potato crop—fortunately at harvesttime.

A tornado's habit of skipping was responsible for one of the most remarkable observations ever made. Will Keller, a Kansas farmer, was out in a field in the afternoon of June 22, 1928, when he saw a tornado heading in his direction. He ran to his cyclone cellar, but just as he was about to close the door he turned for a last look as the destroyer swept down on him. Here is his account of what he saw [quoted by Justice]:

> As I paused to look I saw that the lower end which had been sweeping the ground was beginning to rise. I knew what that meant, so I kept my position. I knew that I was comparatively safe and I knew that if the tornado again dipped I could drop down and close the door before any harm could be done.
>
> Steadily the tornado came on, the end gradually rising above the ground. I could have stood there only a few seconds but so impressed was I with what was going on that it seemed a long time. At last the great shaggy end of the funnel hung directly overhead. Everything was as still as death. There was a strong gassy odor and it seemed that I could not breathe. There was a screaming, hissing sound coming directly from the end of the funnel. I looked up and to my astonishment I saw right up into the heart of the tornado. There was a circular opening in the center of the funnel, about 50 or 100 feet in diameter, and extending straight upward for a distance of at least one half mile, as best I could judge under the circumstances. The walls of this

---

[3] This was a true tornado, not a thunderstorm squall, which is called a tornado in West Africa.

opening were of rotating clouds and the whole was made brilliantly visible by constant flashes of lightning which zigzagged from side to side. Had it not been for the lightning I could not have seen the opening, not any distance up into it anyway.

Around the lower rim of the great vortex small tornadoes were constantly forming and breaking away. These looked like tails as they writhed their way around the end of the funnel. It was these that made the hissing noise.

I noticed that the direction of rotation of the great whirl was anticlockwise, but the small twisters rotated both ways—some one way and some another.

The opening was entirely hollow except for something which I could not exactly make out, but suppose that it was a detached wind cloud. This thing was in the center and was moving up and down.

At least two other men have had the eye of the funnel pass over them and lived to tell their tale.

A motorist, traveling with his wife, noticed a large dust cloud in his path but drove ahead. As soon as he entered it he realized his mistake as flying debris broke the windshield and windows. He bent down for protection, but during a comparative lull he looked up and saw boards, branches of trees and a head-sized boulder floating round the car. This was almost certainly the moment when the eye of the funnel was directly overhead. Then the whirling outer winds struck and he and his wife were flung out of the car into the road (quoted by E. V. Van Tassel).

Robert Jackson was caught in a Kansas tornado on May 20, 1957, and saved himself by lying down with his arms gripping the roots of a tree. He said that the tornado's eye was comparatively calm, like a hurricane's (quoted by Lowe and McKay).

Various observers have remarked on the electrical discharges accompanying tornadoes. Hazen argues that some of the effects usually attributed to the wind may actually be the result of electrical properties in the tornado. Wenstrom says that explosions occurred on the ground beneath which a tornado was forming, but before it had actually touched the earth.

H. C. Russell says that a man in Australia saw a tornado strike a dead pine tree. Afterward he rode up to the tree and found fire and smoke at the base; he was certain there was no fire before the tornado struck.

Tornadoes are described by early Greek writers; although, being a maritime people, they were more concerned with waterspouts. Some meteorologists consider that there are tornado references in the Old Testament. Was the fiery whirlwind that snatched Elijah up to heaven a lightning-filled tornado? Ezekiel's strange description in Chapter 1 of "the likeness of four living creatures" may be the attempt of a writer, more familiar with religion and its symbols than with meteorology, to describe strange events in the heavens. Verse 4, at the beginning of Ezekiel's description, reads:

And I looked, and, behold, a whirlwind came out of the north, a great cloud, and a fire infolding itself, and a brightness *was* about it, and out of the midst thereof as the colour of amber, out of the midst of the fire.

It needs no great imagination to see here a sand-filled ("amber") tornado with lightning playing around the cloud. G. B. Bathurst, who analyzes the whole description, wonders if this is the earliest fully reported tornado—the date would be about 600 B.C.

Tornadoes sometimes form when great heat is generated, as in volcanoes and fires. The heat sends hot air rushing upward and this starts the typical tornadic whirling action. Writing of the new Mexican volcano Parícutin, Frederick H. Pough says that he saw a great rush of gas from the crater which formed a miniature tornado some 20 feet in diameter and roared away "as if it had irresistible force." Charles Lyell says that during the far greater eruption of the Indonesian volcano Tambora in April 1815 tornadoes formed which tore large trees from the ground, covered the surrounding seas with debris, and tossed houses, men, and cattle into the air (C. E. Wurtzburg and J. T. Ross).

On that black day, September 1, 1923, when the Tokyo-Yokohama area of Japan was devastated by earthquake, fire, and flood, the final horror came from the "dragon twists"—fire-induced tornadoes. The immense heat of burning Tokyo sent hot air rushing upward at some 150 m.p.h. to form an immense pile of artificial cumulus cloud that bulked larger and taller than Everest. Terrified survivors of the earthquake and fire saw writhing pillars of black smoke, skyscraper tall and wide as office blocks, bearing down on them. In one area alone a tornado was estimated to have killed 40,000 people (Noel F. Busch).

More remarkable, from a meteorological aspect, was what happened during the great oil fire at San Luis Obispo, California, which lasted for five days during April 1926. This was described by J. E. Hissong of the local Weather Bureau office. The fire, which spread over some 900 acres, had been started by lightning and nearly six million barrels of oil were burnt, 15 million dollars' worth of property destroyed, and two people killed.

Hundreds of whirlwinds were seen over or near the fire and "many of them had all the characteristics of true tornadoes. The gyrating, writhing, funnel-shaped clouds with the white condensing vapor in the vortices were plainly visible against the background of black smoke. Some of the funnels appeared to be not more than one foot in diameter at the smallest part, and some were reported as giving the impression of ropes dangling from the clouds of smoke." Some of the tornadoes carried debris for about three miles. Fruit trees were uprooted and some were twisted so that their boles cracked.

One of these tornadoes writhed beyond the area of the fire, lifted a cottage several feet, carried it about 50 yards and then dropped it as a total wreck, killing the two people inside. Another tornado picked up a house and, according to onlookers, raised it 300 feet, carried it 100 feet, then dropped it completely demolished.

These artificially induced tornadoes also occur in forest fires. Howard E. Graham of the Fire Weather Service, Portland, Oregon, and a companion watched a forest fire on August 23, 1951, at Vincent Creek.

From our vantage point about 200 yards away it was evident that violent whirling surface winds existed near the fire over a diameter of some 100 to 200 feet. In the middle of this circulation was a dark tornado-like tube extending upward, whose top was obscured by drift smoke above approximately 1,000 feet. The winds in this tube were so extreme that a green Douglas-fir tree, which at breast height was about 40 inches in diameter, was quickly twisted and broken off about 20 feet above the ground. Near the whirlwind the fire flames leaped several times higher than those in surrounding areas. A large treetop burst into flame like the flash of a powder keg when the whirl passed by. Within the tube, gases and debris were moving upward at a high velocity. The whirling column remained nearly stationary during its activity, moving little more than 50 yards; had that not been the case, extremely rapid fire spread might have resulted. The whirlwind rapidly disappeared and as rapidly re-formed a moment later, repeating this procedure at least three times during a 10-minute interval.

Graham points out that such fire whirlwinds over large fires are infrequent, and other conditions, besides intense local heat, must therefore be satisfied before they form. These probably involve relatively high temperature, wind currents, and topography.

Sir Napier Shaw says that there was a suggestion during the First World War to create tornadoes artificially for the discomfiture of the enemy. One ingenious inventor claimed that shells fired vertically in rapid succession would produce a vortex and start the tornadic process. Apparently the thought did not occur to him that in the unlikely event of the success of his scheme the tornado might sweep against his own lines.

Tornadoes occurred in the Second World War as a result of fire-bombing. The normal fire raids, terrible as they were, could be dealt with, but occasionally these raids turned into the dreaded fire-storms against which all human aid was vain. The first occurred in Hamburg during the large bomber raid on the night of July 27, 1943. There had been a heat wave and the night was sultry. This doomed Hamburg. The rain of high explosives and incendiaries, and the fires they started, turned sultriness into violent heat. The resultant fire storm burnt out eight square miles of the city.

David Irving says:

As a result of the sudden linking of a number of fires, the air above heated to such an extent that a violent updraught occurred which, in turn, caused the surrounding fresh air to be sucked in from all sides to the centre of the fire area. This tremendous suction caused movements of air of far greater force than normal winds. In meteorology the differences of temperature involved are of the order of 20 to 30 degrees C. In this fire-storm they were of the order of 600, 800 or even 1,000 degrees C. This explained the colossal force of the fire-storm winds.

In typical tornado fashion, the funnels twisted large trees out of the ground and tossed them as giant torches into the air; tore the clothes off people fleeing for shelter; and overturned cars and trucks. Nor was this all. The oxygen at ground level was burnt up and thousands suffocated in the shelters. Not surprisingly, a contemporary German account says what happened on this night went "beyond all human imagination." (Sir Arthur Harris)

A tornado also formed after the atomic bombing of Hiroshima and was strong enough to uproot large trees.

According to the U. S. Weather Bureau, in the 46-year period 1916–1961, 11,056 tornadoes were reported in the United States. The actual number of tornadoes during this period was, of course, much greater, as many occurred in uninhabited areas or, for one reason or another, were never reported (see p. 67). During these 46 years property damage amounted to roughly 700 million dollars (about 15 million dollars a year) and 9,397 people were killed (about 200 a year). Statistics show that, on average, about 13 people are injured for every one killed.

A township can be wiped out by a tornado. Look what happened when a twister ripped across Udal, Kansas, on the night of May 25, 1955. Out of a population of 610, 80 died and 270 were injured. Of the 187 houses, 170 were smashed to rubble, 16 damaged beyond repair—one escaped unscathed. The estimated damage was $2\frac{1}{4}$ million dollars. *Time* magazine (June 6, 1955) reported:

> Old Railroader Fred Dye was snatched out of his shoes, whirled outdoors and thrown alive up a tree. Barber Henry Norris went to bed, woke up unhurt in the street: "I don't know how I got there." Will Sweet and his wife cowered in a back bedroom until it was over, then opened the door and found the rest of the house gone. Norman Lanning huddled with his wife and three children against the kitchen wall by the refrigerator, which skidded away; the wall was the only thing left standing in the area, and it saved them. "Oh God," said Lanning. "How lucky we were."

They certainly were. Urban J. Linehan, in his study of tornado deaths, says that ten people were killed in one house during a tornado in Colorado.

The utter devastation left by a great tornado. During the tornadoes which swept across parts of Texas, Oklahoma, and Arkansas on April 9, 1947, nearly two hundred homes were reduced to rubble like this, 169 died, nearly one thousand were injured.   *United Press—American Red Cross*

Tornadoes, like lightning, sometimes strike more than once in the same place. On May 4, 1922, Austin, Texas, was hit twice in half an hour, as was Baldwyn, Mississippi, on March 16, 1942. Ellis County, in Oklahoma, was damaged by a tornado on April 9, 1947; then on May 31 the same area was hit again, but, owing to the extensive damage from the earlier tornado, there was virtually nothing left to destroy (Wolford).

What is the first known American tornado? According to David Ludlum, an authority on early American weather, it was one that struck a meetinghouse in Massachusetts in 1643. He adds that, although an Indian was killed, the tornado "was regarded more as a curiosity than a significant event." Later generations of Americans were to learn differently.

Ludlum has also drawn my attention to a vivid description of a tornado by George Milligen-Johnston in his *A short description of the Province of South Carolina,* published in 1770. It struck Charleston on May 4, 1761, "a terrible phenomenon resembling a large column of smoke and vapor. Its prodigious velocity gave it such a surprising momentum as to plow Ashley River to the bottom, and to lay the channel bare." It went on to hit warships offshore, sinking five and dismasting several more. The tornado then struck southwest leaving a wide swath of destruction "tearing up trees, houses and everything that opposed it; great quantities of leaves, branches of trees, even large limbs, were seen furiously driven about, and agitated in the body of the column as it passed along." (I have abbreviated and modernized the account.)

The most deadly of these early tornadoes occurred on May 7, 1840, at Natchez, Mississippi, killing 317 people (Lorin Blodget and Natchez *Courier,* May 8, 1840).

The most destructive tornado known in American history, and possibly in world history, occurred on March 18, 1925. It formed about 1 P.M. in southeast Missouri and in a little over three hours had blasted an almost straight and continuous path of 219 miles across southern Illinois, finally blowing itself out about 30 miles inside Indiana. During its course, the storm cloud varied in width between half a mile and a mile, and its speed between 57 and 68 m.p.h. Thus in length of path, width of cloud, and speed of travel this tornado was exceptional, being very much above average in all three. "Very few people reported seeing anything like a funnel-shaped vortex cloud in the course of this storm. Apparently the storm cloud was so close to the earth there was no room for a pendent cloud." (Flora)

The toll of this great tristate tornado was: 689 people killed, 1,980 injured, and property losses of some 17 million dollars.[4] Some 3,000 houses were destroyed or damaged and four small towns practically wiped out. The saddest feature of this terrible disaster was that, although the tornado lasted over three hours and traveled 200 miles, nobody gave warning. Fortunately, such an elementary lack of foresight is virtually impossible today.

Flora says that the 60 tornadoes which struck the Deep South on February 19, 1884, killed 800 people. The tornado of September 1, 1952, which hit Carswell Air Force Base in Texas wrecked 106 heavy bombers and caused altogether nearly 50 million dollars' worth of damage.

---

[4] The most deadly of tornadoes occurred recently—the Midwest tornadoes of April 11, 1965, which killed 240, injured 5,000 more. The tornado of June 9, 1953, which ripped through central and eastern Massachusetts was the most expensive in terms of property damage—52 million dollars' worth. Anthony F. C. Wallace's detailed report on this tornado contains much information on a community's reaction to a tornado disaster.

Tornadoes [61]

Not bombs but wind did this. On March 20, 1948, a tornado lashed into Tinker Air Force Base, Oklahoma, leaving fifty aircraft completely destroyed, fifty others damaged.   *U. S. Air Force*

The worst tornado in Canadian history struck Regina, Saskatchewan, on June 30, 1912, killing 28, injuring hundreds, and causing damage estimated at four million dollars (the equivalent of about 16 million dollars today).

Both Flora and Wolford have sections on non-American tornadoes, including references to the literature. Wegener says that there are records of 258 tornadoes and waterspouts in Europe between 1456 and 1913. Undoubtedly, the actual number was much greater. In New Zealand, with an area less than that of Nevada, an average of nine tornadoes are reported each year. As New Zealand is sparsely populated, the yearly total is probably nearer 25 (C. J. Seelye).

The British Isles, especially the east Midlands of England, have had many tornadoes through the centuries. The earliest one of which there is authentic record struck London on October 17, 1091. Roger de Hoveden says that 600 houses were blown down, as well as many churches. And John of Worcester says that in May 1140 at Welsburn (now Wellesbourne), Warwickshire, "a very violent whirlwind sprang up, a hideous darkness extended from the earth to the sky and the house of a priest was violently shaken, and

The Elements Rage   [62]

all of his outbuildings were thrown down and broken to pieces." He adds that the church roof was carried away, some 40 houses severely damaged, and large hailstones fell, one of which killed a woman. Undoubtedly many tornadoes went unrecorded in those distant days, as the country was sparsely populated and scribes were few.

About 60 tornadoes were reported during the 83 years from 1868 to 1950. I say "about" because more than one report may refer to the same tornado. London was hit three times during this period. In the evening of October 22, 1928, a small tornado traveled in a direct line from Victoria to Euston, causing damage of about £15,000. Large quantities of masonry were blown into the streets but no one was killed: most people were sheltering from the heavy rain.

According to the British Meteorological Office: "Destructive tornadoes have been reported in the British Isles (mainly south and central) with a frequency somewhat greater than once in two years: because of their very local nature, however, some may be unrecorded and their actual frequency of occurrence is probably appreciably greater than this." (D. H. McIntosh)

Two British tornadoes (with accompanying smaller ones) have been the subject of detailed investigation, resulting in government reports. The South Wales tornado swept 100 miles along the boundary of England and Wales from Barry to Chester on the evening of October 27, 1913. It grew out of a violent thunderstorm which traveled from Devon to Cheshire. The tornado left a path of damage for 11 miles in Glamorganshire, 11 miles in Shropshire and 5 miles in Cheshire. There were also signs of another tornado in the same area in Wales, but this was less violent. The main tornado traveled at an average speed of about 35 m.p.h. and had a maximum width of 1,000 feet.

At Treforest the iron chimney stack of the generating station was blown down and the whole western side of the building, made of corrugated iron sheets, collapsed outward. A few miles away the tornado completely wrenched off the corrugated iron roof of a store. Later such a piece of metal was found over half a mile away firmly wrapped round a fallen telegraph pole.

The tornado moved on. It lifted the roofs off houses; wrecked a church, piling up the pews against the west wall; picked up cows, carried them over a high hedge and dropped them in a field, killing three; uprooted trees, blowing one 80 yards; twisted the tops off other trees, leaving only the trunks standing; picked up one large tree and dropped it in the middle of a field. Before the day was done this tornado had claimed five lives.

In the afternoon of May 21, 1950, three tornadoes occurred which have been more thoroughly investigated than any others in British history. With some breaks, the path of the main tornado stretched from Wendover, Buckinghamshire, to Ely, Cambridgeshire, 65 miles away, in about 2½ hours—one of the longest paths ever recorded for a tornado in the British Isles

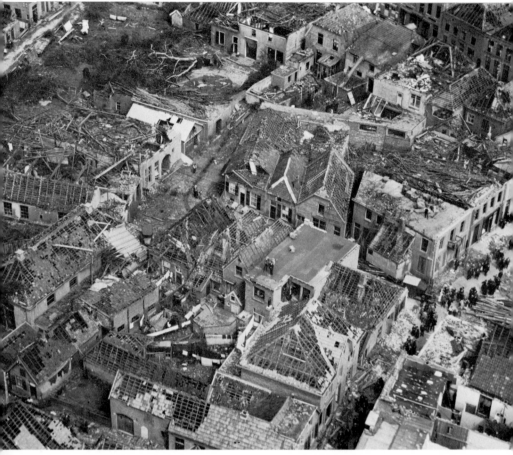

Havoc in Borculo, Holland, after the tornado of August 10, 1925. Although not so frequent, and rarely as violent, as those in North America, Europe is no stranger to twisters.   *KLM Aerocarto N. V., The Netherlands*

or the continent of Europe.[5] The tornado varied considerably in width and speed, maxima being 80 yards and not less than 110 m.p.h. It was accompanied by heavy rain, lightning and hail—some stones were about two inches in diameter (H. H. Lamb).

L. C. W. Bonacina quotes the following eyewitness description by people who saw the tornado near Wendover:

---

[5] Although no further damage was reported, the tornado was seen lowering and withdrawing into the cloud base at more distant points, and was last seen over the sea off Blakeney, Norfolk—some 120 miles from its starting point. Incidentally, the longest recorded European track is about 300 miles (Wegener).

All of a sudden it became as dark as night, and before we had time to wonder what was about to happen there was a terrific crash of thunder followed by an avalanche of large hail, which devastated all the telegraph wires along the road and lay inches deep on it. Then when all this had abated sufficiently we ventured to look at the sky, to see the black clouds literally spinning like a top and scores of tree tops being snatched off their trunks and hurtling through the air.

Total damage in these tornadoes was estimated to be in excess of £50,-000. Damage and destruction to trees was particularly severe; in one place an orchard was uprooted and near by a swath, some 15 yards wide, was torn through a wood. Full-grown oak trees were felled, and the branches and most of the trunk of an oak a yard in diameter were twisted off. At Linslade, Buckinghamshire, 50 houses were unroofed; a brick-built bakery demolished; and cars, and a horse box complete with horse, were lifted and tossed about.

One of the most macabre tragedies in the whole violent saga of tornadoes occurred in an English village. It created such a sensation that several tracts were written about it (J. B. Rowe, and L. C. W. Bonacina). The village schoolmaster also composed a poem about the tragedy. This was painted on boards and has been seen by many thousands of visitors to Widecombe (Eliott Colpoys Wood).

The tornado struck on Sunday, October 21, 1638, at Widecombe-in-the-Moor on the southern flank of Dartmoor.[6] The congregation was gathered in the church and the vicar had just begun the service when suddenly everything went black and the building was hit by wind and lightning of the utmost violence. A ball of fire moved through the church and then burst with a thunderous explosion. "Which so much affrighted the whole Congregation that the most part of them fell downe into their seates, and some upon their knees, some on their faces, and some one upon another, with a great cry of burning and scalding, they all giving up themselves for dead."

If a bomb had exploded in the church the damage and carnage could hardly have been worse. The roof and tower were wrecked, stone and masonry showered down both inside and outside the building.

The tornado and lightning ball killed and maimed scores of men and women—and a dog. People were snatched from the pews and whirled about. Some were set down completely unharmed, others were dashed against walls and pillars. A man's head "was cloven, his skull rent into three pieces, and

---

[6] On Sunday, August 4, 1557, two other church services in Suffolk were wrecked by similarly catastrophic storms, including tornadoes. At Bungay "the church did as it were quake and stagger, which struck into the hearts of those that were present such a sore and sudden fear, that they were robbed in a manner of their right wits." Details and references are given by J. B. Harvey.
For a somewhat similar incident during a church service in Norfolk on July 2, 1665, see D. Justin Schove.

his braines throwne upon the ground whole, and the haire of his head, through the violence of the blow at first given him, did sticke fast unto the pillar or wall of the church; so that hee perished there most lamentably."

The lightning ball added to the havoc, as witness the description of what befell Mistress Ditford. "Her gowne, two wastcoates, and linnen next her body, burned cleane off; and her back also very grievously downe to her waste burned and scalded, and so exceedingly afflicted thereby, shee could neither stand nor goe without helpe, being lead out of the church." The tracts say that many other people were "burned and scalded in divers places of their bodies." Altogether about 60 were killed or injured.

All this took place in a few seconds, and while those who were left alive were still numb with uncomprehending horror, the church was filled with "a very thick mist, with smother, smoake and smell." The latter, reminiscent of brimstone, came from the lightning and bursting fireball. But to the 17th-century worshipers it was the signature of the Devil himself. Many believed—understandably enough—that the Last Judgment had come and they were in the very flames of Hell. Centuries later a child in a Devonshire school was asked: "What do you know of your ghostly enemy?" He replied: "If you please, ma'am, he lives to Widecombe" (Wood).

The tracts end with a familiar prayer, charged with a new and terrible meaning:

> From lightening and tempest, from Plague, Pestilence and Famine, from Battell and murder, and from suddaine death, Good Lord deliver us.

F. F. Tuckett was in a chapel on a mountain near Susa, Italy, when lightning struck and the effects were similar, though not so tragic.

> We were blinded, deafened, smothered, and struck, all in a breath. The place seemed filled with fire, our ears rang with the report, fragments of what looked like incandescent matter rained down upon us as though a meteorite had burst, and a suffocating, sulphurous odour—probably due to the sudden production of ozone in large quantities—almost choked us.

In view of the danger and damage from tornadoes some meteorologists have wondered if it is possible to prevent them. But the total masses of air involved are so vast that nothing short of a massive nuclear explosion could influence them—in this case better the disease than the cure! However, it may be possible to attack a tornado once it is formed by seeding the parent thunderclouds.

In the United States much attention has been given to broadcasting advance tornado warnings. One result has been that more tornadoes have been found! Writing in 1958, Morris Tepper says that since about 1920 the average number of tornadoes reported annually has risen more than fivefold. This can only mean that many tornadoes used to go unreported. During the period 1682–1874 about 150 tornadoes were recorded; during 1916–1961, 11,056.

In Kansas City, Missouri, there is a Severe Local Storm Warning Center which tries to forecast areas where tornadoes are likely, and then sends out appropriate warnings. The areas may be more than 100 miles across. Some of the information comes from specially equipped research airplanes, loaded with weather instruments, which deliberately fly into likely clouds, avoiding, of course, the deadly funnel. It has also been suggested that rockets equipped with television cameras could be used to view storm areas.

Electrical discharges from a tornado cloud send out radio waves of unusually high frequency. As these can be detected many miles away it is possible to pinpoint the dangerous cloud and send out the necessary warning. Radar also is used, but is more useful for tracking tornadoes already formed than for detecting them.

Flora, who for 47 years was a meteorologist of the U. S. Weather Bureau in tornado-prone Kansas, considers that a modern reinforced steel and concrete building should be relatively safe even if directly in the path of the worst tornado. As proof, look at what happened in Albany, Georgia, during the violent tornado of February 10, 1940, which destroyed 32 city blocks. Right in the path of the storm was the Hotel Gordon, six stories of steel and concrete. On each side of the hotel, buildings were lifted into the air and demolished, yet apart from extensive damage to its windows the hotel suffered hardly at all. The best way to seek safety in such a building is to crouch against one of the inside partitions, preferably in a southwest corner.

Flora gives the following advice to anyone who is out in the open when a tornado is around:

> The best thing is to lie down in a ditch or gully, the deeper the better. But in such a crisis, you can't be too particular. I knew a man and his wife who were trapped in a storm near Topeka. They crouched in a shallow excavation that had been used for storing apples, and although it was not more than three feet deep, they escaped injury, while their house and barns were carried away. If you have no other alternative, run as fast as you can to the northwest, at right angles to the movement of the storm. When the tornado is only a few hundred yards in width, it is possible to evade it in this manner.

The advice to run in a northwesterly direction is because tornadoes in the United States usually travel from southwest to northeast. If a tornado is seen in the distance which appears to be standing still but grows wider and noisier, then it is probably moving directly toward you. So, again, run to the northwest. If, however, the tornado is seen to be moving, it will probably

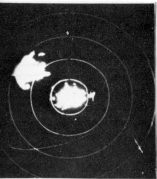
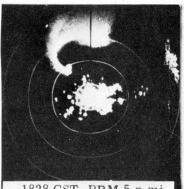
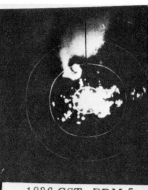

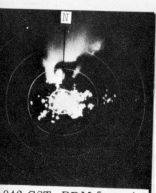

Successive photographs of development and decay of tornado funnel as seen on radar screen. The tornado occurred at Meriden, Kansas, on May 19, 1960.   *U. S. Weather Bureau*

bypass you. As the forward speed of a tornado averages under 30 m.p.h., people in cars should be able to outdistance it fairly easily. Incidentally, anyone witnessing a tornado should send full details—and any films and photographs—to the nearest meteorological office.

Further advice to anyone caught in the open by a twister is given by Talman.

> If flight is impossible, persons caught in the open are advised to lie flat on the ground, face down, preferably in a ditch or other depression, and as far as possible from trees and telegraph poles. The body, and especially the face, should be protected with blankets, automobile cushions, or anything else at hand in order to prevent one's flesh from being penetrated and lacerated by the quantities of sand, gravel, fine splinters and the like that, flying at the speed of a bullet, usually fill the air during the passage of the storm.

The Elements Rage

TORNADO
SAFETY RULES

TO KNOW WHAT TO DO WHEN A TORNADO IS APPROACHING, MAY MEAN THE DIFFERENCE BETWEEN LIFE OR DEATH ! !

I If you are near a tornado cellar :

When time permits, go to a tornado cellar, cave, or underground excavation which should have an air outlet to help equalize the air pressure. It should be kept fit for use, free from water, gas, or debris; and preferably equipped with pick and shovel. THERE IS NO UNIVERSAL PROTECTION AGAINST TORNADOES EXCEPT UNDERGROUND EXCAVATIONS.

II If you are in open country :

1. Move at right angles to the tornado's path. Tornadoes usually move ahead at about 25 to 40 miles per hour.

2. If there is no time to escape, lie flat in the nearest depression such as a ditch or ravine.

III If in a city or town :

1. Seek inside shelter, preferably in a strongly reinforced building. STAY AWAY FROM WINDOWS!

2. In homes: The corner of the basement toward the tornado usually offers greatest safety, particularly in frame houses. People in houses without basements can sometimes be protected by taking cover under heavy furniture against inside walls. Doors and windows on the sides of the house away from the tornado may be opened to help reduce damage to the building.

3. Standing against the inside wall on a lower floor of an office building offers some protection.

IV If in schools :

1. In city areas: If school building is of strongly reinforced construction, stay inside, away from windows, remain near an inside wall on the lower floors when possible. AVOID AUDITORIUMS AND GYMNASIUMS with large, poorly-supported roofs!

2. In rural schools that do not have strongly reinforced construction, remove children and teachers to a ravine or ditch if storm shelter is not available.

V If in factories and industrial plants :

On receiving a tornado warning, a lookout should be posted to keep safety officials advised of the tornado's approach. Advance preparation should be made for moving workers to sections of the plant offering the greatest protection.

VI Keep calm! It will not help to get excited. People have been killed by running out into streets and by turning back into the path of a tornado. Even though a warning is issued, chances of a tornado striking one's home or location are very slight. Tornadoes cover such a small zone, as a rule, that relatively only a few places in a warned area are directly affected. You should know about tornadoes though, "just in case". See other side for details.

VII Keep tuned to your radio or television station for latest tornado advisory information. Do not call the Weather Bureau, except to report a tornado, as your individual request may tie up telephone lines urgently needed to receive special reports or to relay advisories to radio and television stations for dissemination to thousands in the critical area.

UNITED STATES DEPARTMENT OF COMMERCE
WEATHER BUREAU

U. S. GOVERNMENT PRINTING OFFICE : 1962 O - 638697

For sale by the Superintendent of Documents, U.S. Government Printing Office, Washington 25, D.C. - Price 5 cents

Tornado warning.

In tornado-prone regions storm, or cyclone, cellars are built. Sometimes they are reinforced basements, sometimes underground rooms separate from the house. Flora and Finley give full directions for the making of such shelters as well as many other safety hints. Incidentally, Moore, writing from a very wide knowledge of tornadoes, says that he has never known of anybody being killed by a tornado while sheltering in the cellar of a frame house.

Far flimsier structures have, at times, provided shelter. A man was driving his car in Kansas one summer when he saw an ominous cloud approaching. Fearing it might be a tornado, the motorist abandoned his car (why he did not make full speed for the horizon I don't know) and ran for cover in a nearby school. The door was locked, so he dived into the coal shed at the rear of the building. A moment later the tornado struck. The car was blown off the road, the school was wrecked, but the coal shed and the motorist were unhurt.

Chapter 3

Waterspouts

A waterspout, or water tornado, is one of the most remarkable spectacles that any ocean traveler can behold. From the dawn of history men have set down their experiences of this freak creation of wind, weather, and sea. Lucretius, writing in the 1st century B. C., says: "It happens at times that a kind of column let down from the sky comes down into the sea, around which the waters boil, stirred up by the heavy blast of the winds; and if any ships are caught in that tumult they are tossed about and come into great peril."

Other ancient writers, however, regarded a waterspout as a gigantic serpent, sea dragon, or other monster. The Arabians regarded it as a manifestation of a Jinnee: a spirit capable of assuming various forms and exercising special power. It is thus referred to in the *Arabian Nights*.

W. E. Hurd, an American authority on waterspouts to whose researches I am deeply indebted, quotes the following picturesque description from an early writer:

> A great black dragon is seen to come from the cloud and put its head into the water, and its tail seems as though it were fixed in the sky; and this dragon drinks up the waters so greedily, that it swallows up along with them any ships that may come in the way, along with their crews and cargo, be they ever so heavy.

Small wonder that readers of such perfervid descriptions regarded a waterspout as a creature to be avoided at all costs. Various suggestions were made about propitiating or scaring away the all-devouring sea monster. Sprinkling the spout with vinegar (how?) was one nostrum, while other advisers favored loud noises. Drums and gongs were beaten, swords clashed, and seamen shouted and stamped on the deck in attempts to scare the fearsome monster away. Even today some seamen think that gunfire will break a spout, but Hurd says that he knows of no instance where a waterspout was destroyed either by atmospheric shock following gunfire, or through shot actually hitting it.

[*71*]

A rare aerial view of a waterspout.   *Royal Air Force*

Waterspouts are not confined to the high seas, they occasionally form on freshwater lakes and rivers. There have been many on Lake Erie in North America; seven were seen in one morning (*Monthly Weather Review,* June 1928).

When the characteristic whirling motion starts, the rotating air in the vortex cools by expansion, and the consequent condensation of the water vapor forms the funnel-shaped cloud. In some waterspouts this cloud is only a filmy screen through which distant objects can be plainly seen, although where the spout touches the water a large amount of spray is swept up into the vortex. Like tornadoes, waterspouts sometimes occur in association with hurricanes. (See A. H. Gordon, 1951, for a discussion of waterspout meteorology.)

Waterspouts which leave the water for the land become tornadoes, and tornadoes passing over water become waterspouts, and are the most violent form. C. L. Jordan tells me: "A large percentage of the tornadoes reported in peninsular Florida bear greater similarity to waterspouts than to the tornadoes which cause great damage in the Middle-western portion of the United States each spring." F. B. Dinwiddie has written about these tornado-*cum*-waterspouts.

In tidewater regions, such as southeast Virginia, a tornado sometimes changes into a waterspout and back again many times as it crosses bays and rivers. J. J. Murphy says that on September 5, 1935, a tornado formed near Norfolk, Virginia, and destroyed trees and sheds. It crossed a creek, sucking up water until the bottom was exposed and then gouged a channel in the mud. The waterspout lifted small boats onto the shore, ripped off part of a heavy pier and—a tornado once again—destroyed several buildings. Crossing Hampton Roads it turned into a waterspout again, then into a tornado which flung rolling stock off the tracks in a railroad yard. As a waterspout again, it sucked up another creek and as a tornado damaged some airplane hangars on shore. When last seen it was heading up Chesapeake Bay as a waterspout.

In the chapter on tornadoes I described another tornado-*cum*-waterspout that sank five ships. Incidentally, John Hersey says that the tornado which formed over Hiroshima turned into a waterspout as it passed over the nearby river.

Waterspouts have been known to form in various kinds of weather; in cyclones and anticyclones; in calms and gales; in cloudy and in cloudless skies; in warm and cold weather; at night and in the day. Waterspouts may travel with or against the surface winds; they are sometimes harmless, sometimes dangerous; they assume a wide variety of shapes and sizes and may vary widely in behavior.

In the North Atlantic waterspouts occur most frequently between May and October in regions of high water temperature. The band of maximum activity extends from the Gulf of Mexico through the Florida Straits to the Bahamas and thence to the northern limit of the Gulf Stream.

Gordon says that during the 48 years, 1900–1947, British ships reported 994 waterspouts, an average of about 20 a year. During the 11 years, 1948–1958, 197 waterspouts were reported near the coasts of the United States, including 73 in the Gulf of Mexico, 14 off California, 2 off Alaska and 1 off Hawaii—an average of less than 18 a year for such a vast area (Laura V. Wolford). It is not surprising, therefore, that the sight of one of these weather freaks brings all hands to the rails! Of course, many more waterspouts occur than are reported—the great majority are formed to burst unseen.

Waterspouts cannot be ignored even by a modern liner. The damage is caused by the whirling winds, the sudden reduction in air pressure, and the deluge of water, although the explosive effects of tornadoes are absent. Hurd gives the following examples of encounters between ships and waterspouts.

The White Star liner *Pittsburgh* was struck by a huge waterspout at night in mid-Atlantic on March 30, 1923. Her bridge was wrecked, the chart room badly damaged, electrical connections destroyed, and the officers' cabins flooded. The crow's nest was filled with water and it was believed that many tons of water dropped simultaneously upon the forward superstructure. The liner had to stop her engines for an hour while the worst damage was repaired. The deck officers estimated that the mass of water in the spout was between 40 and 50 feet wide and over 70 feet high.

Most records of waterspouts relate to sailing ships, which is understandable as they were obviously more vulnerable. Small sailing ships have become total wrecks when hit by large waterspouts. Some have capsized, others have had masts torn away and hulls tossed violently about. While in the South Atlantic the barque *Lilian Morris* encountered a giant waterspout said to measure nearly 500 feet in diameter at the base. Although the barque collided only with the edge of the spout, the terrific whirl of wind struck her like a giant fist. Her foretopgallant mast, the mizzen topmasts, and all her canvas were torn away. One of the crew was swept overboard and drowned. The master of the ship "was blown round the poop like a piece of paper . . . sky and sea seemed one, resembling a smoking furnace." Eventually the ship was brought safely to harbor under jury rig.

Alfred Wegener says that on May 30, 1841, a waterspout at Courthézon, France, lifted a 23-ft. boat out of the river Rhone and smashed it against the land.

Sometimes small vessels have been sunk without the waterspout actually hitting them. Hurd says that when the schooner *Alice* was near Newfoundland a waterspout, passing within 10 feet, damaged her so badly that she became a total loss. The crew were rescued the following day.

One other instance of a waterspout's fury: on April 4, 1902, the American steamship *Hestia* was steaming off Cape Hatteras at sunset when a large waterspout was observed traveling straight for the ship. The captain found it impossible to avoid a collision and ordered all hands below. He remained on deck until the last moment.

The oncoming spout was about 50 feet wide with an almost black core about two feet across. As it struck amidships the captain dived below. There was a deafening roar, strong gusts, and a sudden shock as the spout passed over. After the attack the captain came on deck again. Two large hatch tarpaulins and a plank of wood, eight feet long by ten inches wide, were high in the air, and the log line from the taffrail, complete with weighted spinner, was suspended in space like an imitation of the Indian rope trick!

Although the waterspout cannot be disregarded, it would be wrong to imagine that it is more than a very minor hazard of the sea.[1] But it is an extremely interesting marine phenomenon. To the onlooker the formation of a waterspout is an awesome spectacle. From the sky, which is generally cloudy, a funnel-shaped mass descends toward the sea. The sea itself is disturbed and immediately beneath the dipping funnel the water may foam and turn white. As the funnel comes lower the water rises to meet it. At last the rising cone of water and the low-swinging, writhing tube of air meet and the waterspout is then fully formed. Around the base is the "cascade," or circular whirl of spray, which is considerably wider than the spout itself.

Most textbooks state that the funnel of a waterspout is composed of condensed water vapor from the air and is not, as is popularly thought and as its name implies, a huge column of solid water. But it appears that spray can be drawn up to a considerable height. In the Cottage City waterspout which appeared off the coast of Massachusetts on August 19, 1896, the height of the cascade was estimated to be over 400 feet.[2] When it is remembered that a violent tornado can lift a railway engine, it should not be difficult for a large spout, although admittedly less powerful, to lift sea water to a considerable height.

Hurd says that snow, hail, and chunks of ice have fallen from waterspouts, or from waterspout clouds.

Waterspouts appear in various shapes and sizes. A spout seen off Rabat, Morocco, on December 18, 1917, was about 1,000 feet high but only three feet in diameter. One seen off San Luis Obispo, California, was reported to be 2,000 feet high and 500 feet wide, and another seen on July 16, 1915, from the British steamship *Gordon Castle* was reported to be 50 feet high and 100 feet wide. There are other reports of waterspouts with greater width than height, but it is probable that the observers saw only the cascade, the funnel being invisible.

At least one waterspout was nearly a mile high. It was seen off Eden, New South Wales, on May 16, 1898, and a theodolite reading from the shore gave its height as 5,014 feet. It was some 10 feet wide (H. C. Russell).

Probably the largest waterspout on record was one observed by Captain Cleary of the British steamship *River Avon* on January 28, 1888, in the

---

[1] Gordon (1948) suggests that in the days of propeller-driven aircraft flying at medium or relatively low altitudes waterspouts may have been responsible for some unexplained disasters. "Disappearance of aircraft without warning could quite reasonably be expected from collision in the dark with a waterspout column owing to its high rotational velocities."

[2] Probably no waterspout has been so thoroughly studied as this one. Frank H. Bigelow, of the U. S. Weather Bureau, after considering all the available information, gave the following computations of its size: approximate length of tube, 3,600 ft.; diameter of tube at base of cloud, 840 ft.; diameter of middle of tube, 144 ft.; diameter at surface of water, 240 ft.; diameter of base of cascade, 720 ft.; height of cascade, 420 ft. It traveled at about 1 m.p.h.

Waterspouts   [75]

Atlantic Ocean near Bermuda. It was estimated to be over a mile in diameter and raised the water to a great height. Everett Hayden, who quotes this record, says that many waterspouts were reported at the time.

According to William Ferrel, in comparatively dry air tall narrow waterspouts tend to form, in humid air wide short ones. The air was of comparatively low humidity when the Cottage City waterspout formed.

A waterspout has been seen shaped like an hourglass—two cones with the waist midway between sea and sky. Double- and even triple-walled spouts have been reported, and also two funnels connecting two clouds without touching the sea at all. Hurd says one waterspout palpitated in the middle as if it were breathing. One of the strangest waterspouts was seen off the coast of New South Wales by Capt. R. Taplin, who says:

> As it came bowling along at the rate of 20 m.p.h., we could see the water spouting up in a continuous and uniform stream right up to the cloud. When the waterspout was about two miles to the northwest of our ship, it suddenly presented a very curious and fantastic shape; it became very long, swaying and coiling about like a serpent. All at once it made a complete coil, and in a few seconds one of the most beautiful sights I have ever witnessed during my seafaring career vanished as completely as if it had never been in existence [quoted by Russell].

Waterspouts frequently occur in families, three or four appearing in the same general area at once. Occasionally 15 or more have been reported.

Gordon (1951) says that near the Bahamas on February 12, 1888, the steamship *Earnmoor* reported 30 waterspouts. Many others have also been reported in this locality. Sometimes six or more waterspouts depend from one cloud formation, although not all become fully formed, the lower end not reaching the sea.

How fast does the air in a waterspout whirl? It is obvious that the speed of rotation must be high, otherwise the funnel of air could not form at all, or, if it did, it could not be maintained as a vaporous entity. Hurd says that the whirling winds of one waterspout extended upward to heavy clouds through which they bored a hole to the blue sky beyond. The maximum speed is believed to be about 120 m.p.h., which is well below maximum tornadic force.

Waterspouts have been seen moving across the sea at only one or two miles per hour; others rush along at torpedo speed—50 m.p.h. or more. The average appears to be between 15 and 20 m.p.h. The duration of a spout varies between three minutes and an hour, both extremes being exceptional. The average duration is about 15 minutes.

←— Photograph of water spout on the North Pacific coast of Japan. *WMO photograph*

Waterspouts [77]

Waterspouts vary considerably in color. One was described as "a solid column of dense, black cloud," but other spouts have been so semitransparent that the interior of the tube could be seen. Charles F. Holder has a picture of a luminous waterspout; the glow was caused by a multitude of tiny luminous organisms which the spout sucked up. To see such a waterspout coursing over the ocean at night, its whole length outlined in phosphorescent light against the darkness, must be a magnificent spectacle. Various waterspout noises have been reported. Sighings, hissings and sucking sounds, as well as roarings and crashings have been heard.

Perhaps the most interesting phenomena connected with waterspouts are the so-called "rains" of fishes and other objects. That live fish, frogs, and similar small fry should suddenly descend from the sky is so extraordinary that it is not surprising many have refused to believe it.

That fine British 18th-century naturalist, the Rev. Gilbert White, referred to "that foolish opinion of [frogs] dropping from the clouds in rain." He considered that it was the refreshing showers which brought frogs out of their hiding places—which is undoubtedly true—and it was this sudden appearance which gave rise to the story of the clouds "raining frogs."

In our day, Bergen Evans, famed debunker of pseudoscience, is sceptical of the "rains," or falls. In June 1946, *Science* published an exchange of letters between Evans and E. W. Gudger of the American Museum of Natural History. It was Gudger who, in a series of papers published between 1921 and 1946, made scientists realize that the falls were to be taken seriously.[3] He collected over 80 reports from all the continents, including various islands, extending over 2,350 years. Gudger set out some of the evidence in his letter to *Science*. In his reply Evans seemed to rely chiefly on the assertion, which is probably true, that "no trained observer has yet seen quantities of fish coming down out of the sky." It is fair to add, however, that in his *The Natural History of Nonsense* (1947) he admits that the waterspout theory is "possible though not probable."

To me, such scepticism borders on obscurantism, and implies an inability to evaluate evidence properly. It was the same attitude that prompted the French Academy in the 18th century to deny, in the face of the strongest anecdotal evidence, that stones (meteorites) fell from the sky (see page 171). Here are some examples of falls, although probably waterspouts were not the only winds involved in some of the incidents. There are very powerful updrafts in heavy thunderstorms.

This news item appeared in *The Times* (London) for June 17, 1939. The superintendent of the municipal swimming pool in Trowbridge, Wilt-

---

[3] Although Waldo L. McAtee had published a long article on *Showers of Organic Matter* in the *Monthly Weather Review* in 1917.

shire, reported that in the afternoon there was a heavy shower. He ran for shelter and, as he did so, he heard the sound of what he thought was lumps of mud falling behind him:

> I turned and was amazed to see hundreds of tiny frogs falling on to the concrete path surrounding the bath. It was all over in a few seconds, but there must have been thousands of these tiny frogs, each about the size of the top of one's finger. I swept them up and shovelled them into a bucket.

A typical *Times* correspondence followed this report, the letters continuing until July 11, 1939. One correspondent recalled that Samuel Pepys wrote in his diary for May 23, 1661, that Elias Ashmole, the antiquary, "did assure me that frogs and many insects do often fall from the sky, ready formed."

Two military correspondents wrote of rains they had witnessed in India. Lieut. Col. R. C. R. Owen said that when he was in Bareilly, he rode across the parade ground immediately after a heavy storm and cloudburst. He found three or four acres covered with small fish, about the size of whitebait or small sardines.

General Beauvoir de Lisle said that after a heavy shower at Lucknow in 1908 his lawn was covered with fish about 1½ inches long. There were two or three to the square yard and some were alive. It seemed impossible for them to have come from anywhere but the sky. To make certain, however, the general inspected the flat roof of his bungalow. Several fish were there also.

Gudger (1929) says a friend told him that on the outskirts of Providence, Rhode Island, on May 15, 1900, he was caught in a severe thunderstorm accompanied by torrential rain and a strong wind. Before he could find shelter, he was pelted not only with rain but with fish as well. The fall was very localized, the fish coming down only within about a quarter of an acre. Thousands of fish were collected afterward from streets and gardens. They proved to be fresh-water fish, perch and bullpouts (a species of catfish), and measured from two to four and a half inches. Boys sold them by the pailful, and various shops displayed specimens of the strange visitants.

One of the queerest falls occurred on the afternoon of May 28, 1881, when a shower of periwinkles fell on Worcester, England. (A periwinkle is an edible shellfish about an inch long. Other falls of mollusks are referred to by McAtee.) The incident was thoroughly investigated at the time and was the subject of a leader and long correspondence in the Worcester *Daily Times*—May 30 to June 11, 1881. The storm which bore the periwinkles apparently came via the west coast of Scotland and Anglesey, so that the *nearest* place from which the winkles could have come was about 100 miles

Waterspouts [79]

away. From accounts of eyewitnesses it is known that the periwinkles were borne before the main storm and that they fell from one to two hours before the lightning and rain hit Worcester.

Word of the miraculous shower soon spread, and men, women, and children collected them. Thirty children were seen in one lane, all busy winkle-picking. The periwinkles were found in hedgerows, gardens, fields, and on roads. One man said that he reckoned two sacksful fell in his garden. Some were buried in sand one to two inches deep, many were still alive when picked up. The total weight that fell was estimated to be about half a ton.

To anyone who has read the preceding pages the explanation of these showers will be fairly obvious. A funnel of air which can lift tons of spray to heights up to 420 feet would have no difficulty in similarly raising a shoal of frogs, fish—or even periwinkles.[4] This airborne freight is carried for miles and then, when the funnel dissolves, is showered down on an unsuspecting countryside.

---

[4] G. J. Symons claimed that once the whole of the water in a pond, including fish, was lifted skywards (*Q. J. Royal Met. Soc.,* January 1893).

A tornado-*cum*-waterspout that passed over Wascana Lake, in western Canada, lowered the water level by two feet. It was estimated that over half a million tons of water were thus levitated (A. B. Lowe and G. A. McKay).

←Waterspout in the Mediterranean sighted off port bow of USS *F. D. Roosevelt* on October 5, 1962.   *U. S. Navy*

Waterspouts   [81]

chapter 4

Hail 📎

There are several forms of hail. This chapter deals with large hailstones, nearly as dense as pure ice, which are formed exclusively in severe thunderstorms during hot weather.

Although ordinary hailstorms last for only a few minutes, severe ones sometimes last for several hours, but during these severe storms there may be considerable intervals when hail does not fall. Such storms may sweep across country at speeds up to 50 m.p.h., sometimes traveling 500 miles, but usually they travel slowly and are very local, rarely exceeding ten miles across.

A clue to a large hailstone's origin can be found by splitting it open. It generally consists of onionlike layers of ice built about a tiny central core, or nucleus, which is generally so tiny that it is invisible to the naked eye. How do these successive layers form? A hail-bearing thundercloud sometimes towers over ten miles high, with air currents continuously rushing to the top. As these currents ascend they carry with them water vapor and droplets which, in the higher regions of the cloud, freeze on to a nucleus and gather cloud droplets, forming coatings of ice.

Becoming heavier and getting into a weaker updraft, the incipient hailstone begins to fall, eventually gathering another layer of water, part of which at once freezes on to the ice-cold kernel. Powerful updrafts prevent it from falling to earth and it receives more coatings. This process continues until the hailstone becomes too heavy for the updrafts and it falls to earth.

If the upcurrents of air are relatively weak, only small hailstones, with one or two concentric layers, will form. If, however, very strong updrafts are blowing, remarkably large stones may fall. Sometimes these have only three or four concentric layers which are relatively large; sometimes a large number of small layers. Cicely M. Botley says that 25 layers were counted in one hailstone. Incidentally, a similar layered effect occurs with ice deposits on aircraft.

This is a simplified account of a process which is now recognized as being more complex than was realized by earlier investigators. In particular,

[*82*]

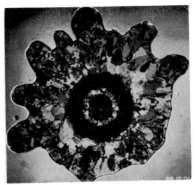

Section of hailstone taken with polarized light.   *Division of Building*
Research, National Research Council of Canada

radar studies have provided valuable information on the mechanism of hail-
forming clouds.

The growing hailstone rarely has a straight up and down movement:
more often it follows an irregular path. Large hailstones often grow without
numerous journeys. Once they have acquired a coating of ice they grow
by accretion in the part of the cloud bearing large amounts of supercooled
water. A very strong updraft is, however, essential to keep the hailstone for
a lengthy stay in the watery part of the cloud. The very largest hailstones
probably grow in a steady persistent updraft which travels along with the
storm. During these aerial excursions the hailstones sweep up ice particles
and liquid (K. A. Browning).

Further information about the growth of hailstones has been obtained
through laboratory investigations. At the Swiss Federal Snow and Avalanche
Research Institute at Davos, Switzerland, a "hail tunnel" has been built. It is
essentially a wind tunnel—maximum air speed 80 m.p.h.—with an adjustable
climate, + 300° C. to − 45° C. The tunnel reproduces the atmospheric
conditions and temperatures in which hailstones are formed and enables
observers to study the hail-forming process. It has frequently been found
in these experiments that hailstones contain water and are therefore heavier
than ice. But, apart from "mushy" hail, it is questionable if this is generally
true in natural hailstones. In some icing conditions in the tunnel, lightning
was seen, discharging from the icing particle to the environment (Roland
List).

In suitable conditions relatively huge hailstones form. These tend to be
less well-rounded than the smaller stones—spheroidal rather than spherical.
Records of stones the size of hens' eggs are comparatively common in
meteorological literature, while others the size and weight of baseballs are
sometimes reported. Most meteorologists accept that the largest authenti-

Hail   [83]

cated hailstone fell on July 6, 1928, at Potter, Nebraska. H. Stevens, the U. S. Weather Bureau's observer there at the time, says: "The monster chunks of ice could be heard hissing through the air, and when they hit in plowed or soft ground completely buried themselves, and sank halfway in on prairie ground."

These monster stones—as large as grapefruit—fell from 10 to 15 feet apart. One was measured, weighed and photographed immediately after falling: circumference 17 inches, diameter nearly 5½ inches, weight 1½ pounds. When cut open it was found to consist of the typical layer construction, thus proving that it was a single stone and not several stuck together.

Large as it was, it is reasonably certain that the Potter stone was below the maximum size for a hailstone. Writing of the giant stones that battered a *Viscount* airplane over Delhi, India, on May 27, 1959, S. Mull and S. M. Kulshrestha say that the largest hole was five inches in diameter but there were larger dents, one measuring 10 by 15 inches. They think that some of the stones were eight or more inches in diameter. Such a hailstone would weigh about two pounds.

Considerably larger and heavier hailstones have been reported. According to a report in the *Indian Journal of Meteorology and Geophysics* for January 1950, hailstones weighing up to 7½ pounds fell in Hyderabad State on March 17, 1939. Somewhat similar weights have been reported for hailstones falling in China and Africa. Some meteorologists, however, are sceptical of such reports and say that "hailstones" of this weight are the result of two or more stones freezing together as they lie on the ground. Moreover, large pieces of ice sometimes fall from aircraft. J. Hallett tells me that one large "hailstone" contained tea leaves! Presumably, waste from the kitchen outlet froze on the way down.

What updraft speed is required to sustain a hailstone in the air until it reaches grapefruit size? No definite answer can be given because the necessary speed varies with conditions, especially air turbulence. G. Grimminger has estimated that a hailstone with a specific gravity of 0.8 (water is 1.0) and a diameter of five inches requires an updraft of 157 m.p.h. in air with very little turbulence, and 278 m.p.h. in very turbulent air. The highest speeds are reached in "chimneys," comparatively narrow areas, 100 to 300 yards in diameter, of uprushing air. Sir Basil Schonland believes that a speed of 260 m.p.h. was required to support the Potter hailstone.

There is independent evidence that very powerful updrafts do occur in thunderstorms. On p. 119 I have recorded the experience of a pilot descending by parachute in a thunderstorm. At times he was sent *upward,* and a descent which would normally have taken 15 minutes took nearly three times as long. Another pilot recorded that he was "flying a plane over western New Jersey [when] I got in the front part of a thunderstorm.

A few of the hailstones which fell at Stegal, Nebraska, on July 20, 1958. Melting has slightly reduced their size.   *U. S. Weather Bureau*

Before I knew it I had gained 4,000 ft. I shut my engine off and dived at *100* m.p.h.—and I was still going up!" (Quoted by Frederick G. Vosburgh). And a six-ton airplane, with both propellers feathered, was kept in the air for over an hour by vertical currents in the Sierra Nevada region of California. But this was not during a thunderstorm (Ministry of Aviation Circular No. 92, 1964).

Some meteorologists, however, are sceptical of claims for updrafts of 260 m.p.h. and more. Commenting on the Potter hailstone, a report in the *Monthly Weather Review* for August 1928 said that the size of the stone was too great to be explained by the strength (*i.e.*, speed) of the upward current, and suggested that the probable explanation was that the hailstone grew rapidly while falling through a thick stratum of supercooled droplets.

Although most hailstones are spheroid, very different shapes sometimes occur: pear-shaped, oblong, pyramidal, as well as stones with many irregularities and protuberances. Others are covered with icy spikes from a quarter to nearly an inch long projecting from a central cone. The causes of these unusual shapes are varying conditions of moisture, temperature, and air currents in the upper atmosphere, and the way the hailstone is formed. Sometimes a hailstone breaks during its descent and a new stone forms around a misshapen fragment. T. E. W. Schumann believes that sometimes the moisture in the center freezes before the stone falls to earth and that the consequent expansion is responsible for some of the strange shapes.

Snowden D. Flora says that during a violent tornado at Eskridge, Kansas, on June 5, 1917, disk-shaped hailstones fell. They were six to ten inches in diameter and two to three inches thick. Plaster casts of some of these were sent to the local weather bureau. Flora says that the casts were made by an undertaker who was thus familiar with the process!

Large hailstones sometimes explode with sounds like pistol shots. W. G. Brown writes of "a fall of large hailstones, which on coming in contact with the windows or walls or pavement in many instances exploded with a sharp report, so loud as to be mistaken for breaking window panes or a pistol shot. As the hail fell, the fragments sprang up from the ground and flew in all directions, looking like a mass of 'popping corn' on a large scale." The explanation may be that they contained air which burst out as the hailstones struck. Another explanation is that ice formed on the outside while there was still water inside. When this froze and expanded, there would be inside pressure which eventually burst the hailstone.

Hailstones sometimes contain foreign matter. Those falling in the vicinity of a nuclear explosion are radioactive. Other hailstones have contained small stones, leaves, twigs, nuts—and even live animals. The speed of the updrafts of air in a violent hailstorm, and the known power of waterspouts and tornadoes to lift various objects and later shower them down upon the earth, render such incidents credible. I understand that the oxygen requirements of small animals are such that the little air available in the hailstones would be sufficient to keep them alive during their journey to and from the clouds.

J. R. Norman, the British ichthyologist, says there is a record of a hailstone as large as a hen's egg which fell during a heavy storm at Essen, Germany, and that inside was a 1½-in. carp. A small turtle is also said to have fallen coated with ice (*Monthly Weather Review,* July 1905).

I have not read of a bird becoming embedded in a hailstone, but such an occurrence isn't impossible. Charles F. Brooks says that during a storm at Worcester, Massachusetts, there was a fall of iced ducks. Had a very strong updraft been blowing it is possible that these ducks would have received several more layers of ice before they finally descended. Then they could have been described as ducks in hailstones—although with rather a large nucleus!

That this is no farfetched idea was proved when five German glider pilots soared into a thundercloud over the Rhön Mountains. Afraid that the violent winds would tear their gliders apart the men bailed out. The powerful updrafts evidently caught the billowing parachutes and carried the men into the region of supercooled water vapor—the raw material of hailstones. The men formed gigantic nuclei, rising and falling like outsized yo-yos until they eventually landed entirely covered with ice and frozen to

Large-size hail wrecks a plane.　　*Marty Haedtler*

death—except one who miraculously survived (Philip D. Thompson and Robert O'Brien).

Hailstones are a severe hazard to airplanes. They have damaged planes flying as high as 45,000 feet—nine miles! Robert Buck, an experienced airline pilot, says:

> Flying through hail is probably the most nerve-racking experience in the sky. The clatter is overpowering.[1] Some hailstones are bigger than tennis balls, and thousands of these, rock-hard and coming at over 180 miles an hour, can damage an aircraft badly.
>
> Years ago a friend of mine flew into severe hail. He decided to turn and get out. The hail had already broken the windshield, beaten the front of the wing, and smashed out the landing lights. As he banked the aircraft to circle back, the fuselage was turned broadside to the hail, which quickly broke every window on the exposed side.

I know of no record of an airplane wrecked by hail but it certainly could happen, and with ever-increasing speeds the danger grows. It has been proved that hail only $\frac{1}{20}$th inch in diameter causes damage. Joseph B. Emerson and Robert K. Souter, in their monograph on hail and aircraft,

---

[1] Other pilots say that the noise is so great that all communication between members of the crew is impossible.

say that one encounter caused damage amounting to 25,000 dollars. Most modern planes are so built that they can continue to operate in most hailstorms, but what if an aircraft collided at supersonic speed with a mass of grapefruit-sized chunks of ice? (A. F. Crossley)

Glider pilots have been dangerously bombarded; one sailplane landed riddled by hail, and others have had their wings torn off. A glider pilot, caught in a thunderstorm over Munich, suffered a hail bombardment which tore holes in the fabric of his rudder and buckled his machine, while the furious gale carried his light machine 150 miles across the Bavarian and Bohemian forests to the banks of the Eger in Czechoslovakia (Peter Supf, and see p. 144).

Although severe hailstorms rarely visit Britain, they do sometimes occur. One which occurred at Barton, Lincolnshire, is commemorated in a monument—surely one of the strangest ever erected. The following inscription on the monument tells the story.

> In memory of the great hailstorm at Barton, July 3, 1883, 10:30 to 11 P.M. Ice 5 inches long, 3 inches wide—15 tons of glass broken—ice weighed 2½ ozs.

The monument is of bricks which were being made at the time of the storm. Some of the large hailstones made deep indentations in the hardening bricks, which thus preserve a record of the storm for posterity.

A severe hailstorm occurred during the early morning of September 22, 1935, over the River Nene valley in Northamptonshire. Thousands of square feet of the glass in skylights, windows, and greenhouses were destroyed. The damage to one building alone, St. Andrew's Hospital in Northampton, exceeded £600. A hailstone picked up at Rushden was stated to be as large as a tennis ball. Partial proof that some of the stones did reach this size is provided by measurements of some of the holes made in various surfaces. Panes of glass showed circular holes three inches in diameter, and a piece of asbestos cement roofing had a hole slightly exceeding four inches in diameter.

The largest British hailstones of which there is authentic record appear to have fallen on September 5, 1958, at Horsham, Sussex. Some were tennisball size, and one weighed 6½ ounces. In their report of this storm F. H. Ludlam and W. C. Macklin say:

> In most places shortly before the onset of the hail and rain there was a sudden squall from between west and northwest, strong enough to break down tree branches and sometimes to uproot trees. People hastening to close windows were driven back to shelter by a bombardment of hailstones, which arriving at a shallow angle broke many panes with such violence that glass splinters were flung against the opposite walls. The larger stones broke roof tiles and carried away the lead frames of small window panes. Car drivers

were brought to a standstill by road-flooding, loss of vision in the torrential rain and swirling foliage, and by the felling of large trees across the road; some cars were covered with dents from the impacts of the hailstones.

But the severest hailstorms occur in regions of great land masses and warm, though not tropical, climates. The frequency of hailstorms varies greatly throughout the world. Whereas some areas, such as deserts, never have a hailstorm, other areas have them frequently. Cheyenne, Wyoming, has hail on about ten days a year, the highest frequency in the United States. Athens, Greece, has hail once every two days during the hail season—December to February.

On May 8, 1926, a very severe hailstorm struck Dallas, Texas. In the business center some of the hailstones were the size of baseballs. They smashed thousands of windows and skylights; cracked or dislodged numerous tiles and slates; shattered street lights and electric signs, and smashed acres of glass in greenhouses. The hailstones were so heavy that they riddled the tops of thousands of cars and smashed many windshields. The total damage in and around Dallas from this quarter-hour storm was estimated to be two million dollars.

South Africa has had many severe hailstorms. During a storm at Durban on June 24, 1929, the noise was described as like "machine-gun fire" with hailstones the size of baseballs raining down. During other storms in South Africa very large hailstones have penetrated corrugated iron roofs "as if they had been made of paper." Probably the most destructive of these storms occurred on November 17, 1949, when the damage was estimated at over £500,000. Several stones fell weighing up to 5½ ounces and others were about half a pound (*Illustrated London News,* July 27, 1929, and Keeve Steyn).

To anyone who has not experienced it, the damage caused by a violent hailstorm is almost unbelievable. On July 14, 1953, such a hailstorm swept over the Alberta Province of Canada, covering a path some 140 miles long and 5 miles wide. The hailstones were as large as golf balls, with some even larger. The storm was accompanied by winds up to 75 m.p.h.

Allen G. Smith, biologist of the U. S. Fish and Wildlife Service, says:

A close investigation of the hail damage on the ground presented a picture of unbelievable devastation. Grasses and herbs were shredded beyond recognition and beaten into the earth. Trees and shrubs were stripped of all leaves and small branches and the bark on one side of the larger trees had been torn away or deeply gouged by hailstones. Plants growing in waters of the potholes and lakes were reduced to nondescript pulp. Emergent vegetation had disappeared, destroyed and beaten under the water's surface by the weight of the hail. Ponds that had been choked with grasses, sedges, cattails, and bulrush since June, were stripped of all evidence of former plant growth.

After a hailstorm in South Africa.   *Pretoria News, National Building Research Institute, Pretoria*

Songbirds, hawks, owls and wildfowl were killed by the thousand. Examination of hundreds of ducks showed that many died through having their skulls crushed. The post-mortems revealed the gruesome fact that the upper mandible had been torn from many adult ducks, leaving only the lower mandible and the tongue.

The number of ducks killed was estimated with reasonable accuracy because the hailstorm occurred in an area where there are regular aerial surveys of wildfowl. Such surveys showed that this storm killed at least 36,000 ducks and ducklings, in addition to thousands of other birds. On July 18, another severe hailstorm occurred in the same area, this time killing an estimated 27,000 ducks and ducklings. Thus in 5 days over 60,000 ducks were killed in an area of 700 square miles.

But large hailstones are not only dangerous to birds. In the Alberta hailstorm a 600-pound hog, caught out in the open, was battered to death. During a hailstorm in Nebraska on August 8, 1917, piglets and calves were fatally injured and scores of rabbits were killed in the fields. Horses and cattle which were caught in open pasture were found after the storm covered with blood and with huge lumps on their bodies (George A. Loveland).

The Elements Rage   [*90*]

William Beebe noticed similar injuries to horses during a severe hailstorm in the Himalayas; their hides were covered with welts as though they had been lashed with whips. Lizards were flattened on rocks and logs, birds and their nests were destroyed, and two large squirrels, weighing about five pounds each, were found dead.

In the discussion following Bilham and Relf's paper on hail given before the Royal Meteorological Society, Sir George Simpson said that he had received a report when he was in India which stated that buffaloes over a large area had been completely wiped out by a hailstorm. If the stones were grapefruit size, pelting down at 200 m.p.h. or more, I suppose this was possible—just! W. G. Kendrew also refers to large animals killed by hailstones.

P. O. Lapie records a remarkable hailstorm which appears to have been intimately associated with a tornado which occurred in the afternoon of May 9, 1935, over a barren plateau in Chad, north central Africa. Giant hailstones fell over a strictly localized area of about a square mile. Hailstones covered this area to a depth of nearly 19 inches. The stones at the edges of this area varied from the size of small peas to that of a man's fist. Nearer the center the size increased, and over a central area of some 2,000 square yards blocks of ice were embedded in the soil. Some of these blocks were said to be 2½ feet thick.

In great hailstorms enormous amounts of hail fall. In the storm in southern Kansas on June 23, 1951, piles of hailstones were a foot thick in places. And after a storm in Washington County, Iowa, on September 1, 1897, there were drifts six feet deep (Flora).

Readers of the Bible, unacquainted with the size that hailstones sometimes attain, may have been puzzled by the ravages said to have been caused by hail during one of the plagues of Egypt (Exodus 9:19 and 25) and by the statement in the Book of Joshua 10:11 about the battle with the Amorites: ". . . they were more which died with hailstones than they whom the children of Israel slew with the sword." The Amorites were caught on a steep mountain path and many were probably killed by falls. But it is known that very large hailstones sometimes fall in Palestine; Douglas V. Duff says that he has seen cattle brained by a Palestinian hailstorm.

There are various other records of people being killed by violent hailstorms. This is not surprising when it is remembered that the impact of a giant hailstone is greater than that from a home-run hit at baseball.

On May 1, 1928, six children were killed and ten other persons injured by hailstones the size of hens' eggs which fell at Klausenberg, Rumania. On July 10, 1923, at Rostov, Russia, hailstones reported to have weighed between one and two pounds killed 23 people and many cattle. Most of the human fatalities occurred to peasants who had run into the fields in an endeavor to save their cattle. And on June 13, 1930, in the Siatista district of Greece, hailstones killed 22 people (Talman, 1931, and Flora, both of whom record other fatal hailstorms).

There are more records of deaths from hailstones in India than from any other country. The most deadly hailstorm of which there is authentic record burst over the Moradabad and Beheri districts of India on April 30, 1888. Two hundred and forty-six people were killed. Some were pounded to death, but the majority were knocked down by stones and wind, buried under drifts, and died of cold and exposure.

J. S. MacIntosh, who was an eyewitness, said:

> A terrific storm of hail [broke] all the windows and glass doors. The verandas were blown away by the wind. A great part of the roof fell in, and the massive pucca portico was blown down. The walls shook. It was nearly dark outside, and hailstones of an enormous size were dashed down with a force which I have never seen anything to equal. . . . The really destructive hail seems to have been confined to a very small area, about six or seven miles around Moradabad. . . . Men caught in the open and without shelter were simply pounded to death by the hail. Fourteen bodies were found in the race-course. The police report that 1,600 head of cattle, sheep and goats were killed [quoted by A. W. Greely].

Probably no country in the world suffers greater financial loss from hailstorms than the United States: larger than that from tornadoes, and in some years approaching that from hurricanes. One hailstorm frequently causes damage of a million dollars or more. To farmers, especially, hail is well-named the "White Plague." Many have had the bitter experience of owning fields of flourishing crops one day, and fields of worthless vegetable debris the next. It is not the rare and widely spaced outsize hailstones— grapefruit size—that cause most damage to crops. The farmers' foe is the marble- and walnut-sized stones which, driven by violent gusts of wind, flatten the fields of grain. The damage to crops—chiefly wheat and corn— averages about three-quarters of all losses due to hail. Kansas, the greatest wheat-producing state, suffers most. Flora says that the hail damage there during the ten years 1944–53 amounted to 101,877,900 dollars.

The most expensive hailstorm in the United States occurred in Kansas on June 23, 1951. It swept for 200 miles from Sedgwick County to Allen County, causing over 1½ million dollars' worth of damage to crops. It then smashed into Wichita and played havoc with cars, roofs and windows. Total damage in this storm—including some wind damage—was 14,340,000 dollars.

This storm, however, was not so violent as the one which hit Topeka on June 24, 1897. Orange- and grapefruit-sized hailstones smashed heavy ½-in-thick skylights and punctured sheet metal and shingle roofs. The glass roof of the operating theater at the Santa Fe Hospital was wrecked. The wooden tops of streetcars were punctured and terror-stricken runaway horses

A field of corn ruined by large-size hail.   *J. C. Allen and Son*

dashed through the streets. Twenty-six people were injured, including a boy whose skull was fractured (Flora).

Hail insurance in the United States began in 1880 and today amounts to nearly a billion dollars a year. Premiums in hail-prone areas are high; as much as 20 dollars for every 100 for full coverage. Policies cannot be taken out by telephone or wire just as the storm clouds gather over the farmhouse, either—there is a 24-hour waiting period between the date of application and the effective date of a policy. Although hail is much less of a risk to British agriculture, at least a dozen offices issue hail insurance.

In hail-prone areas some buildings are specially protected. In areas of South Africa which are subject to severe hailstorms some buildings have their windows protected by wire mesh hailguards.

J. A. P. Laurie has described the tests carried out by the South African

Hail   [*93*]

National Building Research Institute to discover the effects of hail bombardment on various material. Artificial hailstones were formed from clear ice, most of them 2½ inches in diameter and weighing between four and five ounces. These ice projectiles were then fired from a hailgun powered by compressed air at speeds up to 100 m.p.h. The maximum kinetic energy at the moment of impact which could be achieved by the gun was 3,500 foot-poundals.[2] This gave an ample margin for the tests as it was estimated from damage done to roofing in a violent storm that few hailstones hit with an impact greater than 3,000 foot-poundals.

The results of the tests showed that even galvanized corrugated steel was dented at 2,500 foot-poundals, and corrugated aluminum was punctured by a similar impact. Half-inch-thick slates cracked at the same figure, and concrete and clay tiles cracked at 500 foot-poundals. The report adds: "No tests on thatch were carried out but experience indicates that this type of roof is likely to suffer only very slight damage in a severe hailstorm."

Throughout the centuries various rituals have been used in attempts to prevent hail from falling on vulnerable areas, or to prevent it from falling at all. The ancient Greeks used to sacrifice a lamb or pullet when hail threatened. In the Middle Ages peasants erected in their fields tall poles bearing strips of parchment inscribed with incantations against the hail god. In this century peasants in rural Italy have practiced such rites as ringing silver bells, hanging amulets on trees, and sprinkling bits of charred wood from the Yule log on the fields in vain attempts to prevent hail from ruining their vineyards and crops.

Attempts have also been made to ward off hail by mechanical means. At one time church bells were rung when a storm threatened, presumably because it was thought that the vibration might prevent the hail from forming. Kites and balloons with lightning conductors were flown because it was thought they could draw off the electricity in the clouds.

At the beginning of this century the hail cannon was introduced. Italy alone had 10,000. Blank charges were fired and it was believed that the vortex rings helped to prevent the hail from forming (B. C. V. Oddie).

According to Ottavio Vittori, writing in *Nubila,* the Italian journal devoted to hailstorms and allied subjects, there is evidence that pressure waves from explosions (and thunder) affect the composition of hail. Some European fruit farmers claim that after rocket hail-firing "mushy hail" falls, which is so soft that it does little damage to crops.

Since the Second World War other preventive measures have been used. They all have the same principle: to supply more nuclei, similar in shape to ice crystals, on which hailstones can develop. The more nuclei in the hailcloud, the smaller the size of the individual stones. The extra nuclei are sent into the hail-forming cloud in several ways. One method, used chiefly

---

[2] A foot-poundal is equivalent to 420,000 ergs.

in France and Switzerland, is to generate smoke on the ground which wafts billions of dust specks into the clouds. In Italy rockets send high explosives and chemicals into the clouds. In 1955 there were nearly 10,000 rocket sites in northern Italy, from which over 100,000 rockets were fired. Italy also exports these rockets to other countries.

In the United States airplanes have been used to "seed" hail clouds, chiefly with silver iodide or common salt—two pounds of finely ground salt yields a million million particles.

But many meteorologists are not satisfied that such measures have the effects claimed for them. Sir Graham Sutton, Director-General of the British Meteorological Office, quotes with approval the following conclusion of the U. S. Advisory Committee on Weather Control (1957): "Available hail frequency data were completely inadequate for evaluation purposes and no conclusions as to the effectiveness of hail suppression projects could be reached." Similarly, J. C. Thams, a Swiss authority on hail, tells me: "I think the most famous experiments have been carried out on the southern slope of the Alps in our own institute. The last experiment from 1957–1963 with silver iodide gave no significant results that the formation of hail can be prevented by seeding the clouds with silver iodide. I think till now there is no evidence that we can influence the formation of hail." Fame and fortune still await the man who can control hail.

Attempts have been made, notably in the United States, to forecast the occurrence and location of hail. The first forecasts were made in February 1950 at Tinker Air Force Base, in Oklahoma, and were for the benefit of military aircraft. Today there are regular hail-warning systems for both the military and civilians. Information is obtained chiefly by radiosonde: a collection of meteorological instruments which, carried aloft (up to 20 miles) by balloon, transmits weather data to a ground station. Radar is also used to detect hail (Flora). Incidentally, many observers have remarked that hail-bearing clouds have a greenish tinge.

Like hurricanes, severe hailstorms have played an important part in history. Two great hailstorms began in the morning of July 13, 1788, in southwest France and swept in parallel bands, about 12 miles apart, nearly 500 miles to the northeast. The hail affected 1,039 communes, caused great damage to crops and ruined the harvest. The consequent food shortage was a factor in causing the French Revolution in the following year.

After this it is surprising to learn that a most violent hailstorm once brought peace to France. In May of 1360 Edward III was with his army between Paris and Chartres preparing to renew the war with France. On May 8 there was such a violent storm that, according to Sir John Froissart, the famous chronicler of the times: "It seemed as if the world were come to an end. Giant hailstones killed men and horses, and even the most courageous were terrified." The king was so affected that "he vowed to the Virgin that he would conclude a peace." The treaty of Brétigny followed.

chapter 5

Avalanches ⟫

"Hast thou entered into the treasures of the snow?" The question is as old as the book of Job, but it is only during the last hundred years that the full wonder of a snow crystal has been revealed through photomicrography. And as it is trillions of these crystals which, in violent motion, make the snow avalanche, it is necessary to know what they are and how they behave.

One of the pioneers of snow photomicrography was Wilson A. Bentley who for over 40 years lived a hermitlike existence in Jericho, Vermont, among the northernmost mountains of New England, a region favoring the production of the single snow crystals which were essential for his work. He developed a camera capable of taking photomicrographs up to a magnification of 3,600 times. Eventually he amassed some 5,000 negatives, no two of which were identical.

An exhaustive work on the subject was published in 1954—*Snow Crystals* by the Japanese physicist and meteorologist, Ukichiro Nakaya. The investigations, photography, and writing took 20 years. One sentence gives a glimpse of what the work entailed: "It is rather a hard task to continue the examination of the crystal forms of snow without a break during several hours of a snowfall, the temperature being sometimes below $-10°$ C."

Snow is the crystallization of water vapor in the air into geometrical forms. The popular notion that snow comes from rain is therefore incorrect; ice pellets are the product of frozen rain.

Nakaya reproduced snow crystals artificially at temperatures of $-20°$ C. in an abundant supply of moisture. But tiny particles of solid matter, by providing nuclei, enable snow crystals to form without this degree of super-saturation. Over industrial and civilized areas there is an abundance of such material in the form of smoke and dust. In areas remote from civilization the nuclei are provided by a wide variety of natural substances, such as pollen grains and other vegetable matter, grains of earth and mud and salt from wind-blown evaporated sea spray. Incidentally, Nakaya made artificial snow round a nucleus of fine rabbit hair.

The water vapor condenses on the solid nucleus and forms a tiny ice

[*96*]

disk, or needle. Balloonists have sometimes found themselves surrounded by these incipient snow crystals, so tiny that they were made visible only by the sunlight glinting on them. Further condensation takes place on this foundation and thus the crystal is built up.

Snow crystals vary in size from about 0.07 mm., or 3/1,000 in. (about twice the size of a fog particle) to 5.0 mm., or $\frac{2}{10}$ in. in diameter. In the platelike forms the thickness is $\frac{1}{50}$ or less of the width. It has been estimated that all the 5,000-odd crystals photographed by Bentley could be packed into a two-inch cube.

Why is it that so many of the crystals which fall have the same general hexagonal pattern? Writing of the formation of a solid from a gas, Sir William Bragg says:

> The molecules lie side by side in an *ordered array*. Order and regularity are the consequences of the complete fulfilment of the attractions which the atoms or molecules exert on one another. When the structure has grown to a size which renders it visible in the microscope, or even to the naked eye, the regularity is manifest in the form of the solid body: it is what we call a crystal.

Nakaya says that snow appears to be a unique example of a single chemical compound exhibiting so much variation in crystal habit. Despite the similarity in design, no two hexagonal snow crystals, out of the countless thousands which have been examined, have ever been found to be identical.

Formed in the inexhaustible laboratories of the skies, the exquisite beauty of these hexagonal crystals makes even a professional meteorologist break into lyrical prose, as in this passage by Humphreys (1937): "We view with lens and record with camera the perfection[1] and intricacy of these marvellous gems that from an infinite store glisten, not in a lapidary's locked-up booth, but over all outdoors, as far as the eye can see, where sparkle and gleam, for each to have and to hold, more diamonds than ever enriched the marts of Golconda."

In addition to the classical hexagonal appearance, snow crystals form many other shapes: needles, bullets, cones, rods, etc. Nakaya lists and illustrates seven main types with 42 subdivisions.

The different forms of snow crystals are due to varying atmospheric conditions. Generally, the simpler types appear to be formed at high altitudes when water vapor is scarce and the more complex types at low altitudes when there is an abundance of water vapor. Needle crystals are rare in Europe, yet they are common in the mountains of the west coast of the United States, and in an hourlong snowstorm at Mount Tokachi, Hokkaido, Japan, snow needles fell almost exclusively. Nakaya, who records this, has a

---

[1] Snow crystals found on earth are not *perfect*.

section on the meteorological conditions producing various types of crystal (see also L. W. Gold and B. A. Power).

I have dealt in some detail with snow crystals because these are the units of which all snow is composed. But single crystals fall comparatively rarely, except in very cold regions such as the Antarctic, and on mountain tops. Frequently crystals bunch together and fall as "snowflakes." This happens most frequently when the lower air is comparatively warm—the plumelike rays of individual crystals then stick to each other.

When snow first falls the snow cover contains a large proportion of air. Frequently ten inches of newly fallen snow contains only as much water as one inch of rain, although atmospheric conditions obviously cause wide variations.

The specific gravity of fresh snow varies from about 0.06 to 0.10 but the figure for the ice of which it is composed is just over 0.9. (The specific gravity of water is 1.0.) These figures emphasize the great amount of air present in newly fallen snow. Rarely, snow falls which is composed of one part ice and 250 parts air! These facts explain why men who have been buried for 48 hours in snowdrifts have not suffocated.

Great changes take place in snow after it falls. There are names for each of the various stages between its fall and its conversion into water or glacial ice. Gerald Seligman (1936) describes and illustrates 12 varieties, each with its own specific gravity.

Very occasionally a number of snowflakes adhere to form an "aggregate." A snowstorm in which numbers of aggregates fall is an impressive spectacle. One such storm occurred over Berlin in January 1915, when many aggregates fell with diameters of from three to four inches.

During other snowstorms even larger aggregates have been reported; up to 15 inches wide and 8 inches thick (*Monthly Weather Review*, February 1915).

How fast does snow fall? A snow crystal has very small mass and falls very slowly. According to Nakaya a plain hexagonal crystal falls at about half a mile per hour. But snowflakes sometimes fall faster. M. A. Giblett, referring to a fall of snowflakes in London, says that they fell with terminal speeds between 1.1 and 1.8 meters per second, or between 2 and 3½ m.p.h. Rain falls much faster. The terminal speed of large raindrops is 17 m.p.h.— at any speed faster than that they break up and the parts fall more slowly.

Although snow is one of the most delicate and fragile of natural substances, it can at times be one of man's worst foes as the records of floods, avalanche, snowstorm, and blizzard abundantly testify.

The number of snow crystals which fall during a heavy storm is astronomical. Vincent J. Schaefer (1942) estimates that during a ten-hour storm about 10^{15} (a thousand million million) flakes fell on an acre.

During 27½ hours on April 14–15, 1921, 87 inches fell at 10,000-ft-high

Silver Lake, Colorado, the most intense snowfall for the United States since records have been kept. The greatest known seasonal snowfall in the United States also occurred during the present century. This was during the winter of 1955–6 when 1,000.3 inches, or 83.3 feet, fell at the Paradise Ranger Station, 5,550 feet up on the southern slope of Mt. Rainier, in southwest Washington.

Even Florida experiences snow. The record snowfall in historic times for the Sunshine State is probably the five inches which fell near the Georgia border on January 11, 1800.

These examples of heavy snowstorms all occurred on the American continent, but one of the world's greatest snowfalls occurred in England. In March 1891, the deep ravine on Dartmoor known as Tavy Cleave was stated by the Rev. S. Baring-Gould to have been filled with snow to the almost incredible depth of 300 feet—and modern authorities are inclined to believe him. (See E. G. Bilham, and *Geographical Journal*, May-June 1946, p. 258.) Marcel de Quervain, however, tells me that he believes figures for the depth of snow are often very different from the actual deposit, and should therefore be regarded with caution—wind drifting is a big factor.

The sheer weight of snow is a danger to buildings. The snow massed on a roof amounts exceptionally to 80 pounds per square foot, which means that a roof with an area of 800 sq. ft. (that of an ordinary three-roomed dwelling-house) is supporting some *30 tons*.[2] And 80 pounds per square foot, while exceptional, is far from the record. In mountainous regions of Japan 240 pounds per square foot has been recorded—nearly 100 tons on the roof.

In snow-prone countries, such as the United States, Canada, and Switzerland, the building codes require that roofs be strong enough to support a given weight of snow per square foot. That such codes are necessary was tragically proved on February 28, 1959, at the Listowel Arena, near Toronto, Ontario. Because of a heavy snow, the roof and walls of the ice rink suddenly collapsed without the slightest warning. A hockey game was being played at the time, and eight people were killed and many more injured (W. R. Schriever, *et al.*).

It is massed snow which causes the most familiar form of the avalanche. Snow avalanches used to be divided into two categories: the *ground* avalanche of wet snow which slides over the ground and carries quantities of earth, stones and other debris with it; and the *powder* avalanche which consists of dry powdery snow, great clouds of which fill the air as the avalanche descends. But this twofold division is an oversimplification. Some avalanches are a combination of two, or even three, types, and others are too complex for any classification (see de Quervain for a detailed classification).

---

[2] Marcel de Quervain comments: "A quite common figure in the Alps!"

A powder snow avalanche plunges down a Swiss mountainside.

An avalanche occurs when a mass of snow which has been pent up on a mountainside loses its hold and hurtles down. Wet snow has been known to avalanche on a slope of only 15°, while hard snow that has lain for a long time often remains on slopes up to 50°.

Irregularities formed by rocks or mounds act as anchoring points and tend to arrest any tendency to avalanche. Similarly, bushes and large trees

Swiss Federal Institute for Snow and Avalanche Research, Davos, Switzerland

standing close together act as arresters. Another important factor is the structure of the snow covering. Many avalanches come only from the upper layers of snow which, of course, do not touch the ground at all.

When a snow mass is poised ready to avalanche almost unbelievably small disturbances can provide the necessary triggering action. In the Rocky Mountains, the vibrations caused by trains start numerous avalanches. The passage of a man or an animal, such as a fox, can set an avalanche in motion. Such disturbances may even take place at some distance *below* the mass of snow. Other avalanches have been caused by the fall of a branch of a tree or even the fall of loose snow from trees.

Loud sounds are also said to sometimes trigger an avalanche. It has been observed that while shooting down avalanches by gun or mortar fire the report alone is sometimes sufficient to bring the snow down. But it is possible that in these cases the shock wave of the explosion is the causative agent.

It has been said that the sound of a human voice is sometimes sufficient to start an avalanche, but there is no definite evidence of this having ever happened. There is, however, plenty of evidence that most fatal avalanches are started by the victims themselves. It is very easy for a skier to set off an avalanche that is ready to go. The records show that comparatively few accidents are caused by naturally released avalanches falling on unsuspecting victims.

Normally, an avalanche goes through three phases before coming to rest: gathering speed, travel at maximum speed, and reduction of speed. The maximum speed varies considerably. The slowest avalanches are those composed of damp snow—although very wet snow avalanches can travel at great speed—and the fastest are those composed of dry powder snow. But the angle of the slope on which the avalanche occurs is an important factor in causing variations of speed.

Some avalanches—chiefly of wet snow—travel at speeds which would enable a fast skier with a fair start to outrun them. But maximum avalanche speed is probably about 200 m.p.h. There is a tendency—understandably—to exaggerate avalanche speeds. Avalanches vary greatly in width—from ten feet to a mile or so.

The distance avalanches travel necessarily varies greatly. Sometimes after descending a slope one may run for a mile or so across level ground. The Altels ice avalanche of 1895 crossed a valley and then ran up the opposite slope. Snow avalanches sometimes do the same, especially in deep, narrow, V-shaped valleys. Survivors have reported that the snow "came up from below."

The snow in a big avalanche may have a volume of over a million cubic yards and weigh hundreds of thousands of tons.[3] Its movement is a combination of sliding, flowing, and bouncing. This action sometimes pulverizes the snow into such fine particles that it penetrates closed doors and windows, and sometimes suffocates people while they sleep.

Avalanches exert great pressures. A mixed ground and powder avalanche at Zuoz in the Inn Valley, Switzerland, in 1951, which traveled at

---

[3] Edwin Bucher tells me that the snow in a big avalanche may weigh a million tons—the equivalent weight of over twelve *Queen Elizabeths,* the world's largest liner!

about 170 m.p.h., exerted approximately 1,100 pounds pressure per square foot and destroyed a stone building in its path.

Wet-snow avalanches often carry a mass of debris, scraped from the ground as they pass. Sometimes the front is 60 feet high and exerts a frontal pressure of some 4,500 pounds per square foot. Far greater pressures have been reported. Avalanche defenses at Fionnay, Switzerland, designed to resist pressures of 8,000 pounds per square foot, were destroyed by an avalanche of wet snow and rock. An avalanche compressed in a gully developed pressures up to 22,000 pounds (nearly 10 tons) per square foot! (A. Voellmy, and A. Roch, 1961 and 1964)

Most avalanches end as cone-shaped masses. The snow in the "tip" may be 50 feet deep, and it is in this that any victims of the avalanche are often buried. Rescuers probe with long sounding rods in endeavors to locate victims.

Dogs are the best means of finding people buried in snow; they can recognize a man even when he is buried ten feet deep. In Germany, France, Switzerland, Austria, and Italy dogs are trained and registered. There is a well-known story told in Austria of how the postman of Zürs was one day overwhelmed by an avalanche. His dog came to the snow and remained standing at a particular spot. It refused to move. For three days it remained there, and eventually the townspeople dug into the snow beneath—to find the dog's master still alive. But it must be emphasized that this is most unusual; usually unless an avalanche victim is rescued in 20 minutes the odds are that he will never be rescued at all.

Another famous avalanche story—with a macabre ending—concerns the attempt to climb Mont Blanc on August 20, 1820. An avalanche swept three guides into a glacial crevasse where they perished. From the known rate of travel of the glacier, it was forecast that the bodies would be carried slowly down, and should appear about 40 years later at the foot in the valley of Chamonix some five miles away. And, sure enough, 41 years later they duly appeared—according to some reports "still looking in the bloom of youth" (references in T. Graham Brown and Gavin de Beer).

Many stories are told of remarkable escapes in avalanches. One recounted by J. Cecil Alter in the sober pages of the U. S. Weather Bureau's *Monthly Weather Review* concerns a man taking a shower at Bingham, Utah, on the morning of February 17, 1926. Suddenly a powerful avalanche swept down Sap Gulch and ran for two miles. It lifted the man from his shower, carried him 150 feet on the crest of the snow and set him down comparatively unharmed.

In powder snow avalanches a potent cause of destruction lies in the mixture of snow particles and air (an aerosol) forming a dust cloud which behaves as a heavy gas, sweeping down the mountainside at near-tornadic speed ahead of the snow sliding on the ground.

Avalanches [103]

After the avalanche that fell on Airolo, Switzerland, on February 15, 1951.

The most violent wind occurs when an avalanche is stopped abruptly, as when the snow mass falls almost vertically onto a valley floor. The air explodes in all directions like bomb blast—and with all its vagaries. One house may be torn from its foundation, another only feet away left untouched.

It is thought by some investigators that the snow itself causes an explosive blast: air, which is imprisoned and compressed in the center of the avalanche through the pressure of the moving outer layers of snow, eventually bursts out with explosive violence.

Whatever the true explanation of its origin, there is no doubt about the astonishing effects created by the blast. Frequently, the tops of trees in the path of an avalanche are snapped off, although the snow itself does not

The Elements Rage   [*104*]

Photopress, Zurich

reach so high. Often, however, destruction is caused by the snow dust which moves swiftly and envelops objects in its path. Sometimes the lateral components of the blast uproot trees hundreds of yards on either side of the avalanche. Thirty summer chalets were seen to disintegrate through the impact of the blast from an avalanche which came to rest 200 yards away (*The Observer*, London, March 19, 1939).

In a restricted valley near the Grimsel Pass, Switzerland, avalanche blast destroyed a small bridge and hurled part of it about 150 feet up the mountainside. Sir Arnold Lunn tells me that the snow of the avalanche never reached the bridge.

This incident helps to render more credible the story of an Alpine stagecoach which was blown—coachman, horses and all—across a stream.

Avalanches   [105]

The avalanche which caused this was said to have fallen so far away that the coachman neither saw nor heard it.[4]

Perhaps the greatest destruction caused by avalanche blast occurred in 1819. Part of an Alpine glacier fell over a precipice and landed on an uninhabited area. But the houses in the nearby village of Randa were shattered by the terrific blast of air pushed ahead by the mass of glacial ice as it plunged and hit the valley floor. The steeple of a stone church was flung to the ground, and heavy millstones were tossed about like leaves in an autumn gale. The village was almost totally destroyed.

Yet, such are the vagaries of blast, it is possible for a man to be within a few feet of an avalanche and to feel nothing. F. F. Tuckett, an experienced mountaineer, says that he was on the Eiger, Switzerland, when a great avalanche—estimated at half a million tons—fell so near him that he was covered with powdered snow. But ". . . there was nothing of the nature of those great blasts which we are told not unfrequently immediately precede or follow the larger avalanches, and often cause even more destruction than the latter."

Mark Heller, of the Avalanche Committee of the Ski Club of Great Britain, comments:

> Powder snow avalanches are very rare (though very dramatic). The annual death toll is due almost entirely to windslab avalanches of sizes varying from a few feet to the gigantic. That these are formed on lee slopes by wind-carried snow which is compacted over a layer of "ball bearings" and often covered by subsequent snowfalls should be much more widely known.[5]

"Ball bearings" refers to long coarse granulated snow or "depth-hoar" crystals which can act as ball bearings should the top layer start to move.

Avalanches are rare, but are not unknown in Britain. Near Lewes, Sussex, there is an inn called The Snowdrop—a memorial to one of the greatest avalanches England has known. On December 24, 1836, after a great snowstorm, a huge mass of snow slid down from the South Downs and buried a row of cottages, causing the death of eight people.

In the United States death and destruction from avalanches were almost unknown until the beginning of the later (non-Californian) gold rush —about 1860. Then, for the first and last time the mountains of the Western

---

[4] Ordinary snow avalanches, unless they fall over steep gradients or carry heavy debris with them, make little or no noise, although a hissing noise is heard with some. Ice avalanches fall with a noise like thunder. "Avalanche blast can travel great distances. It can, and frequently does, precipitate avalanches on the opposite side of a wide valley. Its power is almost unbelievable." Seligman.

[5] Advice to skiers about avalanches is given in various publications. One of the best and most recent was in the British *Ski Notes and Queries,* December 1964.

states were heavily populated.[6] In the booklet, *Snow Avalanches* (1961), the U. S. Forest Service says:

> From the Sierras and the Cascades to the Rockies, miners swarmed into the high country and built their camps. . . . . Verifiable records of avalanche accidents in the vicinity of Alta [Montana], for instance, go back as far as 1874, when the mining camp was practically obliterated by avalanches; more than 60 lives were lost. During the next 35 years, avalanches killed 67 more persons. Three slides in three different years wiped out more than 10 persons each.

In 1937 Alta became the site of the first avalanche observation and research center in the Western Hemisphere, although it was not until 1945 that detailed research began.

The worst avalanche disaster in the United States is known as the "Wellington Snowslide." It occurred at the railroad station of Wellington, Washington, in the Cascade Range on March 1, 1910. A great mass of snow fell on the station, and three large locomotives, several carriages, a water tank, *and* the station building were swept over a ledge into a canyon 150 feet below. Over 100 people were killed.

But it is the avalanching snow of the European Alps which has claimed the greatest number of victims, especially in the years before the introduction of scientific preventive measures. The main reason is that the Alpine slopes and valleys are dotted with farms and other dwellings. Another reason is the number of avalanches: tens of thousands a year in Switzerland alone.

In 1689 a tremendous avalanche wiped out Saas, in Valais, together with its inhabitants. In 1719 the town of Loèche, in Valais, was destroyed by an avalanche and 60 people lost their lives. A year later, at Obergestein, another of these "thunderbolts of snow," as Lord Byron called them, demolished 120 houses and killed over 80 people.

During the First World War more soldiers were killed by avalanches in the Tyrolean mountains than by all the shells, bullets, bombs, and other missiles of the combatants fighting in that area. The winter of 1916 piled snow deeper than for half a century; snow-wise mountaineers knew the eastern Alps were a deathtrap. Yet the stern exigencies of war forbade retreat. On December 13 the snow began to thaw and 105 avalanches plunged down the mountainside. Some of these were deliberately released by the combatants; probably the first time in military history that avalanches were used as heavy weapons. Many hundreds of soldiers died that day. And in the four years of war the White Death claimed thousands of lives. Exact figures are unobtainable but, according to the archives of the combatants, the figure did not reach 60,000 as is often claimed.

---

[6] They are now *visited* by thousands of skiers, but avalanche warning and control systems have greatly reduced the danger.

Another view of Airolo after the avalanche.   *Willi Borelli*

The worst European avalanche disasters in many years occurred during January and February of 1951. In this period dangerous avalanches fell from the Valais Alps in the west to the Austrian Alps in the east. They were the result of exceptional weather conditions. On January 19 masses of warm air from the Atlantic and masses of cold air from the polar regions met over the Central European Alps. This meeting of vast masses of warm and cold air was accompanied at a height of some 16,000 feet by a violent wind blowing at over 115 m.p.h.

P. Boettcher, describing these conditions, writes:

> As the front, and with it the area of precipitation, ran parallel to the upper-wind direction, it persisted almost without change of position, from 19–21 January. This circumstance was the main cause of the tremendously heavy precipitation in the Alps. Moreover, throughout these three critical days, a north-south pressure gradient prevailed in the Alps, so that the wind was blocked on the north side of the mountains, which yet further increased the volume of precipitation.

In these exceptional conditions dangerous masses of fresh snow fell, producing longer avalanche paths than usual. And because of the extreme depth of freshly fallen snow there were avalanches on comparatively gentle slopes.

The Elements Rage

Damage and casualties were reported from Germany, France, Italy, Austria and Switzerland, the last two countries suffering most.[7] In Austria farms, churches, power stations, and whole villages were overwhelmed. Thousands of acres of forest were swept away, over 100 people killed.

No country in the world is better equipped than Switzerland to meet the avalanche danger. The Swiss have a very efficient avalanche-warning system. But all the defense services of the snow-wise Swiss were unable to avoid loss and some deaths in the exceptional circumstances of 1951. When the final tally was complete, Switzerland's ancient foe had damaged or destroyed trees over an area of 750 hectares (three square miles), buried more than 2,500 hectares (ten square miles) of cultivated land, killed 530 cattle, destroyed 894 buildings, and killed 92 people (de Quervain and Th. Zingg).

Throughout Europe 265 were killed by these avalanches. According to the Swiss Snow and Avalanche Research Institute, they had been the worst since 1720, and Boettcher says: "Never before has the operation of avalanches extended simultaneously over so wide an area, and in this respect it is no exaggeration to speak of this as the greatest avalanche disaster on record."

But compared with other natural hazards, the losses caused by avalanches are not great. It is estimated that they cause a yearly average of 150 deaths throughout the world. Property damage is comparatively trivial. These small losses are not due to any scarcity of avalanches, but because the vast majority occur in uninhabited regions, and the danger from those that occur where men live is lessened by forecasting and precautionary measures. For every avalanche that becomes news, tens of thousands remain unreported because they are harmless.

No country has suffered more from avalanches—or studied them more intensively—than has Switzerland. But even here the scientific study of avalanches did not begin until after the First World War. Much defense research and other snow studies are done at the Federal Snow and Avalanche Research Institute on the Weissfluhjoch, 8,000 feet above Davos. There are three main defenses: forecasting, artificial release, and protective structures.

FORECASTING

It is generally possible for experts to know when and where avalanches are likely, and reports on their development can then be sent out to threatened areas. In Switzerland avalanche bulletins are distributed to the Press every Friday and whenever the snow situation calls for one—two to three bulletins a week on average.

---

[7] Joseph Wechsberg's *Avalanche* tells how the little Austrian village of Blons was overwhelmed on January 11, 1954. The main avalanche struck at 200 m.p.h.: 50 died—one in six of the inhabitants.

Forecasting is aided by the knowledge that many avalanches descend on the same course year after year. This particularly applies to wet-snow avalanches. In the inhabited districts of the Swiss Alps nearly 10,000 habitual paths are recognized. But it must be emphasized that avalanches do not always confine themselves either to the width or length of their habitual paths. During the terrible Swiss avalanches of January 1951, several plowed through heavy timber where no avalanche had been known for hundreds of years. (For avalanche forecasting in the United States, see *Snow Avalanches.*)

ARTIFICIAL RELEASE

If snow masses can be brought down while they are comparatively small, dangerous avalanches will be avoided. Such harmless avalanches are induced by artillery or mortar fire, by rockets or mines. If conditions warrant it, officials on some of the Swiss mountain railways go out every morning before the traffic starts and direct fire at dangerous places on the higher snow slopes. In addition to direct fire, land mines are used to cause small avalanches. The mines are placed in position, and when the forecasting experts decide the time is right they explode the mines electrically from a distance.

PROTECTIVE STRUCTURES

These prevent dangerous snow masses from forming. Trees growing close together, as in a thick wood, provide the best defense. Not only can no avalanche originate among them but they arrest all except the most powerful ones. Trees are accordingly grown at various strategic points, such as the places above villages where avalanches might originate. Protective woods on Swiss Alpine slopes have been strictly preserved for centuries; at one time the penalty was death for cutting trees in them.

Artificial barriers are constructed on slopes where avalanches may occur. These usually consist of rows of heavy walls which break up the masses of snow into small harmless units. The snow mass is thus held at numerous points, and nowhere can a slide develop and peel off the whole surface. Long walls are also built at an acute angle to the snow slope, thus deflecting avalanching snow so that it descends where it can do the least harm. Some Swiss houses have the side facing uphill built like a wedge, so that any avalanche which strikes it is split, the two halves harmlessly by-passing the house. Railways and transalpine highways, which are vulnerable targets, are often protected by tunnels or built-up galleries so that avalanches slide harmlessly over the protecting wall.

Despite the damage it causes, snow is, on balance, a decided asset. On the score of natural beauty alone, think of what an irreparable loss it would be never again to see a snow-capped mountain or a landscape carpeted with glittering snow. Look again at those photomicrographs of snow crystals and imagine our loss if we could no longer gaze upon such delicate and exquisite beauty. Think of a snowless world where never again could children enjoy a snow fight or roll a giant snowball; where the thrill of the toboggan run, or the swish of a ski breaking the crust of a virgin snowfield was a thing of the past, and you realize that a little danger and inconvenience are a small price to pay for such natural joys.

Snow also confers practical benefits on mankind. In some parts of the world snow is a valuable aid to transportation. In skiing snow enables man to travel at his maximum speed unaided by mechanical means: for one kilometer with a flying start at Cervinia, Italy, on July 18, 1964, Luigi de Marco traveled at 108.589 m.p.h.

Snow is of considerable value to agriculture. The large amount of air trapped in the crystals makes snow a very good insulator—twice as efficient as sand. This insulation keeps the temperature of the soil almost constant, however much that of the air may change. Moreover, when a blanket of snow covers the ground it greatly reduces heat loss from lower ground levels. Frequently when snow, which has lain for several weeks finally melts, the ground is free of frost.

"This absence of frost has an important influence in preventing spring floods. The water of the snow melting in the warm sunshine of approaching spring is absorbed freely into the soil. As a result pastures and lawns may emerge from the snow cover verdant with young grass." (Charles F. Brooks) Snow also holds water that is needed for irrigation later in the year. It thus forms a valuable reserve of water in some districts, especially in mountainous country.

Snow avalanches are most common, but there are two other forms which, mass for mass, are more dangerous: ice avalanches and rock avalanches. Ice avalanches come from glaciers, parts of which sometimes break and hurl down millions of tons of ice.

The most disastrous ice avalanche of this century, and one of the worst in recorded history, occurred on January 10, 1962, in western Peru. Here the ice-covered peak of Nevado de Huascarán, Peru's highest mountain, thrusts four miles into the sky. On the floor of the valley eight villages clustered round Ranrahirca, a township of about 2,500 souls.

At 6:13 p.m. on the fatal day a vast mass of ice broke from the north peak. As it fell, it carried away more ice and blocks of granite and slate. It was estimated that the total volume was some six million cubic yards— equal to four Empire State Buildings—and weighing four million tons. As the colossal mass struck a funnel-like gorge, a terrifying roar echoed across the surrounding countryside.

Then, fantastic as it sounds, the millions of tons of ice *bounced* off the

White river of death. Part of the ice, rock and mud avalanche that overwhelmed a valley and killed three thousand, five hundred people in western
Peru January 10, 1962.   *Servicio Aero-fotografico Nacional, Lima, Peru*

side of the gorge, struck again, bounced, struck—altogether five times during
its zigzag ricocheting, mile-a-minute course. Then the avalanche plunged
straight down. This monstrous journey was subsequently reconstructed by
a survey on the spot.

Each time it struck, rocks, soil and other debris scoured from the
gorge added weight and volume to the avalanche. Four mountain villages
were instantaneously crushed and buried. Then it spilled onto the valley
floor an irresistible flood of mud, rock and ice a third of a mile across and
up to 130 yards deep. One moment Ranrahirca was a happy thriving township of a thousand or so buildings and over 2,000 people, the next it was a
vast graveyard covered with an impenetrable gray carpet. Only a score of
buildings and 100 people on the outskirts of the town survived.

After cutting down Ranrahirca, the avalanche traveled a further mile
to the Santa River. The final toll of this avalanche was seven villages, one
town, 10,000 (estimated) livestock, and about 3,500 dead (Olivier Dollfus
and Carlos Peñaherrera Del Aguila, and Bart McDowell).

By then the vast mass of debris was a mile wide and some 15 yards
deep. It was estimated that in all about 12 million cubic yards weighing

The Elements Rage   [*112*]

more than 20 million tons were involved. The avalanche covered about 11 miles in some 15 minutes.

Rock avalanches, or rockslides, are rare but potentially the most dangerous of all. Some of the worst have occurred in Switzerland. Sometimes, in these tremendous rock falls, a considerable part of a whole mountain plunges down. This happened at Plurs, Switzerland, when, on September 4, 1618, nearly half the side of a mountain fell and obliterated the town. Out of a population of some 1,500, only four were left—those who were away from Plurs at the time (Helmut Presser). Then on September 2, 1806, one side of the Rossberg in the Alps in central Switzerland collapsed. The vast mass of rock traveled across a valley, then totally engulfed four villages, killing over 500 people. The valley floor was raised by more than 100 feet (Heinrich Hirzel).

Another Swiss rock avalanche occurred on September 11, 1881, near the village of Elm. Overshadowing the village was the Plattenbergkopf, outermost buttress of a great mountain mass, the Glarner Alpen. Owing to careless slate mining halfway up, the top of the Plattenbergkopf became undermined. There were sporadic falls of rocks and the villagers vaguely realized that sometime the mountain would fall. But the moment of truth was at hand.

September 11 was a rainy Sunday. Rocks fell more heavily than usual and the mountain groaned and rumbled. Sightseers gathered and were "rewarded" by the sight of part of the east side of the Plattenbergkopf breaking away. No one was hurt although rocks fell almost at the feet of some of the onlookers. Seventeen minutes later a larger mass fell from the west side of the mountain. By now even the hardened villagers felt some alarm and many flocked to the hillside opposite the groaning mountain. Little time was left.

The two large rock falls had left the top of the Plattenbergkopf balancing on a tiny neck of rock, like the top half of an hourglass. Millions of tons of rock teetered for four minutes, and then hurtled down. The huge avalanche fell as far as the quarry; then the upper part shot forward horizontally across the valley, hit the Düniberg obliquely and was deflected down the valley, covering about a mile in less than half a minute. Elm was annihilated, and half of another village was destroyed.

A few men raced the inexorable tide and won. The survivors, particularly the village schoolmaster, have left a vivid description of what happened when the mountain fell. A great wind preceded the avalanche, whirling people into the air, uprooting trees, and lifting houses from their foundations. Some houses were carried whole through the air and set down safely beyond reach of the avalanche. Other houses were seen to bend and shake, then "break up like little toys" before the avalanche reached them.

People caught by the flying rocks were killed instantly—"as an insect is

Rock avalanche—the most deadly of all avalanches. Thousands of tons of rock fell from the mountainside during a series of rockfalls near Almens, Switzerland, in April, 1950.   *Photopress, Zurich*

crushed into a red streak under a man's foot." A house was cut in two by the sharply defined edge of the avalanche.

As abruptly as it had started, the avalanche ceased. For less than a minute the valley was filled with a continuous roar—then "silence and stillness supervened. Survivors stood stunned where they were. Nothing moved. Then a great cry and wailing arose in the part of the village that was left. People began to run wildly about, some down the valley, some up. As the dust cloud grew thinner the wall-like side of the ruin appeared. It was quite dry. All the grass and trees in the neighbourhood were white with dust."

About ten million cubic yards of rock fell on Elm and its valley, burying some 150 men, women and children—and a million square yards of green fields—under a solid gray rock carpet (Martin Conway, Ernst Buss, and Albert Heim).

The most famous tragedy from a rock avalanche in North America occurred in Canada, when, on April 29, 1903, part of Turtle Mountain, Alberta, fell on the township of Frank, some 3,000 feet below. Turtle Mountain is composed of a thick layer of limestone overlying layers of softer rock and coal. The slope of the upper part of the mountain is steep, averaging some 50°; the section which fell was even steeper. There was a coal mine at the foot of the mountain, and it is probable that the excava-

Some of the huge boulders which fell, each capable of wrecking a house.　*Photopress, Zurich*

tions caused the soft underlying rocks to collapse under the enormous weight of the limestone. Turtle Mountain was almost ready to go. H. E. Vokes says:

> The unseasonable weather determined the hour at which the calamity occurred. The unusual warmth of the past few days caused extensive melting of the winter snows, and this melted water had penetrated the open joint cracks. Then on the 28th there was a sharp change to cold weather, and the thermometer fell to zero in Frank on the morning of the slide. The water in the joint cracks froze. As it froze it expanded, tearing loose the last supports which held the mass in place, freeing it to hurtle down into the valley as one great avalanche of destruction.

An estimated 90 million tons of rock hurtled down at a speed of 90 m.p.h. The mass of limestone was estimated to be half a mile square and about 500 feet thick in the center. As the locomotive-sized rocks crashed down, the roar was heard 25 miles away. The avalanche sealed the entrance to the mine, crushed the southwestern half of Frank, killed nearly 70 people, plowed *beneath* the Oldman River, and carried water and river bottom 400 feet up the opposite side of the valley.[8]

---

[8] On page 232 I have dealt with what happened when a similar mass fell into Lituya Bay, Alaska.

Avalanches

A small rock avalanche plunges down the Grosse Windgälle, Switzerland.   K. Reimann

And the 19 men in the mine? The first thing they knew, 300 feet down, was a great blast of air that roared through the tunnel like a tornado, throwing men and horses to the ground. The entrance was sealed by a jumble of broken rocks. Two possibilities were open to the miners: to attempt to clear the entrance or to try to hack a shaft to the surface from further back in the mine, where the slope was steeper and the rocks therefore less thick. They chose to dig the shaft, and worked in desperate shifts from about seven in the morning until five in the afternoon, when the first man came out and looked up at the mountain that had almost been his tomb. Its eastern face was entirely different, and the valley was now a chaos of rock fragments. This largest known rockslide on the North American continent covered over one square mile and had an average depth of 65 feet.

Chapter 6

Lightning ⟩⟩

To the ancients, lightning was something supernatural. The blinding light, brilliant as the sun, and tremendous roaring surely could come from no lesser source than the gods. But were Jove's bolts a punishment or warning? For many centuries lightning divination was part of Roman statecraft, and about 300 B.C. the College of Augurs was entrusted with this task. As late as the 18th century a thunderstorm was the signal for a furious outbreak of bell-ringing. Medieval bells were frequently inscribed *Fulgura frango*—"I break the lightning." Many bell ringers were killed as a result of strikes on church towers.

The true cause of lightning was not known until the middle of the 18th century. Before then various picturesque theories had been held concerning its origin, such as clouds rubbing together, an atmospheric explosion of "nitrous and sulphurous vapours," or an emanation from the earth. It was not until the experiments of such men as Benjamin Franklin that the origin of lightning was established.

Franklin's experiment has become a legend. Exactly what happened on that day in June 1752 when he flew "the most famous of all kites" is not known for certain. Probably the best account is by Joseph Priestley, who obtained the details from Franklin himself, although not until nearly 15 years after the experiment was made.

> Preparing a large silk handkerchief and two cross-sticks of a proper length on which to extend it, he took the opportunity of the first approaching thunderstorm to take a walk in the fields in which there was a shed convenient for his purpose. . . . The kite being raised, a considerable time elapsed before there was any appearance of its being electrified.
>
> One very promising cloud had passed over it without any effect; when, at length, just as he was beginning to despair of his contrivance, he observed some loose threads of the hempen string to stand erect, and to avoid one another, just as if they had been suspended on a common conductor.
>
> Struck with this promising appearance, he immediately presented his knuckle to the key and the discovery was complete. He perceived a very evident electric spark [quoted by Carl Van Doren].

[*117*]

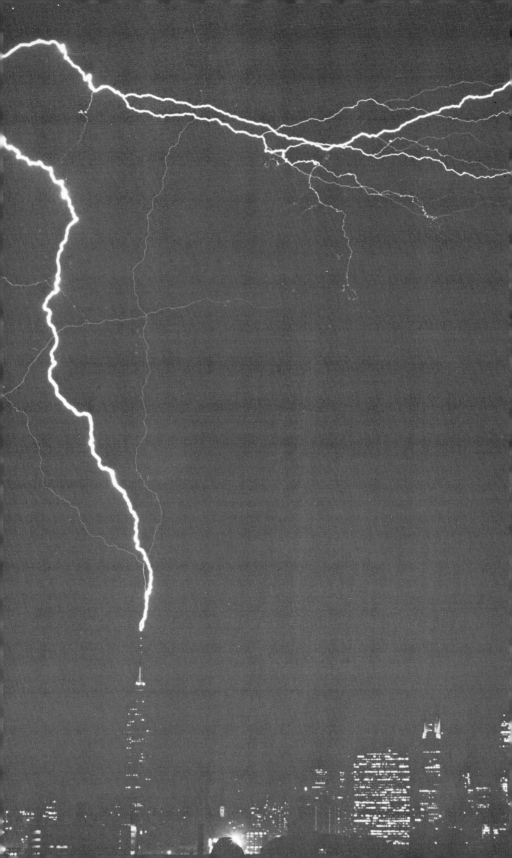

Experiments of this type became quite popular, probably because the experimenters did not realize the danger. One man secured 30 sparks 10 feet long, and several hundred shorter ones, in an hour. The loud reports emanating from the house of another experimenter frightened the neighbors into protesting; they were afraid they would be killed by the lightning he was trying to domesticate. One Russian experimenter Georg Wilhelm Richmann was, in fact, killed while experimenting with a "thunder machine." His collecting rod was apparently struck by lightning as he approached it and a discharge leapt to his head, killing him instantly (B. B. Kudryavtsev).

Lightning is now regarded as the electrical discharge from a charged thundercloud. Sometimes lightning occurs without rain; for example, through electrification caused by the collision of ice crystals, and in the dust clouds over an erupting volcano. Thunder is the noise caused by the effect of the discharge—the *spat-spat* of a gigantic spark plug.

Since the end of the Second World War thunderstorms have been investigated by radar, rocket, balloon and airplane, and some of their phenomena have been reproduced in the laboratory. Consequently much is now known about the mechanics of thunderstorms—and lightning—although there is still uncertainty about some of the details.

A thunderstorm generally forms when an updraft of warm moist air (which provides the energy) rises into cold air. The resulting thundercloud —cumulo-nimbus—sometimes towers 13 miles above the earth. The base of such a cloud may be anything from ½ to 2½ miles above the ground, and may cover an area of 100 or more square miles, and contain over half a million tons of water.

The cloud base looks like a huge cauliflower or an enormous white anvil, topped by the "cirrus umbrella" composed of countless millions of ice crystals. These giant cloud masses are cells of turbulent energy whose electrical potential is measured in millions of volts. A large thunderstorm releases as much energy as a megaton bomb.

A thundercloud is composed of active centers, or cells (sometimes one but generally up to five), which go through several stages, lasting about an hour. The mature stage, during which lightning occurs, lasts for about 15 minutes. A cell may be anything between 1 and 5 miles wide. The rising air gathers much momentum; frequently there are currents shooting upward at 60 m.p.h., occasionally at 150 m.p.h. or more. There are also down currents, but they are less violent. As the moist air rises, it cools and eventually ice crystals form. Then rain and hail fall, and the stage is set for lightning.

There must be very few people who have suffered the terrifying experience of falling through a thunderstorm and lived. But it happened to U. S. Marine Corps jet pilot William Rankin. The engine of his single-seater

---

Lightning

fighter failed at 47,000 feet—9 miles, or 1½ times the height of Everest—and he bailed out. His preset parachute did not open until he had fallen to 10,000 feet. Normally, he should have reached the ground in about 13 minutes but, caught in the thunderstorm's turbulent air and tremendous updrafts, the nightmare journey took him nearly three-quarters of an hour. At times Rankin was actually going up.

> I was blown up and down as much as 6,000 ft. at a time. It went on for a long time, like being on a very fast elevator, with strong blasts of compressed air hitting you. Once when a violent blast of air sent me careering up into the chute and I could feel the cold, wet nylon collapsing about me, I was sure the chute would never blossom again. But, by some miracle, I fell back and the chute *did* recover its billow.
>
> The wind had savage allies. The first clap of thunder came as a deafening explosion that literally shook my teeth. I didn't *hear* the thunder, I actually *felt* it—an almost unbearable physical experience. If it had not been for my closely fitted helmet, the explosions might have shattered my eardrums.
>
> I saw lightning all around me in every shape imaginable. When very close, it appeared mainly as a huge, bluish sheet several feet thick. It was raining so torrentially that I thought I would drown in midair. Several times I held my breath, fearing that otherwise I might inhale quarts of water.

What causes lightning? This century has witnessed a dozen or so theories and argument still continues. One widely accepted theory is that when droplets of water are frozen in the thundercloud electricity is generated. This has been proved experimentally in the laboratory. To quote the British meteorologist, B. J. Mason (1955):

> Having worked out the rate at which these particles would grow in a typical thundercloud, I used the results of these laboratory tests to calculate how quickly charge would be generated and separated by these hailstones while they were falling towards the cloud base. The answers were encouraging. It seemed that such a process would be capable of producing the necessary quantity of electricity in the time required by the electrical and radar observations. . . .
>
> There is some reason to hope that we are at last on the right track. At least many of the experts are now agreed that the generation of thunderstorm electricity is closely connected with the formation of soft hail, although there may be some doubt as to the exact mechanism. However, one cannot help feeling that nature, who has guarded this particular secret so well and for so long, may not give it up so easily. It is one thing to have a plausible theory, and another to prove it beyond all reasonable doubt. There is still a long way to go.

Broadly, the top of the thundercloud is charged with positive electricity, the bottom with negative. And in many thunderstorms there is a small charge of positive electricity between top and bottom of the cloud. But how is the normally insulating air transformed in a fraction of a second into a white-hot conductor?

On the earth directly below the cloud there is a buildup of positive electricity, forming a "mirror image" of the negative charge above.[1] As the cloud drifts over the earth, the positive charge follows it like a shadow, climbing any prominences, such as church steeples and chimneys, which will bring it nearer to the cloud. Enormous differences of electrical potential between earth and cloud are built up, with a maximum of about 100 million volts. Something has to give. Suddenly a faint, electrically conductive channel, called the pilot, forms in the air. Then a thick white-hot dart, or leader, shoots downward from the cloud for a distance varying between 50 and 1,000 feet. This is quickly followed by another leader which elongates the path; then others follow, until eventually it is within 50 feet or so of the earth. The leader track, as it is called, consists of 40 or more successive darts, and this is what gives lightning its characteristic zigzag shape. The leaders travel at some 100 miles per second, although the speed is not constant over the whole of the track. The complete process takes about $\frac{1}{100}$ of a second. If a subsequent stroke in the same discharge passes down the already prepared track, it travels much faster, around 1,000 miles per second.

What is the role of the leaders? They make a path of electrified particles (ions) through the nonconducting air, blazing an electrically conductive channel along which the main lightning stroke can flow.

When the leader track is within a short distance of the earth, streamers (a leader in reverse) leap up from the earth, sometimes snaking 200 feet high.[2] One eventually makes contact with the leader track and then the main lightning stroke—a brilliant spear of light—soars *upward* at a maximum speed of some 80,000 miles per second, or more than a third the speed of light. D. J. Malan tells me that the highest return-stroke speed he and his colleagues have measured is 87,000 miles per second. Flashes from cloud to cloud consist of leaders only.

This process explains the well-known branching appearance seen on many photographs of lightning. The branches are made by the zigzag path of the various dart leaders. I have seen a photograph of lightning compared with a tracing of the River Amazon and its tributaries. They were almost identical. As the main flash ascends it energizes and lights up the branches made by the leader track. These branches, of course, point downward, and this explains why photographs of lightning often give the impression that the main flash is directed toward the earth instead of upward toward the cloud.

---

[1] Normally, the earth has a negative charge, but a thundercloud causes the ground beneath it to develop a positive charge.

[2] Sometimes, from very high ground and tall structures, the predominant leader strokes are from earth to cloud.

A single discharge, consisting of leader and main stroke, generally lasts a few thousandths of a second.

Occasionally, the separate strokes in a multiple discharge can be seen, and recorded by an ordinary camera. This happens when a strong wind moves the zigzag "rope" of superheated air which channels the lightning strokes. Camera movement also accounts for some of the photographs.

Various figures have been given for the diameter of the lightning channel (Leonard B. Loeb, 1964). The matter is complicated by several factors. The diameter of the channel is probably not consistent for the whole of its length. In addition, the bright central core of the channel is surrounded by a corona envelope (glow discharge) which may extend 10 to 20 feet. The diameter of the channel is exaggerated in photographs because of halation —the reflection and dispersion of the intense light on the negative. R. H. Golde, a British authority on lightning, tells me he considers that the intensely bright central core of the lightning channel is about half an inch wide. He bases this figure on experimental work with electrical arcs—a lightning discharge is, of course, a natural electric arc.

Where does the "light" in lightning come from? The tremendous blast of the stroke—millions of horse-power—causes the surrounding air molecules to glow. The same process is seen on a miniature scale in the light produced in an old-fashioned arc-discharge lamp.

The lightning causes a drop in the electrical charge in the thundercloud. It recharges in about 20 seconds and it is then ready for another flash.

People who have been in the midst of a violent thunderstorm have experienced this "recharging" for themselves. Ann Strong, who was caught on a mountainside in British Columbia during such a storm, says of the lightning:

> After each strike we moved in silence for a while, with only the tearing wind and slashing rain. Then the rocks would begin a shrill humming, each on a slightly different note. The humming grew louder and louder. You could feel a charge building up in your body. Our hair stood on end. The charge increased, and the humming swelled, until everything reached an unbearable climax. Then the lightning would strike again—with a crack like a gigantic rifle shot. The strike broke the tension. For a while we would grope forward in silence. Then the humming would begin again [quoted by Colin Fletcher].

F. F. Tucker was on a mountain near Susa, Italy, where there was a massively built chapel some 15 feet in diameter. A heavy thunderstorm came on and the summit of the mountain was electrified.

> As the clouds swept by, every rock, every loose stone, the uprights of the rude railing outside the chapel, the ruined signal, our axes, my lorgnette and flask, and even my fingers and elbows, set up "a dismal universal hiss."

It was as though we were in a vast nest of excited snakes, or a battery of frying pans, or listening at a short distance to the sustained note of a band of *cigali* [cicada] in a chestnut wood—a mixture of comparisons which may serve sufficiently to convey the impression that the general effect was indescribable.

Some series of discharges last for a second and contain 40 successive strokes. Mason says that 47 strokes have been recorded in one discharge. Thirty-one consecutive strokes have been photographed in three-fifths of a second. These are, of course, extreme figures. Generally, multiple-stroke lightning occurs much more frequently in tropical thunderstorms. In Johannesburg, South Africa, 50 per cent of all flashes have 5 strokes or more; in London, England, 50 per cent have 3 or fewer. Incidentally, lightning *does* strike twice in the same place; the Empire State Building in New York is often struck as many as a dozen times during a single storm. And some people have been struck more than once, and lived to tell two—or more— tales!

Throughout the world there are an estimated 16 million thunderstorms a year, and at any given moment about 1,800 are taking place. The humid tropics have more than any other region, many places averaging some 80 thunderstorm days a year. The place with the largest number of thunderstorm days is Kampala, Uganda, averaging 242 a year (C. E. P. Brooks, and World Meteorological Organization, Geneva).

Strange as it sounds, however, this does not necessarily mean that Kampala is the most thundery place on earth—if a single clap of thunder is heard in the far distance by an alert meteorologist, that rates as a thunderstorm day in the tables. D. J. Malan tells me: "I once met an engineer from Central Africa who remarked on the violent thunderstorms we get in Johannesburg. When I told him that according to the book they were supposed to get more thunderstorms, he would not believe it. Another engineer with an extensive knowledge of power-line problems connected with lightning in Africa told me that South Africa and Rhodesia experience far more interruptions per 100 miles of line per year than Central Africa."

For comparison, the number of thunderstorm days in Great Britain vary from 5 (*e.g.*, central Scotland) to 20 (*e.g.*, southeast England). In the United States the West Coast has about 3, the central states about 45, and Florida about 70 thunderstorm days a year.

In a storm there are sometimes thousands of flashes. During the great British thunderstorm of July 1923, 6,924 flashes were recorded over London alone—once 47 strokes were counted in a minute. During a great storm on December 25, 1923, at Pretoria, South Africa, 360 flashes occurred in three minutes and for about an hour 100 flashes a minute were recorded. And Cicely M. Botley tells me that during a thunderstorm in southeast England on September 5, 1958: "From Tunbridge Wells at one time the whole

Lightning [123]

northwest horizon was ablaze. The strokes were too rapid to be distinguished."

Lightning activity of this order belongs to what Bernard Vonnegut and Charles B. Moore have called "giant electrical storms." The clouds of these storms rise to twice the height of ordinary thunderstorms, the updrafts are three or four times as fast (up to 300 m.p.h.), and the electrical activity is more violent and continuous. These giant storms are associated with the most powerful type of tornado, such as the one which wrecked part of Worcester, Massachusetts, on June 9, 1953. Electrical activity is frequently observed with tornadoes and it has been suggested that they may actually be caused by thunderstorm electricity.

The visible length of a lightning stroke varies considerably. In the cloud-to-earth discharge it is rarely more than a mile, although flashes four miles long have been reported. When lightning occurs in a mountainous region the flash may be 100 yards long—or even less if the clouds are very low. The longest strokes occur when lightning flashes from one part of the cloud to another, or from one cloud to another. In the first instance, a length of 10 miles has been recorded; in the second, 20 miles. Most discharges are either within the cloud or between clouds. Sometimes one lightning flash taps the electrical energy of several storm cells (M. Brook and Bernard Vonnegut). Very rarely one of these long horizontal flashes finally turns earthward, striking the earth from a blue sky. Hence the probable origin of the phrase: "A bolt from the blue."

The color of the flash varies widely, the most usual is white; the combination of the spectra of nitrogen and oxygen. Red and yellow flashes are often seen in South Africa when the air is heavily charged with dust. A reddish or pinkish discharge occurs when air rich in water vapor is ionized and adds the spectrum of hydrogen to that of nitrogen and oxygen. Every color in the spectrum has been reported but, after white, the main colors are yellow, pink and red. E. L. Hawke tells me that, in England, blue lightning is a common feature of exceptionally violent thunderstorms.

Before dealing further with lightning it is necessary to explain the accompanying thunder. Some picturesque theories have been advanced to account for this loudest of all the common sounds of Nature: a cloud bursting; ice and hail crashing together; and two clouds bumping against each other. In the 19th century there were many advocates of the "vacuum theory": lightning caused a vacuum and thunder was the result of the divided atmosphere coming together with a bang.

The real cause is the intense heat of the lightning stroke—ranging up to 30,000° C.—which makes the air along the path of the discharge expand with the violence of an explosion, radiating pressure waves through the atmosphere. Thunder seldom reaches the ears as a single clap. If it does the lightning was uncomfortably close and the sound is a sharp and terrific

The result of a lightning stroke. When Fred Berry of Suncook, New Hampshire, was struck, his shoes were blasted off, yet his only injuries were two badly cut feet. *International News Photos, General Electric Co.*

crack, like a field gun fired a few feet away. This sound comes from the *shock wave* of the white-hot expanding channel. It is supersonic but attenuates rapidly with distance. At a distance of about 500 feet the familiar sound of thunder (caused by the pressure waves) is heard. As sound travels at 1,090 feet per second, the distance of the lightning can be estimated from the interval elapsing between seeing the flash and hearing the thunder, counting a mile for every five seconds. Incidentally, at close range a sound as of cloth tearing is heard a fraction of a second before the main thunder.

Modern studies of thunder have shown that it is a complex phenomenon presenting several problems. Why is it that gunfire can be heard for 30 miles or more (exceptionally 100 miles), whereas thunder usually cannot be heard for more than about 12 miles?[3] Why is there a long roll of thunder when its

---

[3] Exceptionally, however, thunder is heard at much greater distances—some observations indicate 70 or so miles. Such thunder comes only from powerful earth-to-cloud strokes (L. C. Veenema and J. J. Taljaard). Not all lightning is followed by thunder, as some strokes, especially horizontal ones, are not powerful enough to heat the air sufficiently.

Lightning

cause lasts only a fraction of a second? And why doesn't the sound vary considerably according to the position of the hearer? Why is a clap of thunder frequently accompanied by a sudden downpour of rain?

These are some of the questions set by a study of various observations on thunder. Thanks largely to the work of the American physicist and acoustics expert, Wilfred J. Remillard, there are now reasonable answers to most of the problems.

Unlike gunfire, which is concentrated at one place, thunder is radiated from a vertical branching path a mile or more high, and frequently there are multiple strokes. In some great storms lightning strokes follow each other so quickly that thunder is continuous for minutes on end. During a storm over London during the night of August 2, 1879, thunder was said to have been continuous for 20 minutes. And Hawke tells me that during a storm in Hertfordshire during the night of June 12, 1964, thunder was timed that lasted continuously for 28 minutes.

During a thunderstorm the atmosphere is in a turbulent condition, with various refracting, reflecting, and scattering mechanisms operating—especially wind, rain and hail. Moreover, there is evidence that the sound of thunder is refracted upward and thus may pass over the head of a distant listener. And hills, valleys, and mountains between the lightning and the observer materially affect the acoustics of thunder. "Zones of silence" also occur, so that thunder which is not heard by one observer may be heard by another farther away from the lightning.

Remillard (1960) estimates that about $\frac{1}{400}$ of the total energy dissipated in a lightning stroke goes into the production of thunder. This may not seem much until it is realized that this means about *30 million horsepower* is momentarily expended in some thunderclaps. No wonder the compression waves from thunder sometimes knock men and animals off their feet.

Only two types of lightning are generally referred to: *fork,* in which the path of the discharge is visible; and *sheet,* in which all that is seen is a sudden diffused illumination of the clouds. But lightning experts refer to at least nine types.

Streak lightning appears as one or more vivid lines or streaks. It is the form most often seen, the straightforward cloud-to-earth and return earth-to-cloud stroke or strokes—or cloud-to-cloud, or cloud-to-air stroke, or strokes. The cloud-to-earth, and return, strokes are the most powerful form of lightning and the heaviest thunder is caused by them.

Ribbon lightning is streak lightning occurring in a very strong wind which moves the conducting channel (the ionized path) so that the individual strokes are sometimes seen separately.

Heat lightning sometimes plays along the horizon on summer evenings during hot weather when no thunderclouds are visible. It is generally explained as the reflection of lightning flashes occurring below the horizon. Some meteorologists, however, believe that this form of lightning is the result of glowlike discharges in the sky.

Sheet, or wildfire, lightning is generally the reflection of a hidden flash of streak lightning. The effect can be very beautiful, especially when it occurs at night.

Leonard B. Loeb thus comments on American usage of these terms:

> Sheet and heat lightning are in this country colloquial expressions describing distant flashes mostly *intracloud* flashes, or flashes obscured by cloud and distance, including those on the horizon. The light may even be reflected by a denser cloud mass. The colors are generally pinkish owing to the influence of water vapor or to absorption. Since the flashes are not streaked and appear to cover plane areas by scattering and reflection, the word sheet has been given. Summer thunderstorms after dark are common in this country and distant storms without audible thunder and local manifestations are associated with the heat. Hence the name *heat* lightning.

Return lightning, or more correctly *return shock,* is the name given to the small discharge which sometimes comes from objects on or near the ground when a main flash occurs. John G. Albright says:

> Horses or other animals, even several hundred feet from a tree in an open pasture, experience a shock at the same instant that the tree is struck by lightning. Just previous to being struck, a considerable charge of electricity is concentrated on the tree and is shared in a degree by all the objects in its vicinity. When the tree is struck, all the objects in the vicinity are also discharged, the charges on them passing down through the ground.

The earth itself also sometimes transmits the shock to objects some distance from the actual point of contact.

The above types of lightning are comparatively common, but the following types are so rare that their occurrence is generally reported in some detail in the meteorological journals.

Beaded, chain or *pearl,* lightning appears as a flash broken into more or less evenly spaced dashes. One theory is that the main flash is succeeded by luminous points along the path of the discharge. Another theory is that variations of brightness along the path give the appearance of pearls on a string. This "pearl-necklace" effect lasts for a second or so, and is usually due to an end-on view of part of the path. The effect was seen and filmed when lightning struck the plume of water from an undersea explosion (George A. Young).

Rocket lightning is a form which is slow enough for its movement to be visible, as with a rocket.

Ball is the most spectacular of all and is dealt with at length on pages 134–141.

On rare occasions, after the main storm has passed, an extremely violent flash of lightning occurs, the so-called "parting shot." It is so vivid that even in daylight it appears as a blinding flash. The accompanying thunder is also far louder than ordinary claps. Charles F. Brooks says:

> The cloud from which this lightning comes is the rear portion of the far-flung spreading top of a storm of great intensity, the center of which may be miles away. It is characteristic of heavy thunderclouds that they mushroom out like a vast-spreading umbrella. When their electrical charges are powerful they may let loose a bolt which will reach the earth, though it must jump a gap of four or five miles. Such a bolt is, of necessity, of particularly destructive force, for the difference in potential between cloud and earth must be enormous, even when compared with that of the usual jump of a mile. The thunder may be heard 20 miles away.

Brooks is, of course, using the word "bolt" in a figurative sense. Nothing solid comes down with lightning, which is a purely electrical phenomenon.

Dark or *black* lightning, as it is called, is merely a photographic freak resulting from the reversal of the image and has nothing to do with lightning.

Man has made his own lightning, which enables him to probe the secrets of Nature's bolts. This knowledge has resulted in reducing considerably the lightning hazard to property and also to telephone, telegraph, and power lines.

At General Electric's High-voltage Engineering Laboratories at Pittsfield, Massachusetts, controlled lightning flashes are produced as follows: Thunderclouds are simulated by capacitors (electrical storage devices) in which high voltages are built up pending their swift release as artificial lightning. The capacitors are insulated with a nonflammable fluid and stand in groups 34 feet high, forming an impulse generator rated at ten million volts. The stored energy is 165,000 watt-seconds, which, if released slowly, would operate a 100-watt lamp for nearly half an hour. Actually, the discharge is released in some eight millionths of a second. The effect is as if all the power stations in the United States had turned on their power for eight microseconds to produce an electric spark.

During the New York World's Fair in 1939 this "tame" lightning generator was installed to thrill visitors. The following is a description of the scene by Karl B. McEachron, who was a leading authority on artificial lightning.

> The appearance of the demonstration hall in which the big generator performed, with the lights lowered, the red signal lamps glowing, and with the tall, forbidding stacks of black and chromium glittering evilly, was enough

in itself to quicken any watcher's pulse. And the odor of ozone which pervaded the atmosphere as a result of past demonstrations served to increase this feeling of tension and uneasiness. During the 15 seconds required for the big lightning generator to reach its full charge, the ominous hum of the apparatus put nerves on edge.

The stacks of capacitors were discharged just as are Nature's clouds, each discharge making a bright arc 30 ft. in length from the foremost point of one generator to a similar point on the other. In one of the demonstrations, a hard maple post was split by the artificial lightning. There was always a fine line in each piece of the split wood after this demonstration had been completed, indicating the path of the discharge. The wood along this path had been turned into gas, and it was the expansion of this gas which caused the wood to split.

If this is a typical description of the scale and performance of artificial lightning, what must be the power of natural lightning? Here the "capacitors" may be one cubic mile and the flash several miles long. The result is the discharge, in a fraction of a second, of the greatest concentration of power in Nature. Against the 15 seconds required to charge the generator for artificial lightning, a thundercloud requires about 20 seconds. The charges involved are, of course, much greater in a thunderstorm.

The following table, collected from various sources, shows *maximum* figures for normal lightning discharges.

Amperes	—250,000
Coulombs	—400
Joules	—1,000 million (10^{16} ergs)
Volts	—100 million
Temperature	—30,000° C. (about five times the surface temperature of the sun)
Watts	—Ten (British) billion (about 13,000 million horsepower)

Very rarely there are giant strokes, originating from the top of the thundercloud, in which these values may be exceeded; for example, 3,000 million joules (K. Berger and E. Vogelsanger).

Strange as it may sound, the actual quantity of electricity which flows in a lightning flash is very small. Various authorities give estimates ranging up to 1,000 coulombs.[4] It averages only 20 coulombs, which is much less than that supplied by the battery to the self-starter on a car! But, owing to the enormous potentials (millions of volts), the vast energies released by the lightning flash in a few thousandths of a second perform amazing feats. Some of these are due to the violent wave of compressed air which is driven outward from the flash. People hit by this wave have sometimes been hurled a dozen feet or more.

---

[4] A coulomb is the unit of quantity in measuring electricity—the amount which passes when one ampere flows for one second.

Lightning

Leonard B. Loeb says that where a lightning stroke encounters high electrical resistance, the equivalent of the explosive force of a ton of TNT is sometimes expended. This figure helps to render credible some "lightning stories" which otherwise would be hard to credit.

Hard stone is sometimes reduced to powder when struck by lightning. Many instances have been reported in which lightning has knocked holes in stone or brick walls; sometimes the walls look as if a shell had been fired through them. When the belfry of a church was struck, a lump of stone weighing over 200 pounds was flung onto the roof of the apse 60 yards away. When one of the pinnacles of a church in Cornwall was demolished by lightning, a stone weighing nearly 350 pounds was hurled 60 yards over the roof, and another stone was flung nearly a quarter of a mile.

In the days of wooden sailing ships lightning was a major hazard of the sea. In 1838 the 800-pound topgallant mast of H.M.S. *Rodney* was struck, and instantly converted into shavings. The sea looked as if the carpenters had swept their shavings overboard. Sometimes, when a mast was struck, the violence of the explosion was so great that the heavy iron bands encircling it were broken (William Snow Harris).

François Arago says that on the night of July 11, 1852, at Cherbourg, France, lightning struck the mizzenmast of the *Patriote*. The mast was split along 80 feet of its length, and several fragments were flung great distances. One piece about six feet long and tapering from eight inches square at one end to a point at the other was hurled 270 feet and struck oak planking over an inch thick. "It entered the planking by the thick end, nearly half of its length went through, and it was stopped by a knot in the timber."

Lightning has totally destroyed some wooden ships, and may have caused the otherwise inexplicable disappearances of others. The *Royal Charlotte* was struck in her powder magazine and blown to pieces. H.M.S. *Resistance* was similarly blown up by a flash which reached her magazine.[5]

Between 1799 and 1815 lightning damaged 150 ships of the British Navy. Eighteen were set on fire, 70 seamen were killed and 130 seriously hurt. Not until 1849, when lightning rods were fitted to practically all warships, was the hazard from lightning virtually eliminated.

In addition to the destruction caused by the extreme violence of lightning, further damage is caused by the sudden and intense heating which occurs along the path of the discharge. This intense heating in a fraction of a second is the reason why trees burst when hit; the sap is volatilized and explodes. Sometimes a tree just disappears, with fragments flying for hundreds

---

[5] One of the most terrible disasters caused by lightning occurred in 1769, when the state arsenal at Brescia, Italy, was hit and over 100 tons of gunpowder exploded. A sixth of the city was destroyed and about 3,000 people died. The explosion was probably initiated by the lightning igniting powder suspended in the air, forming a highly dangerous mixture.

of yards. Hard rock is shattered in a similar way. If there is a deep crack containing moisture—ice or water—the lightning can turn it into superheated steam which explodes like a charge of dynamite, smashing the rock.

Chimneys have been shattered when lightning caused the sudden expansion of the moisture in the bricks. Pictures hanging on walls crash to the ground because the nails holding the frames together are fused by lightning. Church bells have stopped ringing because lightning has melted holes in them. Windows have vanished because lightning evaporated the glass. And very rarely a small and flimsily built house is wrecked completely, as if by an earthquake.

Then there were the thunderstruck potatoes. Lightning struck a field of potatoes and burnt the stalks to cinders, but the potatoes underneath were cooked to a turn, just as if they had been cooked beneath hot ashes! I asked R. H. Golde if this story was credible. He said that if the soil was dry it could have happened. In passing, R. Gordon Wasson has written a paper on *Lightning-bolt and Mushrooms: An Essay in Early Cultural Exploration* in which he says that in the Province of Kwangsi, China, there are three species of mushroom linked with thunder. They have Chinese names which, when translated, read: "Thunder mushroom," "Thunder-peal mushroom," and "Thunder-aroused mushroom." This sounds so extraordinary that a Chinese in England was shown the Chinese characters, but not told anything about the context, and he at once translated them as I have here.

Under the heading *The Spoor of a Thunderbolt,* Sterling B. Talmage relates how he traced the passage of a lightning stroke. It first shattered a tree, then plowed a furrow for 16 feet, and then struck and half uprooted a 6-ft. pine tree. Next it passed to some rocks, and one large block, weighing over a ton, was moved 4 inches and apparently broken in the process. Then the lightning plowed through soil thick with grass and moss. This sod carpet was folded back over an area measuring 3 by 5 feet. Altogether the lightning stroke passed over or through rock, wood, and soil for 85 feet from the base of the tree it struck first until it was fully earthed.

Sometimes when lightning strikes the earth it burns a channel with radiating furrows. If the lightning discharges into sand it forms tubes of fused silica (melting point 1,710° C.) to which the name "fulgurite" is given. Fulgurites vary greatly in size and length. The largest known appears to be one found many years ago near Drigg in Cumberland, England, which had a maximum diameter of $2\frac{1}{2}$ inches and was over 40 feet long. A curious effect of lightning is sometimes seen when a haystack is struck. The silica from the grass stems melts and welds together into a large lump. S. E. Ashmore told me: "It is usually in fragments because it breaks up when the stack collapses."

The extreme voltages of lightning make it a very efficient killer. But many of the deaths it causes among human beings could easily be avoided.

Over five hundred sheep were killed when lightning struck a flock in the Wasatch National Forest, Utah, on July 22, 1918.   *C. B. Orentson, U. S. Forest Service*

During some army maneuvers a group of rain-drenched soldiers clustered with their machine gun under a tall pine tree. Lightning struck the tree and side-flashed to the gun and soldiers. Three were killed and 20 knocked unconscious.

Playing on the links during a thunderstorm has resulted in the death of many golfers. The up-swung metal shaft of a golf club is highly dangerous.

Lightning causes severe losses among sheep and cattle. During storms these animals tend to herd together and, if lightning strikes, the shock passes from one animal to another. Once, in the Wasatch National Forest in Utah, a tremendous discharge killed 504 sheep. Animals are more susceptible to lightning than human beings because four legs span more ground—and therefore receive a greater shock—than do two. Hence the advice to stand on one leg, or have both legs close together, during a thunderstorm.

Twenty-five cows were killed when lightning struck an oak tree and then side-flashed to the wet bodies of the cattle. The mechanism of the discharge which caused the fatality is discussed under *Return lightning*.

Sometimes the bodies of beasts killed by lightning are inedible because the bones are shattered and their splinters are intermingled with the flesh. Other bodies have been found split in two as though cleft by a giant axe. (See M. J. G. Lynch and P. H. Shorthouse for a medical discussion of the effects of lightning strokes.)

Birds have been killed by lightning while flying. They have been seen to fall from the sky and when examined were found to be partly roasted. Fish, too, can be killed when lightning strikes their waters: a very small shock is sufficient.

No one can examine the records of lightning without being impressed by its freakish actions. The French astronomer, Camille Flammarion, collected numerous examples, some of which are set forth here.

Lightning set fire to a building and then struck a nearby fire alarm, thus calling out the fire brigade to extinguish the blaze. Two ladies, quietly knitting, had their needles snatched out of their hands. A farmer's laborer was carrying a pitchfork over his shoulder when lightning hurled it 50 yards, twisting the tines into corkscrews. Lightning struck a room where a girl was sitting at her sewing machine, holding a pair of scissors. There was a brilliant flash of light, the scissors were spirited away and the girl found herself sitting *on* the sewing machine.

Lightning can play queer tricks with people's clothing. The sudden intense heating of the air in the fabric causes it to expand so violently that clothes and footgear are blasted off. Men struck by lightning have sometimes been found completely naked, their clothes scattered in fragments over a wide area. Two girls were standing by a reaping machine when lightning struck. The girls were stripped naked and their boots were torn from their feet. They were unharmed—only embarrassed.

Lightning once struck a chain-maker's shop. It welded all the links in a yardlong chain, and another chain became a bar of iron. In the United States National Safety Council's Report for 1943 the story is told of a soldier who was welded into his sleeping bag when lightning struck the zipper!

Yet another strange effect of lightning is the way it magnetizes various metal objects, often with queer results. A shoemaker's tools were once affected in this way. The result was that his hammer, pincers, knife, nails, and other metal implements were constantly sticking together, much to their owner's annoyance. Lightning sometimes magnetizes objects so powerfully that they are capable of sustaining three times their own weight.

D. E. Pedgley says that during a storm at Great Yarmouth, England, on August 28, 1958, lightning caused a clock (presumably electric) to stop, and then, some minutes later, started it again—but the hands went backward, at twice their normal speed!

Occasionally, lightning makes marks on people's bodies which have been thought to be "photographs" on the tissues. The markings usually disappear in a few hours. Flammarion says that a woman near a lightning flash had the likeness of a flower imprinted on her leg. A flower had stood in the route of the discharge and the image remained for the rest of her life. Flammarion also says that there is a well-authenticated case of a landscape being "photographed" on the inside of the skin of a sheep which had been struck by lightning. It is now established that lightning has no photographic properties and meteorologists consider that the images are the result of a branching electrical discharge passing through the tissues. To doctors, such markings are known as Lichtenberg's flowers (Macdonald Critchley).

A minor legend in American folklore concerns the stools supplied to forest-fire watchtowers. The stools stand high off the ground to provide a refuge for the fire warden if attacked by a ball of lightning. The theory is that the ball will snap around the legs like a terrier and then, frustrated, depart through a door or window!

Fantastic nonsense? Anyone unacquainted with one of the most intriguing byways of lightning lore may be forgiven for thinking so, yet the legend may be based on fact. In 1923 Walther Brand published a book listing 215 observations of ball lightning. Several apparently authentic photographs of the phenomena have also been published. Ball lightning must be taken seriously—as the following examples will show.

A girl was seated at a table in a room when she noticed a large ball of fire slowly moving toward her across the floor. Then it rose and spiraled round her before darting toward the chimney. It traveled up the chimney and, on reaching the open air, exploded with a crash that shook the house.

It is natural to dismiss such an incident as the result of an adolescent girl's excited imagination. Yet here are the words of B. L. Goodlet, taken from a lecture delivered before the British Institution of Electrical Engineers in 1937.

> They [*i.e.*, fireballs] are attracted towards closed spaces (*i.e.*, houses) which they enter through the open window or door, sometimes even through small cracks; the chimney is a favourite path, so that the fireballs frequently appear in the kitchen from out of the fireplace. After circling round the room several times, the fireball leaves by some air path, often the one by which it entered.

Before discussing the theory of ball lightning here are further examples of its behavior. The first has a strong resemblance to the girl's story. A man was in his house during a thunderstorm when he heard a loud clap and saw the chimney-board fall down. A globe of fire "as big as a child's head" came out from the chimney and quietly and slowly moved about the room just above the floor. It was bright and shining, but appeared to have no heat.

The following incident is vouched for by the Abbé Lazzaro Spallazani (1729–1799), a professor at the University (and one of the first experimental scientists) of Pavia, Italy. A girl was in a field near Pavia when a glowing ball rolled toward her, "caressed" her bare feet, and then rose under her skirts, reappearing from her corsage. A medical examination showed superficial damage from the right knee to the center of her chest. The corresponding part of her chemise was torn to pieces (quoted by Flammarion, 1873).

After reading the first British edition of this book A. Edward Hobbs wrote to me as follows:

About 40 years ago [1905] in the course of a heavy thunderstorm at Wargrave-on-Thames, I—in company with a professional fisherman—saw a remarkable example of this freak of Nature [*i.e.*, ball lightning]. We were perfectly sober and sane, and had no doubt about the quality of our eyesight! We were in a punt endeavoring to get from a high bank some shelter from driving rain. The ball descended to the opposite bank and apparently was 2 to 2½ ft. in diameter: it ran along the sedgy surface for about 60 yds., then immediately in front of some timber camp-sheathing—which it appeared to impact—exploded with a terrific rolling bang, after which the atmosphere became delightfully fresh and carried an ozonic-chemical smell. The ball was flame color, but the explosion produced a mixture of colors.

Incidentally, Arago thus quotes the French astronomer Le Gentil on a storm he witnessed at Mauritius in 1770. "There was much lightning but instead of being of the ordinary form it consisted entirely of *very large globes of fire* which appeared suddenly and disappeared in the same manner without any explosion."

From these and other accounts it is possible to compile a fairly full description of ball lightning. There are at least two, and probably more, types. Donald J. Ritchie says: "Lightning balls come in two varieties: a red diffuse ball which decays slowly and without apparent damage and on the other hand a bluish-white ball which decays rapidly with an explosive 'pop' and creates great charring and blast destruction to any object near it." It has been calculated that, on exploding, a large ball can produce pressures up to 100,000 pounds (45 tons) per square inch.

The balls nearly always appear toward the end of a storm and vary in diameter from an inch to 40 feet. The average diameter is about 10 inches. They generally last for periods of from a second to three minutes, but Richie says "one large ball was observed to hang near the base of a cloud for 15 minutes." He also says that the calculated surface temperature can be as high as 5,000° C. and one ball "cut a very clean hole through a wall of an apartment house." The color is usually lavender or pale red, but other colors have been reported. The appearance of a ball is often accompanied by a hissing noise. The balls sometimes follow air currents, sometimes move against the wind. Several observers have commented on a ball's rapid rotation compared with its slow progression—reminiscent of a spinning top.

If reports are to be credited, ball lightning is highly dangerous. Flammarion listed some 50 instances of its occurrence in France, among them several which had fatal results. One of the worst was on July 27, 1789, at

Feltri, Marche Trevisane. A glowing sphere "about the size of a cannon ball" fell into a hall containing 600 people. It then exploded, wounding 70 and killing 10. I have mentioned on p. 65 the fireball which exploded in a British church.

To judge by an experience related by W. Morris in the London *Daily Mail* for October 3, 1936, the best way to deal with a fireball is to drown it! At Dorstone, Hereford, Morris saw "a red-hot ball the size of a large orange" cut a telephone wire, burn a window frame and then dive into a butt containing four gallons of water, causing the water to boil for several minutes. When Morris investigated, he could find nothing—the ball had completely disappeared. After 20 minutes the water was still too hot to be touched.

Scientists are cautious—sometimes too cautious, see page 171—of accepting lay accounts of unusual phenomena, but there are several eyewitness accounts of ball lightning by scientists themselves (Ritchie, 1960, A. B. Mallinson). The most impressive of these are by J. Durward, one-time Deputy Director of the British Meteorological Office.

In the summer of 1934 Durward was in Scotland with his son when they were caught in a thunderstorm. Durward saw among some pine trees by a road a ball of fire about a foot across. It moved toward them and struck an iron gatepost just as the boy had his hand on the latch. There was no noise from the impact—but the boy yelled in pain and for several hours afterward he was unable to lower his arm.

That was impressive enough, but four years later and a thousand miles away, at a height of 1½ miles above the earth, Durward had an even more spectacular demonstration of the reality of ball lightning. He was in a BOAC flying boat near Toulouse, France, at 8,500 feet in dense nimbo-stratus cloud (very dark raincloud), when what appeared to be a ball of fire entered the airplane through the cockpit window, which the captain had opened because of poor visibility.

The ball passed so near to the captain that it singed off his eyebrows and some of his hair, then burned holes in his safety belt and dispatch case. Leaving the cockpit the ball passed through a small compartment, on through the forward passenger cabin to the rear cabin where it burst with a loud explosion (E. Gold).

There are several other records of aircraft encountering ball lightning in flight. G. I. Kogan-Beletskii, writing of Russian experiences, says that a lightning ball exploded on colliding with an airplane, hitting one of the propellers, which suffered slight damage. In another encounter a ball exploded near an engine, temporarily stopping it. And here is a report from the U. S. Civil Aeronautics Board dated December 16, 1963. It refers to an experience of an Eastern Airlines pilot over Atlanta, Georgia, on November 1, 1963.

While reducing speed in light of moderate turbulence, the captain observed a ball of fire in front of the nose, smoke in the cockpit, followed by the smell of ozone. Both battery compartment doors, and a hydraulic service door were blown open. There was turbulence, rain, and frozen precipitation at the time of the occurrence. Investigation revealed a loss of 18 inches of the upper part of the rudder, a hole in the radome, and numerous burned areas on the fuselage.

Although admittedly anecdotal—ball lightning is not susceptible of experimental proof—the evidence for its existence appears to be overwhelming. Yet some meteorologists and electrical experts deny this. Why? K. Berger, of Switzerland, who is an acknowledged authority on lightning, has read this chapter and thus summarizes his views:

> I have spent 16 years of panorama-photography of lightning at night, covering an area of at least 10 kilometre [about six miles] radius, on Mount San Salvatore, near Lugano-Paradiso. During the whole of that time I have not seen the least sign of inexplicable lightning phenomena, nor have the trained technical observers working with me. This result is confirmed by many hundreds of photographs showing thousands of lightning strokes.
>
> Furthermore, during my 40 years of research into lightning I never obtained a photograph—nor saw one that anybody else had taken—which I considered could be regarded as proof of the so-called "ball lightning." It is not possible today to prove either the existence or the nonexistence of something called "ball lightning." In all cases where people have claimed to have seen the so-called "ball lightning" and I have been able to question them closely, it has been possible to explain what they saw in a simple physical manner. Unfortunately, it is not possible so to question those who tell fantastic stories from the past.

J. H. Hagenguth, of General Electric, another sceptic, says that engineers interested in lightning—who spent altogether 19 summers in lightning-prone situations, such as the top of the Empire State Building, and experienced some 500 thunderstorms—never saw ball lightning. However, one of the engineers told Hagenguth that occasionally there were lightning strokes which, viewed from a particular angle by an untrained observer, might have appeared to be ball lightning.

This is admittedly negative evidence. Against it there is a formidable body of observational evidence. In 1936 W. J. Humphreys listed 280 reports; and in 1960, of 15,923 employees at Oak Ridge National Laboratory, Tennessee, who were asked if they had ever seen ball lightning, 515 said, "Yes." Questioned about the size, duration, color, and other details of the ball, their answers agreed substantially with those obtained by Brand (Harold W. Lewis).

Humphreys, who was another sceptic, concluded that the great majority of his 280 reports were optical illusions probably caused by overexposure of the eyes to a nearby lightning stroke. Hagenguth says: "By moving the eyes, this image moves along and perhaps appears as a moving ball of fire. The speed of the motion would be that of the eye motion. . . ." That persistence of vision occurs has been reported by airplane pilots, some of whom have been blinded for as long as ten minutes. Hagenguth adds that laboratory tests have shown that when people have witnessed a brilliant spark discharge, it takes up to 47 seconds for the eyes to reject the spark image sufficiently for them to be able to read. A nearby lightning stroke at night sometimes temporarily blinds seamen.

The sceptics maintain that the remainder of the observations could probably be explained by observations of St. Elmo's fire, a more or less continuous discharge of weak electricity. In thundery weather this pale fire (generally blue or green) sometimes clings to trees, airplanes, metal spikes and ships' masts—hence its name; St. Elmo is one of the patron saints of sailors. It has also been seen on climbers on mountaintops. Incidentally, it has been suggested that St. Elmo's fire was responsible for the bush that burned but was not consumed which so greatly impressed Moses (*Exodus* 3:2). And it is probably referred to in the remark of Brutus:

> The exhalations whizzing in the air
> Give so much light that I may read by them
> [*Julius Caesar,* Act II,
> Scene I: 44–45]

What of the evidence for ball lightning from photographs? Sceptics, such as Hagenguth, say that the photographs are actually of such objects as fireworks, street lamps, and so on, and that sometimes camera movement produces strange effects. Many photographs of alleged ball lightning have been taken, but none have been generally accepted by lightning experts (H. Israel).

The most famous photographs are those taken by the late J. C. Jensen, professor in the Department of Physics of Nebraska Wesleyan University, and published by him, with full details, in *Scientific Monthly* for August, 1933, and *Physics* for October, 1933. The professor is now dead, but I have corresponded with his son, Robert R. Jensen, who assisted him at the time.

At about 9:45 P.M. on August 30, 1930, Professor Jensen, using two cameras, was taking photographs during a violent storm near the university. After one flash several bright masses were seen and estimated to be between a quarter and a half mile away. One mass floated slowly toward the earth; others seemed to roll along a pair of electric power lines for about 100 feet, and then fell to the ground and disappeared with a loud report. One mass was estimated to be 28 feet in diameter.

The photographs have aroused great interest—and controversy. One

Professor J. C. Jensen, who took this photograph during a thunderstorm in Nebraska in August, 1930, considered it showed balls of lightning slowly floating to earth.

sceptic suggested to Jensen that the result was caused by a flaw in the photographic emulsion. What, identical flaws on seven negatives of photographs, taken with *two* cameras, and even using two kinds of film! The most widespread theory of the sceptics is that the professor was the victim of a prank by some of his students, who let off fireworks during the storm. But (*a*) the students were on holiday, (*b*) no one could have foreseen the storm, or that Jensen would be photographing it, or the direction in which his cameras would be pointing, and (*c*) some of the balls lasted for at least three minutes, which is much longer than the duration of fireworks which would give a comparable effect over a quarter of a mile away.

Leon E. Salanave, an American authority on lightning, while not saying that the photographs are definitely of ball lightning, tells me:

I have taken considerable interest in the Jensen photographs. I do not think they represent some pranksters' pyrotechnics, as has been suggested. I have made photographs of "fireworks" with a camera and at a distance similar to Jensen's situation, and don't get similar results. I have seen photographs of fireworks that *do* have some aspects in common with the Jensen photos, but I had no information on the circumstances under which such photos were taken. As far as the Jensen photographs are concerned, I have even had the

Lightning

opportunity to study the *original* negatives in detail, so I have first-hand knowledge of what appears thereon.

Finally, Jensen says: "On another occasion during the course of our researches, balls of similar magnitude were seen at a distance of 2½ miles but no photographic record was obtained. In this case also the balls collapsed with a sharp, loud report."

Undoubtedly a large number of observations can legitimately be dismissed in various ways, but there is still a strong case for the existence of ball lightning. Persistent vision doesn't affect the ears, so what is to be said of the loud bang when the ball explodes? It would seem to be stretching coincidence rather far to say that *every* time the alleged ball disintegrated there was a nearby thunderclap—or a car backfiring. And persistent vision can't heat a bucket of water, let alone burn off a pair of eyebrows! Moreover, as Hagenguth admits, it is not easy to understand why "the impression on the retina disappears so often when the ball lightning is about to disappear from view anyway. This is quite a coincidence." It is! In passing, ball lightning appears to be much more frequent in some parts of the world than others —*e.g.,* there are extremely few reports of sightings in South Africa, many in Central and Western Europe. Schouland (1964), who believes that the best reports come from observers in the Alps, wonders if there are specially favorable conditions for the occurrence of ball lightning in these mountains. It is known that exceptional "giant" flashes occur there every few years.

For a final word on the existence of ball lightning here is the opinion of Leonard B. Loeb, of the Department of Physics at the University of California.

> While there are competent experts who are sceptics, the trend of thought during the present era of plasma physics is that some sort of phenomena leading to the more correctly described fireballs do occur in connection with lightning strokes. They may consist of portions of the glowing plasma from the channel of a stroke that have been detached and stabilized by vortical motion. They are of rare occurrence. They have been too often seen and described by competent observers to be classed with flying saucers. They are not illusions. There have been reasonable quantitative theories as to their nature since 1935, and there are more now as more is learned about highly ionized gases. So far they have not been created in the laboratory but such an achievement may lie in the not too distant future.

A plasma is a highly ionized gas; the surface of the sun is a plasma.

Various theories have been propounded to explain ball lightning, some going back to the 18th century. Among these are that it is the burning of nitrogen oxides formed by the lightning stroke; the combustion of marsh gas which has been driven out of the soil by the lightning; a miniature thundercloud operating on its own; or a slowly burning bubble of reactive gas such as oxygen or methane (Harold W. Lewis, D. J. Malan, Herbert Nauer, and Stanley Singer).

In 1955 the Russian physicist, Peter L. Kapitza, suggested that ball lightning is a plasma sphere, formed at the end of a thunderstorm after a powerful flash when the air is highly electrified. Electromagnetic radiation thus generated causes "a cascade of ionization"—the lightning ball—to which energy is fed from the nearby portion of the thundercloud, probably in the form of intense radio waves (see also E. L. Hill). This theory, or modifications of it, appears to be the most likely explanation of these intriguing and baffling balls of light.

Ball lightning is of considerable interest in nuclear physics; some investigators see an affinity with the notorious fireball of a nuclear explosion. Investigations into the mechanism of ball lightning may supply information on the greater control of thermo-nuclear reactions, particularly for production of power. To quote Ritchie (1963): "The manifold directions of research into ball lightning are opening new possibilities for the service of mankind."

The Russian engineer Georgi Il'ich Babat, in an article titled *A Star Ignited by Physics,* has described how an artificial lightning ball could be created in the sky—over half a mile above the earth (see Ritchie, 1960).

The most exciting potential outcome of the modern study of ball lightning is that it may lead to the development of an effective anti-ballistic missile—the so-called X weapon. Various laboratories throughout the world are working on what is virtually artificial ball lightning. The University of California Radiation Laboratory has used a "plasma gun" to project plasmoids at 120 miles *per second.* If it is possible to "home" these onto missiles they should prove the perfect answer to the intercontinental ballistic missile—they can be made so hot that they not only melt, but *vaporize* any known substance! (C. M. Cade)

C. E. R. Bruce, a British physicist, has described discharges in other parts of the universe which make the greatest lightning stroke on earth seem like a spark from a car's magneto. His papers must be consulted for the evidence, such as spectral analysis of light from the stars, known facts of terrestrial lightning and laboratory electricity, etc., and analogical arguments based on this information.

Bruce believes that cosmic dust, which exists in countless trillions of tons, is the cause of cosmic lightning. In a paper titled *An All-Electric Universe* (1960) he says:

> In our atmosphere the discharges may last for seconds, in stellar atmospheres for years, and in galactic atmospheres for tens or hundreds of millions of years, while on a still grander scale they may originally have enveloped the whole universe as we know it. This was the view of universal evolution,

Is this the path and explosion of a lightning ball? This photograph was taken during a storm over Castelford, Yorkshire, in August, 1961, about 2:00 A.M., when the street lights were out. In the foreground is a lighted telephone kiosk and its reflection in the wet street. Mr. Jennings says that there was a loud explosion and the window in his room shook. Some scientists who have seen the photograph believe it is of ball lightning, others think it is the result of a double-exposure, the pulsed line coming from an alternating current. But Mr. Jennings is sure that the shutter of his camera was closed immediately after the photograph was taken. And, how could a double-exposure illuminate the fronts of the houses? The original is a 35 mm. transparency.
J. C. Jennings

first put forward by the author in 1944: that electrical discharges have gradually condensed the matter from the primordial gas and dust of a general universal atmosphere, first into the galaxies, then from the condensed matter of the galaxies into stars. Discharges in the extended atmospheres of stars further condense the matter ultimately to allow of the formation of planets and satellites.

Bruce believes that some of these cosmic lightning discharges are 600 billion (British) miles wide and ten times longer. The temperature reaches 500 million degrees C.—and the discharge lasts for millions of years. . . .

Another interesting speculation about lightning is that it may have been one of the causes of the origin of life on this planet—and elsewhere. Stanley L. Miller, of the G. H. Jones Chemical Laboratory at the University of Chicago, prepared a mixture of the gases which are believed to have comprised the earth's primeval atmosphere. He then sent "lightning" (laboratory electrical discharges) through the gases. As a result some amino acids were formed. And such acids are indispensable for the synthesis of proteins, the essential constituents of all living matter (see also Sidney W. Fox, and Cyril Ponnamperuma).

Despite the potentially deadly power of lightning, the number of deaths it causes each year is small; in Britain deaths from lightning average 11 a year. In the United States the figure is about 230, and damage to property is about 12 million dollars. Judging by police statistics in both countries, the probability of death by lightning is much less than that by murder.

Lightning is also indirectly responsible for much inconvenience through disruption of telephone, telegraph, and power lines. Moreover, lightning is rated in the United States as the sixth most frequent cause of fire, and is responsible for nearly half of all the fires occurring in the national forests. Loeb tells me that in California lightning causes 70 per cent of all forest fires. In the United States in 1961, 14,858 forest fires were caused by lightning; the yearly average is about 10,000.

Probably the most disastrous fire ever started by lightning occurred in San Luis Obispo, California, on April 7, 1926. This fire lasted 5 days, spread over 900 acres, burnt nearly 6 million barrels of oil, destroyed 15 million dollars' worth of property, and killed 2 people (J. E. Hissong).

It might be thought that lightning is a considerable danger to aircraft, but this is not so. To quote the British Ministry of Transport and Civil Aviation's circular *The Effect of Thunderstorms on Aircraft Operations* (1957): "Whilst many aircraft have been struck by lightning there is little positive evidence of serious damage to metal aircraft by the strike itself and the occupants are safeguarded by the aircraft bonding requirements." However, the official report on the crash of a Boeing 707 in Maryland on December 8, 1963, said that the probable cause of the accident was lightning igniting the fuel/air mixture in a reserve tank (Civil Aeronautics Board Report, March 3, 1965).

Although not dangerous, the buildup of St. Elmo's fire on an aircraft is sometimes very frightening. First the plane begins to glow with pale light, and sparks play across the glass. From inside the cockpit the display looks like miniature forked lightning. Then the sparks become larger and there is a constant flickering off the nose. On occasions a display at night is bright enough to illuminate the inside of the aircraft. Meanwhile radio reception is impossible; all the pilot can hear in the headphones is a high-pitched squeal. Very occasionally, there follows a large nerve-jarring flash and explosion[6]—the aircraft has discharged the buildup of electricity in the form of a lightning stroke. Afterwards a hole is often found in the trailing edge of a wing, or in the tail: the take-off point for the stroke. But the only real damage is to human nerves.

What *is* dangerous in thunderstorms is the turbulence: up and down gusts of wind that have literally torn aircraft apart. Aircraft have been wrecked by flying from an updraft into an adjoining downdraft. First the airplane is carried wildly aloft—it can be several miles—and before the pilot can regain control it is caught in an equally powerful downdraft and smashed into the ground. Even 100-ton jetliners are easily flung about the sky by the violent winds of a thunderstorm (Warren R. Young).

Codes for protection against lightning in almost every conceivable circumstance are published in the United States by the National Fire Protection Association, and in Great Britain by the British Standards Institution.

There are several lightning warning devices. One of these gives an audible warning, and is based on the electrical output of the thundercloud, which increases as the storm approaches. A low-pitched growl is heard when the storm is first detected, and then, as it approaches, the warning note increases in urgency until, with lightning about to strike, it becomes a high-pitched screech (D. J. Malan).

If indoors during a thunderstorm it is best to avoid the fireplace. The chimney, being the highest point of the house, is the most likely target for lightning, and if it is hit the charge will strike earthward down the chimney unless a better conductor is found on the way. It is wise in a storm to stay away from walls, fireplaces, radio and television sets, telephones, radiators, and any large metal objects. Do not use anything connected to the electricity supply. In violent nearby storms, if there is a basement, go there and wait till the worst is over. The center of a room is safest, providing it does not place you between a conductor leading from the roof and another opposite leading to the ground. A chair standing between a fireplace and a radiator would be in a hazardous position if lightning struck down the chimney. Do not take a bath, go for a swim or indulge in any form of water sport during a thunderstorm.

Humphreys (1940) says: "If one has to be outdoors and exposed to a violent thunderstorm, it is advisable, so far as danger from lightning is con-

---

[6] "The discharge itself is quite a sight, and in my experience has usually taken the form of a ball of blue fire on the nose of the aircraft. This has started off about the size of a hen's egg and has built up rapidly (in two to three seconds) to about the size of a football before exploding with a brilliant flash and a deafening explosion." Statement by D. Mason, an experienced pilot.

cerned, to get soaking wet, because wet clothes are much better conductors, and dry ones poorer, than the human body. In extreme cases it might even be advisable to lie flat on the wet ground." Botley says: "A well-known Everest climber [F. S. Smythe] probably owed his life to his clothes being wetted by rain. During a storm in the Alps he was knocked out by a near discharge, but soon recovered. He was told afterwards by a scientific friend that had his clothes been dry he would probably have been killed, but, as it was, his wet condition enabled some of the discharge to pass to earth."

Other safety hints are: avoid high ground, open spaces, tents,[7] small sheds, and lone trees. About 25 per cent of all lightning fatalities are people sheltering under trees. Keep away from wire fences; if you're within 100 feet of one you may get a shock from a bolt that struck half a mile away. And even when the storm is over, a fence is sometimes lethal to touch, having stored a dangerous charge.

If you are out shooting, fishing, or playing golf, drop all metal. While I was writing this book the well-known footballer, John White of Tottenham Hotspur, was killed by lightning while playing golf. If swimming, or out in a boat, head for shore at once. If you can, make for a dense wood and stand near trees which are shorter than the average. You are relatively safe in a deep valley. A car or coach is also safe as, if it is hit, the lightning is directed straight to earth.

When lightning is very severe and close, sit (or better, lie) on the ground, or preferably in a ditch—better be soaked than shocked! And remember: if you heard the thunder the lightning didn't strike you. If you saw the lightning, it missed you. And if it did hit, you're not likely to know it now.[8]

---

[7] Bell tents are particularly dangerous, owing apparently to the metal-capped pole and the damp canvas. Many soldiers were killed in such tents during the Boer War (H. A. Spencer).

[8] There are rare exceptions to these dictums, see Jean-Martin Charcot.

chapter 7

Floods 🔊

Water is one of the most abundant and important substances in man's life—and one of his worst enemies. The well-known chemical formula H_2O indicates that water is compounded of gases: the ratio by volume being two parts of hydrogen to one of oxygen. For all practical purposes water is noncompressible; although at the bottom of deep oceans, with the weight of miles of sea above, it is slightly compressed.

Water is heavy, which is why, en masse, it is so destructive. A cubic foot of water weighs about 62 pounds, the actual weight varying slightly with temperature and the amount of dissolved salts. A large bathful (a cubic yard) weighs three-quarters of a ton, and the water in a tank $30 \times 25 \times 20$ feet (15,000 cubic feet—about the size of a six-room house) weighs over 450 tons.

Throughout the world floods cause greater loss of life and property than any other natural disaster. There are two main types: inundation from the sea, and overflowing of inland waters. Occasionally the two types combine. Inland floods are of two kinds: predictable, occurring at the same period each year (*e.g.,* the Nile); and sporadic. This chapter is concerned only with inundation and dangerous sporadic floods.

The most violent flooding from the sea occurs with storm surges arising from exceptionally strong and persistent winds, earthquakes or volcanic eruptions. These floods are dealt with in the relevant chapters. Sea floods also occur when wind and tide combine to drive water inland.

England is no stranger to sea floods. There were great and disastrous floods on the east coast during the Middle Ages. In the 11th century there were extensive inundations, the worst occurring in 1099.

In November 1236 an inundation of the sea in Norfolk destroyed flocks of sheep and herds of cattle, tore trees up by the roots and demolished houses. In one village alone about 100 people died. Another terrible inundation occurred in this and other areas in December 1287. Again houses were destroyed, and in the village of Hickling the water was so deep that it overflowed the high altar in the priory by a foot or more. Some 500 people perished in East Anglia in this most fatal of all British floods (C. E. P. Brooks and John Glasspoole, and C. E. Britton).

The European country which has suffered most from sea floods is low-lying Holland. On December 14, 1287, the Zuiderzee area was inundated and 50,000 people drowned. On November 18, 1421, the southwestern part of Holland was inundated: 72 villages were destroyed, 10,000 people drowned. At intervals during the following centuries the sea struck again and again. Stronger and better defenses had been built and in 1953 the Dutch may well have thought their ancient enemy was tamed. Then came the weekend of January 31 and February 1. But first it was England's turn.

On the morning of January 31 tremendous gales swept down the east coast of Scotland—the worst northerly gales ever recorded in the British Isles. The wind at times reached over 100 m.p.h. During the day the wind blew along the northern part of the North Sea, driving thousands of millions of tons of water to the south. The records of tidal stations shows that the effect was to raise the mean level of the North Sea by two feet, thus causing a surge against the coast, which reached its peak in the funnel between southeast England and southwest Holland.

Hilda E. P. Grieve, whose book, *The Great Tide,* is the standard work on the east coast floods, comments:

> It is important to emphasize the meteorological buildup from 29th–31st. Vital factors were the long duration and persistence of the wind, the course taken by the centre of the depression, the driving of 15 [British] billion cubic feet of water *from the Atlantic into the North Sea* (this is what raised its level two feet) and the momentum given to the surge by the continuing force of the wind—*i.e.,* it didn't all just happen on the 31st.

But wind alone, violent and persistent though it was, could not have caused these great floods. Several other factors combined to make the North Sea burst its containing walls—a combination of events that might not occur in hundreds of years. The surge coincided with a high tide and an atmosphere depression: as the air pressure fell, the sea rose. (Roughly, one inch change of pressure results in one foot change of sea level.) Hydro-graphic experts say that the floods would have been even worse—several feet higher—had they coincided with the highest spring tides.

On the east coast of England many square miies of low-lying land, most of it below tide level, were flooded from Yorkshire to Kent. The sea either broke the coast defenses or swept over them. They were breached in 1,200 places, which is understandable when it is remembered that great waves exert pressures of *tons* per square foot (see pages 23–24). Inland, the

Floods [147]

sea penetrated a maximum distance of 10 miles. Altogether some 300 square miles were flooded.[1]

The height of the sea as it struck the land varied, but at King's Lynn the tide reached 31 feet. Here the River Ouse broke its banks and a 7-foot-high wall of water swept through the town. The power of such high seas, driven by hurricane-force winds, was enormous. At Wells-by-the-Sea, a 160-ton vessel was deposited on the quay. Thirty-foot-high cliffs near Lowestoft were cut back 30 feet, and a neighboring seven-foot cliff was cut back 86 feet. Dunes and walls were washed away, beaches scoured to bare earth, and buildings shattered (J. A. Steers, and Hilda Grieve).

The toll was 307 killed, over 32,000 evacuated, 24,000 houses damaged, and nearly 250 square miles of agricultural land spoiled for years. Estimates of the total cost of the damage vary, but it was in the region of £40 million.

The floods had hit hard at England, but on the other side of the North Sea they hit harder still. The sea, Holland's ancient enemy, struck its cruelest blow for centuries. Violent on-shore winds, which in gusts reached 90 m.p.h., blew for some eight hours. Then, at high tide, the heaped-up waters battered against the Dutch dykes. These had withstood everything the sea and wind could throw at them for many rough years, but on this terrible Sunday tide and tempest combined to breach them in scores of places along the coasts of Zeeland, Zuid-Holland and Noord-Brabant.

Dutch dykes are of three kinds: "watchers," the biggest and strongest, bear the main assault; "sleepers" act as a second line of defense; and "dreamers," which are comparatively small, surround individual farms and fields. But once the watchers are breached, sleepers and dreamers are soon overwhelmed. Most of the dreamers are strongly reinforced on the seaward side, but once the sea has broken or overtopped them they are soon undermined from the rear.

Once a dyke is breached, however small the break, the sea soon enlarges it until water pours through.[2] That is why dykes must be kept in constant repair—front and back—and the slightest weakness dealt with. This fact is behind the legend of the Dutch boy who plugged the hole in the dyke with his finger.

On this fateful Sunday morning the sea rose until it was level with the 10-foot-high dykes. Then came a very sudden and unexpected surge which burst over 50 dykes almost simultaneously and sent a great sea raging over nearly half a million acres. This caught many people unaware, despite

---

[1] "It is estimated that 206,161 acres were definitely flooded (and possibly another 11,732)." (J. A. Steers)

[2] Writing of sea walls and banks Steers says: "Rat holes, drying cracks, and untended weaknesses of any sort may lead to disaster." He adds that even paths through dunes may "lead directly to incursions of sea water."

The Elements Rage

Aftermath of the great Dutch flood of February, 1953.   *KLM*
Aerocarto N. V., The Netherlands

the warnings of the Saturday night, and nearly 2,000 were drowned. H. A.
Quarles v. Ufford, of the Dutch Meteorological Institute, says: "It is
probable that no floods of such an intensity have occurred during the past
400 or 500 years."

Once past the dykes the sea flowed for miles over land which, through
the centuries, had been painfully wrested from the water. Highways were
flooded, villages destroyed or marooned, buildings borne down, and livestock drowned in tens of thousands.

The cost of this invading sea was 1,835 killed, 72,000 evacuated, more
than 3,000 houses destroyed and 40,000 damaged, and 625 square miles
flooded. Nine percent of all agricultural land and three per cent of the
dairy land were covered by the sea. Over a quarter of a million livestock and

poultry were lost. The total damage in Holland was estimated at £150 million. In Belgium 22 people were killed, and damage was £20 million.

Although very destructive, sea floods are much less frequent than those resulting from the overflow of inland waters. With the occupancy of more and more land near rivers, these floods become ever more costly and dangerous. In the United States alone flood damage averages over 300 million dollars a year—in 1955 it was over a billion dollars.

The causes of inland floods are: rain, melted snow and ice; the accidental damming of rivers (landslides and earthquakes occasionally do this); rivers changing course; the buildup of river bottoms through accumulation of silt; and the bursting of river banks, dams, and the containing walls of lakes and reservoirs. I have dealt with the floods caused by volcanoes erupting beneath glaciers on page 243.

In all but the most sudden and violent floods—as when a dam bursts —ground conditions are important. Rocky and frozen ground, and surfaces already saturated, can absorb little water and thus the flood spreads. But dry absorbent soil generally takes excess water so fast that floods are prevented or, if they do occur, they do not spread far—unless, of course, there is a catastrophic amount of water.

Rain is the primary cause of most inland floods. It is formed when moist air rises and so becomes cooler, the moisture being eventually released as rain. Such evaporation from the whole earth amounts to 16 million tons per second continuously. To the meteorologist, rainfall is the total product of such precipitation—including snow, hail and sleet—and the amount in any given area is measured by what is received in a rain gauge.

Throughout the world, including the oceans, the average estimated annual rainfall is about 40 inches per year. But the extent of rainfall varies greatly from area to area. It is least over large, flat inland areas; most over areas where steep mountain ranges stand in the way of continuous warm, moist winds. In large deserts rainfall is practically nonexistent—perhaps an inch every two years.[3] At Cherrapunji in the Khasi hills, Assam, some 450 to 500 inches fall per year—and in some years twice that amount.[4] Among the world's large cities an average of 1.2 inches falls per year on Cairo, 95 inches on Singapore. London averages 24, Paris 24 and New York 43 inches.

The official record for 24 hours in the British Isles is 11.0 inches, which fell on July 18, 1955, at Martinstown, Dorset, most of the rain falling in a few hours over a small area during a thundery deluge. Severe flooding occurred downstream near Weymouth, but the underlying chalk absorbed much of the water and prevented a catastrophic flood. There is evidence that even greater rainfalls have occurred in short periods over small areas.

---

[3] Rain has never been recorded at Calama, Atacama Desert, in Chile.

[4] From August, 1860 to July, 1861, 1,041.78 inches fell—nearly 90 feet of rain.

As mentioned on page 21, the spiraling winds of hurricanes carry enormous quantities of water vapor from the oceans and pour them on the land as torrential rain. But hurricanes are not the only cause of great rainfalls. Whenever the meteorological conditions are right (or wrong!)—vast rising masses of moisture-laden air—there is heavy rainfall. Occasionally, however, abnormal conditions cause exceptionally heavy falls over small areas, as in "cloudbursts."

The maximum speed of a falling raindrop in still air is about 17 m.p.h.; at any faster speed it breaks up and the droplets descend more slowly.[5] But if currents of air rise at a speed greater than 17 m.p.h. they prevent rain from falling, and thus it accumulates in the rain cloud. If the air currents then *suddenly* cease, a vast accumulation of rain hurtles down in a matter of minutes. On a hillside the torrents are sometimes so powerful that they wash away all soil and vegetation.

On the evening of July 3, 1892, the village of Langtoft, in Yorkshire, was overwhelmed by a flood of rainwater, a so-called cloudburst. No rainfall station reported any exceptionally heavy fall. Some hill fields were washed away to the bare rock; two cottages were swept away, only the brick floors remaining; at one time there was $7\frac{1}{2}$ feet of water in the village; some of the houses were left with a two-foot thick carpet of mud (J. Dennis Hood, and John Lovell).

G. J. Symons suggested that this devastation was caused by a fall on a neighboring hillside of not less than 100 inches. Other meteorologists were sceptical, yet calculations by water engineers on the erosion effects of cloudbursts indicate that Symons' views were probably right, at least in order of magnitude.

Nor is that all. A British authority on weather lore, E. L. Hawke, unearthed a little-known pamphlet written by Robert Harrison and published at Oxford in 1682: *Strange relation of the suddain and violent tempest which happened at Oxford, May 31 anno domini 1682.*

The "suddain and violent tempest" occurred in the afternoon accompanied by "a huge blustering and boisterous wind." The rain "seemed one continued spout or stream; so that in less than half a quarter of an hour these pouring cataracts raised the water in a round and uniform vessel of about four feet diameter near two feet higher than before." Harrison adds that the consequent floods battered down bridges and demolished houses.

The valuable remark about the vessel, which in effect acted as a primitive rain gauge, enables a fair estimate to be made of the amount of rain which fell in a given time. Harrison's figures mean that about 1 foot 9 inches of rain fell in some seven minutes, which is a rate of three inches per minute. This rate exceeds all instrumental records for world rainfall. Apart

---

[5] Sometimes downdrafts carry rain with them and it falls at 60 m.p.h. or more, frequently causing torrential downpours.

from the Oxford record, the greatest *half-hour* measurement for British rainfall is 3.15 inches recorded at Eskdalemuir Observatory, Dumfriesshire, Scotland, on June 26, 1953.

The official record 24-hour rainfall for the United States is 23.22 inches, at New Smyrna, Florida, on October 10–11, 1924. Even greater 24-hour rainfalls have been claimed; for example, 38.7 inches during a hurricane at Yankeetown, Florida, on September 5–6, 1950. The record rainfall for five minutes is 2.03 inches at Alamogordo Creek, New Mexico, on June 5, 1960; that for one minute is 1.23 inches at Unionville, Maryland, on July 4, 1956 (this is also a world record). The world record rainfall for 24 hours is 73.62 inches at Cilaos on the island of La Réunion in the Indian Ocean on March 15–16, 1952 (J. L. H. Paulhus).

Cloudburst and terrain sometimes combine to cause "flash floods." The Southwestern United States is especially prone to these sudden, and sometimes catastrophic, floods. Heavy rain suddenly falls over a comparatively small area which drains into steep valleys and gullies. These are quickly choked by a torrent which sometimes sweeps for miles. Thus an area which has had no rain for weeks may suddenly be overwhelmed by a deluge.

In the greatest flash floods the water scours the valleys of virtually everything movable: earth, vegetation, trees, rocks, and miscellaneous debris. Sometimes a mass of earth large as a house is washed out and carried away whole—still with a tree embedded in it, standing upright.

On July 29, 1883, a flood at Kanab, Utah, rushed down a canyon and washed out a channel 30–40 feet below the former bed of the creek. Bishop W. D. Johnson was an eyewitness:

> The torrent of water in volume, rapidity and noise resembled the whirlpool rapids of Niagara. Whole portions of soil with willows standing erect came floating down the stream; some of these floating islands were several rods in length by one or two wide. It beat everything I ever saw. It lasted for some seven or eight hours. . . . The canyon was cut out at the old city dam some 50 odd ft. down and 16 rods [264 ft.] wide. The canyon is so changed you would not know it (*Deseret News,* July 31, 1883).

During a flood in Davis and Box Elder Counties, Utah, on August 13, 1923, thousands of great boulders were carried along. At least a score weighed from 20 to 60 tons, and the largest, a rectangle of rock 14 feet long, weighed between 90 and 100 tons. It was carried a mile down a gentle slope of 6° to 8° (Ralf R. Woolley).

It is not the water alone which provides the great carrying power of flash floods. As the water courses down the valleys and gullies, earth, sand, clay, and mud mix with it until a mudflow is formed: a thick mud porridge which flows with almost irresistible force and in which large boulders seem to float like corks. Inevitably, as the flow thickens and reaches lower ground it slows down. It then spreads and moves like a huge sheet of wet mortar or concrete, sweeping all but the most solidly based objects before it. Trees are carried away, either uprooted or snapped off at the ground; walls are crushed in; houses and small buildings are pushed off their foundations.

Great Britain has suffered many catastrophic floods from inland waters. One of the worst occurred on March 18, 1864, when Dale Dyke, about eight miles from Sheffield, Yorkshire, burst and killed some 240 people (Samuel Harrison).

Another disastrous inland flood occurred during the night of August 15, 1952, in North Devon, at and around the seaside town of Lynmouth.[6] The rain gauge on Longstone Barrow, Exmoor, the tableland above Lynmouth, recorded 9.1 inches of rain during the 24 hours. Such rainfall has been exceeded only four times since official records began in Britain 100 years ago. Remember that ordinary steady rain for 24 hours means less than one inch in a rain gauge. Nine inches represents over half a million tons of rain per square mile.[7]

The state of the ground made conditions worse. It was already waterlogged, and just below the surface a layer of rock prevented any appreciable percolation of water. Moreover, the East and West Lyn Rivers, and their tributaries, fall 1,500 feet through funnel-like gorges into Lynmouth in under four miles.

Down these gorges on that terrible night pounded millions of tons of flood water. In dry summer weather the rivers have a depth of a few inches; now, at times, a solid wall of water up to 40 feet high raced down to the sea at 20 m.p.h.

Such a torrent is irresistible to everything except the heaviest and most solidly based objects. The water gouged out huge rocks and boulders—some weighing 15 tons—and carried them to the seashore. (A 7½-ton boulder was found in a hotel basement.) Telegraph poles and motorcars followed. Trees felled by earlier gales, and others washed out by the roots, were swept into the sea. The next morning, half a mile out to sea, hundreds of trees, presumably weighted down by rocks and soil entangled in their enormous roots, had their upper branches showing above the waves—a fantastic sea forest of stunted trees. As heavy debris was swept into the waters it had added to the lethal force of the flood. Structures that might have withstood the waters were knocked down by trees acting as outsized

---

[6] Great floods have occurred at Lynmouth in past centuries but very few people then lived there (J. F. Chanter).

[7] Throughout the whole area rainfall was about 3.7 inches, weighing about 90 million tons. In one or more small areas rainfall probably exceeded 9.1 inches. (A. Bleasdale, and C. K. M. Douglas). Charles H. Dobbie and Peter O. Wolf, however, believe that the heaviest local fall was about four inches in *an hour*.

battering rams, and rocks that hit as hard as artillery shells—weight making up for speed.

In the four miles between Exmoor and Lynmouth there were 17 bridges. The first one soon gave before the battering of the debris-strewn waters and added its weight to the force of the torrent. The next bridge then collapsed, then the next, until every one of the 17 bridges was battered down. At times the mass of debris jammed to form a temporary dam. When the piled-up thousands of tons of water eventually broke through there was a huge surge which carried all before it. At a bridge in Lynmouth, however, the debris was so great that the flood waters divided, temporarily forming another river.

Cottages, houses, and other structures within range of the flood were soon destroyed. Overwhelmed by a house-high wall of water, battered by heavy trees and masonry from bridges, and struck by five- and ten-ton boulders, even the sturdiest dwellings collapsed and crashed into the raging tide.

Look at what happened to the Floyds' house. It was on the road between Lynmouth and the edge of Exmoor, and in normal times the West Lyn flowed near by, 30 feet below road level. Nine people were in the house. At 9:30 on Friday evening Fred Floyd, the son, looked out and saw that the river was level with the house. Water was pouring over the road. He went with his father to rescue his mother who was in the downstairs bedroom. It was too late. A vast wall of debris-strewn water hit the house and it disintegrated. All within were swept into the flood.

One moment the house was intact with seven adults and two children within its walls; seconds afterwards it was gone, and of the nine people only one survived. This was Mr. Tom Floyd, aged 63 years. He remembers his son's last words:—"We must get mother out" and then seemed to be going down into a pit of water. He remembers, too, being syphoned upwards, and grabbing some masonry which proved to be the back of where his house had been. Regaining his feet, he found himself in the roadway in front of the cottages, and when being forced along by the rushing water he was caught by his daughter standing at her door a few yards along. Another astounding fact is that Floyd's dog Tim, a four-year-old Cairn terrier, also in the room with them when the building collapsed, had got to the same refuge ahead of him. With the terrific rush of water outside, the depth of that gorge and the debris being carried along, it is nothing short of a miracle that either master or dog survived [Eric R. Delderfield].

The flood waters dug deep into the earth. Road surfaces were scoured away, and the soft earth of the verges was gouged as by a giant excavator, some gullies being *20 feet* deep—right down to the bare rock. The Lynmouth sewerage system and water mains were wrecked.

A vivid illustration of this gouging effect of the flood occurred at a Lynmouth garage. Here gasoline tanks were scoured from their foundations and swept away without a trace.

As in most disasters, there were many odd happenings. In one wrecked house a table, on which was a bowl of eggs, was left standing—and not one egg was even cracked. Elsewhere a cottage had been swept clean away yet the wooden gate still swung from its hinges.

In a car park at one moment all was darkness, the next a blaze of light. Water had shorted the electrical systems of some of the cars thus switching on the headlights. A single car, lights blazing, was seen coming down a hill into Lynmouth. It slid under the flood and, lights still on, traveled like a weird submarine beneath the racing waters. Then suddenly its lights failed and, except for the lightning flashes, intense darkness prevailed again.

When dawn broke after this Walpurgian night the scene on the foreshore was fantastic. It was littered with the debris of scores of wrecked homes and buildings; smashed cars; telegraph poles, tree trunks, branches and complete trees; the smashed and mangled remains of the undergrowth from the surrounding countryside; some 200,000 cubic yards of silt, mud, gravel, and stones, in some places massed 25 feet high; some 40,000 tons of rocks and boulders, some weighing 15 tons (a heap of boulders against the Lyndale Hotel contained 6,000 cubic yards); iron girders and bridges; broken masonry and the bodies of birds, fish, animals—and people.

The flood altered the landscape. S. H. Burton, an authority on Exmoor, says: "I knew Lynmouth well, but when I visited the town soon after the disaster, I could not find my way about. Combined bombardment from the sea and air could not have wrought more fearful devastation than these twin rivers in that dreadful night."

And the toll of this greatest of British inland floods? Ninety-three buildings destroyed or irretrievably damaged; 28 bridges destroyed or badly damaged; 132 vehicles destroyed, and 34 men, women, and children killed or missing. On the credit side, the Lynmouth Relief Fund received from subscriptions throughout the world, £1,336,425. Lynmouth was rebuilt and precautions taken which, it is hoped, will prevent Exmoor's wild waters from ever again destroying the little town.

North America has suffered greatly from floods. Severe flooding frequently results from hurricanes, owing to the immense rainfall in a short time, sometimes 20 inches in 24 hours. The ground is waterlogged and is quickly flooded. Rivers, lakes, and reservoirs are filled to overflowing. Soon

Rushing flood waters cut highway near Yuba City, California, during the western states floods of December, 1955.   *American Red Cross*

the whole countryside is awash, and what were previously roads become canals where the only transport is rivercraft. Under pressure from the water, dams, bridges, and buildings give way. Frequently, in great hurricane floods, the pounding waters wash wooden houses from their foundations and they sail away like huge misshapen boats.

John Hersey says that during the flood caused by hurricane Diane in August 1955, a wooden four-story hotel at Winsted, Connecticut, floated away and was borne downstream in the Mad River. After traveling three-

The Elements Rage   *[156]*

quarters of a mile it settled on a playing field. It was upright but had only two stories—the two lower ones had been broken off or worn away during the ride.

In hurricane floods the water at times rises dangerously fast. During the New England hurricane of September 1938, a man at Buzzards Bay, Massachusetts, crossed a street in ankle-deep water to rescue a child from a car. When he returned a minute or so later, the water was up to his chest. F. Barrows Colton, who recounts this incident, tells of other queer happenings during these tremendous floods. Water short-circuited the horns of cars and burglar alarms so that they added their cacophony to the shrieking of the hurricane. A flotilla of wooden cottages sailed up Narragansett Bay, Rhode Island. And a man's wooden legs, which the sea swept away from his house, were found a week later on a beach 20 miles away—*both together!*

The damage caused by the floods of this hurricane, added to that from the winds and inundation from the sea, made it—up to that time—the most expensive storm in the history of the United States. Property damage was estimated at about 350 million dollars.

The greatest floods in North America occur in the area of the Lower Mississippi. Waters from 50 tributaries (including the Ohio and Missouri Rivers), draining a million and a quarter square miles, flow into North America's greatest river, the 2,348-mile-long Mississippi, "Father of Waters." (The Mississippi-Missouri river system is 3,870 miles long.) In flood, the flow of water is some 30 times greater than at low level. (This is greatly exceeded on various other rivers; for example, the Vistula River, in Poland, where the ratio is 1:120.) At no time in recorded history have all the great tributaries of the Mississippi been in dangerous spate simultaneously. Should this ever happen it might well cause the greatest disaster in the history of the United States.

The Mississippi's lower reaches form a gigantic spout through which funnel more than *60 cubic miles* of water during a flood period lasting from 1½ to 2½ months. The flood does not roar down the river like a vast wave; instead, it is a slow inexorable tide, the flood crest sometimes traveling only 30 miles in a day. Occasionally, the waters in the Mississippi rise higher than those in some of its tributaries. Then there is a backflow, the local waters rise higher than their natural banks and artificial levees, and the land is flooded.

This happened in the spring of 1927. Frederick Simpich, of the National Geographical Society, who flew over part of the flooded area, said:

A vast sheet of water as yellow as the China Sea at the mouth of the Yangtze, stretches practically from southeast Missouri down to the Atchafalaya Basin [Bay] of Louisiana. This sea is about 1,050 miles long and in places over 50 miles in width. Over 750,000 people normally live within its limits. Flying

Floods

over it now in an airplane, you see the roofs of their houses, the smokestacks of their sawmills, their church steeples, the tops of their shade trees, and lines of telegraph poles sticking up from the water.[8]

At the height of the flood $1\frac{1}{3}$ cubic miles of water per day was flowing down the river at Vicksburg, Mississippi.

During the relief work boats cruised among the treetops 15 feet above the ground. One experienced steamboat captain lost his way—familiar landmarks were obliterated—and he lost himself and his 300-ton craft in a flooded forest! A girl is reported to have said: "Noah oughta stuck around; he'd 'ave seen a real flood!" Some people actually built an ark for themselves and animals. Unfortunately, it leaked and the would-be Noah fled to the nearest levee, his followers and animals coming after him "two by two." During another flood some people heard a voice broadcast warnings from an airplane and thought it was God announcing a second deluge.

By the time the waters receded and the overwhelming mess and confusion had been cleared, this flood had killed 313 people, displaced 637,000 more, caused property damage of 284 million dollars (U. S. Weather Bureau).

In these floods most deaths came from the breaking of the levees which contain the Mississippi itself. Then water sometimes floods the land at 15 or 20 m.p.h. and people are overwhelmed before they have time to flee. One day, during the 1927 floods, the streets of Arkansas City were dry at noon, and by two o'clock mules were drowning in them before they could be unhitched from their wagons.

These great floods, which lasted from February to July, are often referred to as the greatest in the recorded history of North America. If judged by volume of water involved this is correct, but not in total area of inundation. Figures vary for the area involved in 1927 (between 26,000 and nearly 29,000), but the Mississippi River Commission informs me that in the spring flood of 1882, 34,600 square miles were inundated. Less water was spread wider!

Although so vast in extent, neither of these great floods was the most costly. That unenviable record goes to the Kansas-Missouri floods of June–July 1951; the only billion dollar floods in American history. The precise estimate was 935,224,000 dollars. The small loss of life—28—is eloquent testimony to the devotion and efficiency of the river forecasting and rescue services—and how well the lessons of past floods had been learned (for flood control in the area see p. 168).

---

[8] One of the engineers of the Mississippi River Commission comments: "There is a planned flooding of backwater areas, this overflow is part of the flood control plan. The areas where tributaries join the Mississippi are used as 'mid-river' reservoirs, so to speak."

Surging water, with spray leaping three stories high, from the August, 1955, flood, Putnam, Connecticut. *John P. Callahan—American Red Cross*

Although neither the most costly nor the greatest in extent, the most *famous* flood in the history of North America—and the most tragic in human lives—was the Johnstown flood of May 31, 1889. The main cause was the bursting of a dam, but this was precipitated by intense rainfall. Incidentally, the flood was made the subject of a poem, *The Pennsylvania Disaster,* by William McGonagall—"the best of all bad poets"—of which four lines will be enough.

> The embankment of the dam was considered rather weak,
> And by the swelled body of water the embankment did break,

Floods

And burst o'er the valley like a leaping river,
Which caused the spectators with fear to shiver.

Johnstown was an industrial town of 12,000 people in the Conemaugh Valley in western Pennsylvania at the junction of the Little Conemaugh River and Stony Creek. Surrounding Johnstown were various boroughs and villages with a population of 18,000. Some 400 feet above and 16 miles away was the South Fork reservoir, at that time the world's largest earth dam: 831 feet wide, 100 feet high and 272 feet thick at the base. It held back a maximum of 4½ billion gallons of water weighing 20 million tons.

Long before the fateful day there were warnings that the dam was unsafe. Then, on May 30, came an added strain. A great storm, continuing for two days and nights, poured millions of tons of water on the surrounding countryside. By early morning on May 31 many of the streets of Johnstown were awash, and by afternoon the water was from three to ten feet deep. And, above, the dam was under enormous pressure.

As the day wore on with no letup in the downpour some citizens thought of one of Johnstown's standard jokes: "The dam has busted—run for the hills." And a few families did just that. They hadn't long to wait. At 3:10 P.M. there was a tremendous roar and 300 feet of the center of the dam gave way. A treetop-high flood hurtled down the valley toward its already swollen river.[9] The wall of water thrust before it a blast of air which flung down trees six and eight inches in diameter.

Although the break in the dam was 300 feet wide and eventually became 430 feet, there was so much water that it took about 50 minutes to drain away. Its initial mile-a-minute rush was not maintained. McMaster calculated that its later speed was less than 30 m.p.h. The immense mass of debris that the flood swept along as it bulldozed its way through the valley slowed it down. Sometimes, where the valley narrowed, this mass jammed against the walls and temporarily halted the flood. Then the overwhelming weight of water, still gathering volume from the draining dam, thrust forward again, sweeping all before it.

Before Johnstown there were several small communities. The flood practically washed them out of existence, like a steamroller crushing toy villages. A stone viaduct was snapped in two as if made of dry clay, then ground to pieces. An iron bridge high in the valley was torn from its foundations by a blow from the edge of the flood. Dozens of locomotives and

---

[9] Figures for the actual height vary, H. K. Barrows says "125 ft. or more," other writers say that it was much lower. John B. McMaster, a professor of engineering who made an on-the-spot investigation, says the water "would have made a stream 500 ft. wide, 20 ft. deep and 12 miles long. Sent over Niagara Falls, at the same depth and with the same velocity as the Niagara River now rushes on, it would have taken 36 minutes to go down."

passenger carriages, hundreds of freight cars, and miles of track were swept forward as the monstrous river pounded down the valley. All these added immeasurably to the battering effect of the water.

Near Johnstown stood a factory—the Gautier rolling mills—with massive furnaces, boilers, heavy machinery, and hundreds of large drums of steel cable and wire. The flood hit the steel mill and, according to an eye-witness, lifted and carried it bodily down the valley.[10] At 4:10 P.M. the flood swept into Johnstown, already awash from a day and a night of torrential rain.

An eyewitness, a lawyer named Horace Rose, who looked up the valley just before the flood struck, wrote:

> I saw stretching from hill to hill a great mass of timber, trees, roofs and debris of every sort, rapidly advancing toward me, wrecking and carrying everything before it. It was then in the midst of the Gautier works. A dense cloud hung over the line of the rolling debris, which I then supposed was the steam and soot which had arisen from the hundreds of fires in the Gautier works as the waves rolled over them. I stood and looked as the resistless tide moved on and saw brick buildings crushed in and instantly dashed from sight, while frame tenements were quickly smashed to atoms.

Rose's own large brick and stone house was shattered and he suffered multiple injuries. But he lived.

Some houses, partly sheltered from the full weight of the flood, survived, but many were crushed; some wooden houses, wrenched whole from their foundations, floated on the vast muddy tide like ships. One such house was found afterward tightly wrapped round with telegraph and electric light wires like some gigantic parcel.

Perhaps the most fantastic sight on this altogether fantastic day was the scene at Stone Bridge: 50 feet wide and based on seven 58-ft. stone piers. It carried four tracks of the main line of the Pennsylvania Railroad to Pittsburgh and was built to last for centuries. The bridge withstood the flood then acted as a dam itself, reinforced by an amazing collection of debris.

Jam-packed against the bridge were the spoils of the flood's sweep down the valley. At the bridge the wreckage towered over 70 feet high and behind it were mounds, 20 to 30 feet high, covering more than 30 acres. Steam engines and cars; miles of track and steel cables; the wreck of hundreds of wooden and brick buildings; parts of viaducts and bridges; telegraph poles, trees and timber; the carcasses of horses, cattle, and other farm animals; and

---

[10] When the St. Francis Dam near Los Angeles burst on March 13, 1928, blocks of concrete weighing 10,000 tons were carried over half a mile (Charles R. Longwell and R. F. Flint).

men, women and children—alive and dead[11]—spread for hundreds of yards in all directions in muddy meaningless confusion. Behind all this the dammed-up waters turned Johnstown into a dirty debris-strewn lake covering all but a few roofs, a church steeple or two, and the upper stories of the few remaining tall buildings. In places the water was 20 feet deep with a 30-ft. layer of debris on top. Then, in the early evening, the wreckage at the bridge caught fire—there were oil-soaked timbers, lime, crude petroleum, and live coals at hand. Many escaped the water only to die by the fire.

As with every great natural disaster, the Johnstown flood abounded in freakish behavior—of elements, humans, and belongings. One lady insisted on finishing her hair-do before being rescued from her shattered house. Some women, with little on, refused to be rescued until the men promised (a) to have coats or blankets immediately ready, and (b) to turn their backs during the crucial seconds. Under two wrecked freight cars was a stable containing a cow, a dog and five hens—all dry and well. The only solid footing in one area was a vast carpet of cigars, spilled from a nearby factory. Some of the best beds for several nights were coffins filled with straw. A partially wrecked house floated down the swollen river to Pittsburgh, over 60 miles away. It arrived nearly 24 hours later and inside was a five-month-old baby alive and bawling. During the flood several babies were born prematurely: one was christened Moses and two were named Flood.

Nobody knows how many lives were lost. The lowest official estimate was 2,205, the highest 2,287. In addition 967 were listed as "not known to be found." Property damage was estimated at 17 million dollars—probably the equivalent of 170 million in the currency terms of today.

Among those who helped to clear up the appalling mess were 600 soldiers, 200 lumberjacks, 1,250 railwaymen, 5,000 workmen, nearly 250 sanitary workers—and 125 undertakers.

The toughest problem was the acres of debris left at Stone Bridge after the fire had burnt itself out. On examination it was found that miles of steel wire from the Gautier wireworks, rolled and twisted by the flood, had bound the wreckage together into a vast inextricable mass. The labor of hundreds of men for several days did little more than tidy up the edges. Even the axes of the 200 lumberjacks, plus steam winches and a 75-ton locomotive, were not particularly effective in wrenching apart the wire-bound mass.

The problem was solved by the use of huge quantities of dynamite, up to

---

[11] The two met in one of the more macabre incidents of this fearful day. A young woman was trapped by an ankle and all efforts to free her failed. Then a man swam below the debris to see what was holding her. It was a corpse which, apparently in a last despairing grasp, had seized her at the moment of death. The rescuer dived again and cut the girl free.

A very rare photograph showing the aftermath of the Johnstown flood of
May 31, 1889.   *Engatter and Dillon Photos, Philadelphia*

a quarter of a ton at a time, during the day, and giant bonfires at night. Even
so, it took nearly three months before the wreckage was finally cleared away
and the Conemaugh River could once again flow freely down its valley.

But Johnstown and the Conemaugh valley were not finished with
floods. There were to be several in the next 45 years; then, on March 17,
1936, flood waters again raged down the valley and overwhelmed Johnstown, now grown to a town of 100,000. Melting snow and a heavy rainstorm
had caused both Stony Creek and the Little Conemaugh River to overflow
and Johnstown was awash. Bridges went down; the main telephone exchange was flooded and all lines went dead; the telegraph system failed;
water doused the boiler in the electric power plant and all lights went out;
houses were wrenched from their foundations; the streets were full of
floating debris, including items unknown to the 1889 flood—automobiles,
refrigerators, washing machines, radios—all the grisly panoply of a great
flood once again. At midnight the water was flowing *14 feet* high past the
Public Safety Building (it had been nearly 20 feet high at this spot in 1889).
The cost of this flood was about 25 dead and 50 million dollars' worth
of property damage—say 200 million today.

In November 1943, after five years' work and the expenditure of nearly
8½ million dollars, Johnstown was considered flood-proof. The channels of
the twin rivers were widened, deepened, and their banks paved with con-

Floods   [*163*]

crete. To do this nearly three million cubic yards of earth and rock were removed and enough concrete was used to cover a two-lane highway 62 miles long.[12]

The great Boston molasses flood of January 15, 1919, had nothing to do with the elements, but its unique character earns it a place here.

A great storage tank of raw molasses stood near the inner harbor. The tank was 50 feet tall, 282 feet in circumference and held 2,320,000 gallons. At lunchtime the tank burst and some 15,000 tons of molasses cascaded through the nearby streets—a monstrous thick brown wave some 15 feet high. Initial speed of the molasses was estimated to be 35 m.p.h. and it struck with immense force.

Before the sticky brown flood was spent it had wrecked the elevated railway, caused over a million dollars of property damage, killed 21 people; and given the municipal services the biggest clearing-up job in Boston's history. Years afterward the smell of molasses could still be detected where the flood had pushed its sticky way. And the cause? The tank had been built of thinner plates than had been specified. It was also suggested that fermentation in the tank had built up explosive pressure (Ralph Frye, and Boston *Traveler*, January 15, 1954).

The greatest floods of all occur in Asia, and appropriately enough. Asia was the scene of the Biblical Flood, Noah's deluge, when "the waters prevailed exceedingly upon the earth; and all the high hills, that were under the whole heaven, were covered." (Genesis 7:19) The Hebrew idiom uses universal expressions—"the whole heaven"—for restricted areas; here it is Mesopotamia. There are references in other ancient writings to a great flood in this area.

Archaeology has certainly proved that great floods, including a gigantic one, did occur in ancient times in Lower Mesopotamia. While excavating at Ur of the Chaldees, Sir Leonard Woolley found a heaped-up deposit of water-laid clay with a maximum depth of 11 feet. Such a mass of clay indicates a flood of at least 25 feet in that particular spot. It also proves that the area was overwhelmed by a flood to which there is no parallel in its later history. Sir Frederic Kenyon says that the deposit was not due to a long period of submersion but to a sudden flood.

According to Genesis: "Fifteen cubits upward did the waters prevail"

___

[12] I have used, with permission, Richard O'Connor's detailed account of the disaster: *Johnstown—the Day the Dam Broke* (1957) as background material for this section.

← Flood waters wreck a road between Munich and Salzburg during the European floods of July, 1954.   *Alfred Strobel—Suddeutscher Verlag*

(7:20), which is roughly the maximum height estimated by Woolley. He considers that in the flat low-lying land of Mesopotamia the flood probably covered an area of 300 by 100 miles.

> It was not a universal deluge; it was a vast flood in the valley of the Tigris and the Euphrates which drowned the whole of the habitable land between the mountains and desert; for the people who lived there that was all the world. The great bulk of those people must have perished, and it was but a scanty and dispirited remnant that from the city walls watched the waters recede at last. No wonder that they saw in this disaster the gods' punishment of a sinful generation and described it as such in a religious poem; and if some household had managed to escape by boat from the drowned lowlands the head of it would naturally be chosen as the hero of the saga.

There has, of course, been speculation on the cause of this most famous of all floods. The most likely explanation seems to be that the Tigris and Euphrates overflowed their banks, there was torrential and long-continued rain, and there was a tidal bore or invasion from the sea: ". . . all the fountains of the great deep [were] broken up" (Genesis 7:11).

Since Noah's day, the greatest and most disastrous floods have occurred in the Indian subcontinent and in China. In the summer of 1962, two great floods swept across parts of East Pakistan, inundating a fifth of the whole area, killing 177 people and causing widespread damage.

Less than a year later far worse disasters struck the same area. Typhoons, rain, floods, and rivers changing course made three million homeless, caused immense loss of property and animals, and killed some 18,000 people.

Terrible as these floods were, they are surpassed by some Chinese floods, particularly from the overflowing of the Hwang-Ho, or Yellow River—"China's Sorrow." For 40 centuries or more this river has been wandering over its surrounding plains, an ever-present threat of death and destruction to the 50 million farmers and peasants living on the 50,000 square miles of rich farmland. For, by one of Nature's ironies, the vast slimy sea of liquid mud left after a flood is an excellent fertilizer. The river rises in the Tibetan highlands and, after a circuitous course of nearly 3,000 miles across China from west to east, empties into the Yellow Sea at the Gulf of Po Hai.[13] In places it is a mile wide. It is China's second longest river; the Yangtze River being nearly 3,500 miles long.

The Hwang-Ho is a problem for cartographers, as in its last 400 miles it has changed course by hundreds of miles eight times since 2300 B.C. The two major shifts which occurred in this century, however, were both man-

---

[13] Estimates of its length vary from 2,500 to 2,900 miles.

made. One was in 1938 when the Chinese blew dykes to flood the advancing Japanese armies; the other was in 1947 when the Chinese forced it back to its pre-1938 course.

The river's name comes from the yellow wind-blown loess—a mixture of clay and sand—which the swift current whirls down from Inner Mongolia in millions of tons. Its turbid waters have twice the amount of silt carried by the Mississippi. In some stretches 40 per cent of the weight of the river flow is silt. It is estimated that each year the river washes away over 1,200 million cubic yards of soil. (When the Panama Canal was made, about 210 million tons of earth and rock were excavated.) As the Hwang-Ho slows down on reaching the Great Plain of North China, an appreciable part of the loess falls to the river bed, so that for some 500 miles the channel grows shallower each year. The bed rises an average of about three feet a century, but in some 20 to 30 mile stretches the rise is some six feet *a year*. The result is that at low water the river runs about 15 feet above the general level of the plain; at high water 25 to 30 feet, and in flood way above that.

These conditions make the Hwang-Ho the most flood-prone river in the world. But this is not all: floods sometimes alternate with droughts on the Great Plain. Controlling the Hwang-Ho thus becomes a water engineer's nightmare. It is also his supreme challenge for, as Oliver J. Todd, an engineer who worked on the Hwang-Ho for over 20 years, says: "On the Great Plain . . . lies the greatest outdoor laboratory in the world for flood control."

How long the Chinese have tried to tame the Hwang-Ho is not known, but the Emperor Yü, who was also an engineer, worked on flood control over 40 centuries ago. He is said to have succeeded by dividing the flow and dredging the river bed continually. But it is believed that the river carried less silt in those far-off days than it does now.

The Hwang-Ho holds the unenviable record of causing the world's most lethal flood. In September and October of 1887 the river rose until it over-topped 70-foot-high levees: 50,000 square miles were inundated, 300 villages swept away, some 2,000,000 people were made homeless, 900,000 killed.

World losses from floods, both in lives and money, are immense. In the United States alone they have cost around a thousand million dollars in a year. Much time, thought, energy, and money is therefore devoted to flood control.[14] It would be beyond the scope of this book to deal with this subject in detail. References are given, however, in the bibliography.

---

[14] Flood control, important as it is, is only one category of public measures against floods. Others are insurance, land-use regulation, structural adjustment, and emergency action.

This cow, caught in a tremendous flood on the Cumberland River, Kentucky, in February, 1937, was left hanged when the waters subsided.
U. S. Army Corps of Engineers

Flood control necessarily varies with the situation, such as terrain, stretch of river, surroundings, and previous history. Controls that are suitable to one stretch of river in one country may be unsuitable to a similar stretch in another country, or even in the same country. It is a very different matter, for example, to control flooding near a large city and in unpopulated country.

Nowhere in the world has greater effort been given to flood control than on the lower Mississippi. A glance at a map and a rapid reading of its history show why—over 50 major floods in 250 years of settlement. The first controls were begun soon after the founding of New Orleans in 1717. Ten years later the city was guarded by a levee 3 feet high, 18 feet wide and 5,400 feet long. Today, there are about 1,700 miles of levees on the main Mississippi River, with an average height of 25 feet, a maximum of 40 feet. The base width is about ten times the height. Many have a 25-ft.-wide road at the crown. There are also some 2,000 miles of levees on the tributaries. Many levees are sited a long distance away from the river—up to five miles in some places—to give an additional area for excess water.

The Mississippi levee system is one of the greatest feats of American engineering; it is longer than even the Great Wall of China. Also, it is most profitable—it is estimated that for every dollar spent on the levees there is a return of almost nine dollars in increased agricultural land, improved waterways, and, above all, safety from death and destruction.

Supporting the levees on some stretches of the river are revetments. First the rough bank is graded; then, to prevent caving and erosion, asphalt paving or stones are placed above low-water level. Below, articulated concrete mattresses are laid against the banks down to the river bed.

Two hundred years' experience of the river, however, has shown that more than levees and revetments are necessary to prevent drowning the surrounding country. Engineers have therefore provided controls which can be used when the river rises dangerously. The first control is a series of reservoirs and, should these be filled to overflowing, flood waters can be released into channels and flood plains where minimum damage and disruption will be caused.

Such drastic measures have been needed twice since the modern levee and control systems were installed. In the 1927 flood, to save New Orleans, levees were cut several miles from the city and part of the flood waters flowed on a short course to the sea. Again in 1937, 23 miles above New Orleans, some of the flood waters were diverted into Lake Pontchartrain. This diversion is believed to have kept the flood crest at New Orleans three feet lower than predicted—and may have saved that great city from an appalling disaster.

The main flood controls are, of course, federal projects involving vast labor and expense. But it is not generally realized that smaller local measures can do much to reduce floods. Trees are one of the best natural defenses: forests can absorb three inches more rainfall than moorlands. The planting of deep-rooted grasses, contour plowing,[15] and the building of small earthen dams at strategic spots—all can help to prevent heavy rainfall from causing floods (Peter Farb).

As so often with natural violence, even floods have their benefits. Some of the most fertile land in the world lies beside great rivers, and every time they overflow a fertilizing deposit of sediment covers the area. Nile floods are the basis of Egyptian agriculture; the Nile valley is fertile solely because the world's longest river floods its banks regularly every year.

------

[15] That is, plowing along elevation contours—along hillsides rather than up and down the slopes. Such plowing produces a "terracing" effect which tends to hold or retard water from running downhill.

chapter 8

Meteoroids)》

"I could more easily believe that two Yankee professors would lie than that stones would fall from heaven." This statement is alleged to have been made by Thomas Jefferson, then President of the United States and a scientist, when told that two Yale University professors had reported the fall of over 300 pounds of meteorites at Weston, Connecticut, in December 1807.[1] The remark was typical of the attitude which prevailed in scientific circles at that time (Robert F. Mehl).

Yet the true origin of meteorites had been recognized by the ancients. In a list of treasures compiled by a Hittite king in the sixteenth century B.C. there is a reference to "black iron of heaven from the sky." Livy mentions the fall of a shower of stones in Rome about 654 B.C., and there is a Chinese record of the fall of a meteorite in 616 B.C. which is alleged to have broken several chariots and killed ten men. And references in the writings of other ancient civilizations indicate that meteorites were regarded as having a celestial origin.

There is considerable evidence that the worship of meteorites was one of the first forms of idolatry. The awe-inspiring sights and sounds which accompany the fall of a meteorite would easily convince primitive peoples that it came from the gods. One meteorite was found in an Aztec temple, and others have been found carefully interred in Indian burial mounds in the United States. A meteorite is most probably referred to in the Acts of

---

[1] Meteoricists—students of meteorites, etc.—are not agreed on the exact meanings of the terms they use. Because of these differences the International Astronomical Union has recommended specific definitions, but these have not yet been universally accepted (P. M. Millman). In this chapter I have used the following terminology, which is based on that recommended by the I.A.U.

Meteoroid: any solid natural body smaller than an asteroid (minor planet) moving in space, including the earth's atmosphere.

Meteor: the light phenomenon caused by the entry of a meteoroid into the earth's atmosphere. It is also used as a general adjective, *e.g.,* meteor crater.

Meteorite: a meteoroid that has landed on the earth.

parts. Instead of Biela's single comet there was a pair of small comets, each apparently complete in itself, traveling along parallel paths.

The next time Biela's comet was due to appear, in 1853, the two small comets were again seen, but this time their paths were about eight times farther apart than in 1846. Since then Biela's comet has never been seen. But on the night of November 27, 1872, at the time when Biela's comet should have returned, there occurred a great shower of meteors. So great was this cosmic blitz that at one time during the night a single observer could see a hundred meteors a *minute*, 600 times the average sightings. It is easy for the modern astronomer to see what had happened. Biela's comet had disintegrated into millions of meteoroids. Incidentally, no meteorites have been known to fall from a meteor shower.

The cometary origin of most meteor showers is now generally accepted by astronomers. But this does not account for sporadic meteoroids. Both probably have the same origin. One view is that millions of years ago a planet disintegrated, either by an internal explosion or by collision. The solar system was thus scattered with planetary debris ranging from dust-sized particles to asteroids hundreds of miles across. Another view is that sporadic meteoroids come from the disintegration of asteroids—presumably by collision. Most astronomers regard all meteoroids as originating in the solar system, but others, notably Lincoln LaPaz (1958), believe that some come from outside the system.

It must be emphasized that meteoroid origins are highly speculative. To quote Sir Bernard Lovell: "The general relation of the sporadic meteoric material to the solar system remains an enigma. The problem of whether the material is the debris of a comparatively recent disintegration in the solar system, or whether it is some of the primeval matter from which the solar system was formed remains to be settled." Dating, based on radioactive methods, shows that meteorites are of the same age as the earth and the solar system.

An enormous number of meteors stream into the earth's atmosphere every 24 hours. On a clear moonless night a single observer will see an average of about ten meteors an hour. But his field of view is so restricted that he can see only those meteors which appear in a tiny part of the sky. Moreover, many meteors are too faint to be observed by the naked eye and can be seen only through a telescope or detected by radar. An estimate by Harvard Observatory is that over 100 billion meteors penetrate our atmosphere every 24 hours! (Arthur L. Draper and Marion Lockwood) In contrast, estimates for the fall of meteorites over the whole earth every 24 hours range from 1 to 30.

The average meteor that can be seen with the naked eye is first visible approximately 70 miles above the earth and is seen for about half a second, hence the popular name of "shooting star." Thus, it follows that every

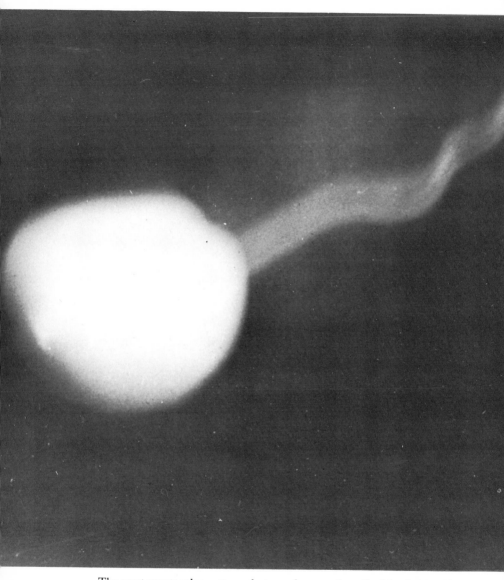

The most spectacular meteor photograph ever taken. On March 24, 1933, a brilliant fireball blazed across the southern United States. At the moment it exploded, some twenty-five miles above the earth, Mr. Brown took this photograph. The explosion was six miles across and the trail was nearly two miles wide. Nininger subsequently recovered about eight pounds of meteorites. *Charles M. Brown, H. H. Nininger, Meteorite Investigations*

The Elements Rage [174]

visible meteor must have sufficient mass to render incandescent a cylinder of air several miles long which can be seen at least 70 miles away. (A meteor travels, on average, ten miles in half a second. Few meteors come nearer to the earth than 30 miles.)

It might be thought that to cause such a great band of light, meteoroids must have considerable mass. Yet most astronomers believe that few are larger than a grain of rice. F. A. Lindemann and G. M. B. Dobson showed that such a minute size is adequate to account for the light. They calculate that an iron meteoroid $\frac{1}{25}$ of an inch in diameter, traveling at 25 miles per second, gives a momentary output of $4\frac{1}{2}$ horsepower.

There is, on average, one sporadic 1-gram meteoroid in every 10,000 million cubic miles of space. In showers the corresponding figure is one million. Probes by space capsules indicate that there is more meteoroidal material near the earth than farther out, although the larger meteoroids are fairly evenly distributed in the solar system (Bernard Lovell, and Fred L. Whipple, 1963).

How is it that so very few meteoroids reach the earth? Our almost complete immunity from bombardment is due to two factors: the earth's protective layer of air and the high speed of the missiles.

Although the atmosphere extends many hundreds of miles above the earth, it is only at about 70 miles that it is dense enough to cause meteoroids to glow. The total effect of this layer of air is to provide the earth with a "cushion" of tremendous stopping power. H. H. Nininger (1944) says: "The air we breathe is the most efficient armor conceivable. In mass, it is equivalent to a thickness of 52 inches of the toughest steel armor-plate, but it affords far more protection than that."

This protective armor of air prevents the vast majority of meteoroids from reaching the ground. But the rare blockbuster (with an initial weight of not less than 20 pounds or so) sometimes gets through. Not always however: the angle of fall is an important factor (see p. 193). Probably only a few ounces of a 20-pound meteoroid reach the earth. Friction first liquefies, then ablates, or rasps off, layer after layer of the outer parts so that only the central core lands on the earth.

Depending on speed, angle of approach, and constitution, some meteoroids weighing more than about one ton retain a proportion of their cosmic speed when they fall. To form a crater there must be a powerful blast at the point of impact, and for this to occur a meteoroid, on landing, must weigh at least 10 tons and be traveling not "slower" than 2.5 miles per second. Kinetic energy, and therefore blast effect, rises steeply with speed.[2] A meteoroid weighing 100 tons and striking the earth at about six m.p.s. would release 5×10^{19} ergs, which is greater than the explosive force of 1,000 tons of TNT.

---

[2] Kinetic energy is the energy an object has when it is in motion.

Whipple (1952) has devised a "meteor speedometer" by which the trajectory, height, and speed of meteoroids can be accurately measured. Two astronomical cameras, located some 20 miles apart, are trained upon the same point 50 miles above the earth. The large distance between the cameras is necessary to give a sufficiently long base for accurate trigonometric computation. Any bright meteoroid passing near the point on which the cameras are focused is automatically photographed.

It takes a long time to obtain results; Whipple (1951) says that in ten years of continuous photography during clear moonless nights about 60 worthwhile results were obtained. A shutter is rotated in front of the lens of each camera 10 to 100 times a second. The bright streak of the meteoroid's path is thus broken into regular segments. From the two photographs it is possible to determine how far the meteoroid traveled, and the segments show the time taken. By this method it has been proved that some meteoroids enter the earth's atmosphere at a speed of nearly 45 miles per second. In recent years the "Super Schmidt" cameras, with their wide field of view and very sensitive lenses, have enabled many more meteor trails to be photographed. And radar telescopes can detect the faintest trails, enabling velocity and direction to be determined without even looking at the sky (J. Davis, and Bernard Lovell).

There are several kinds of light trails. The brief pencil of light—shooting star—that momentarily streaks the night sky is an ordinary meteor. If the meteoroid is coming directly toward the observer it appears as a brief stationary point of bright light. The brilliant torch of light that illuminates hundreds of cubic miles is known as a fireball, which has a luminosity equaling or exceeding that of the brightest planets. Lovell says that a spectacular fireball may be caused by a meteoroid weighing no more than a pound.

The earth moves in its orbit at 18.5 miles per second. Meteoroids enter our atmosphere at any angle. One traveling in the same direction as the earth has a speed relative to the earth of 7.7 m.p.s., but if it enters head-on its relative speed is 44.7 m.p.s.

To realize what this speed means, imagine a race between a meteoroid and a train from New York to Washington, D. C., over 200 miles away. The meteoroid would reach Washington before the last of the train's carriages had left Pennsylvania Station!

It is possible to obtain a rough idea of a meteoroid's relative speed from the color it produces. Why? Because the intensity of the heat—caused by friction with the atmosphere—varies with the meteoroid's speed, and different temperatures produce different colors. Yellow, orange or red indicates one of the slower meteoroids; blue, green or white one of the faster.

Some meteoroids are so retarded by their passage through the atmosphere that they land with no more force than a stone dropped from a high building. On January 1, 1869, some meteoroids fell on a frozen lake at

Hessle, Sweden. Although some of them weighed several pounds they did not break through the ice. Other meteorites have burried themselves several feet in hard earth. A 600-pound meteorite plowed 11 feet into the ground.

When a meteoroid, traveling up to 60 times faster than a high-powered rifle bullet, collides with the atmosphere, the air in its path is violently compressed. It is estimated that for a meteoroid eight inches in diameter the air presses against it with a force of at least 12 tons. Confirmation of such great pressures is given in the following quotation from the (Franklin) *Institute News* for June 1945: "An iron sphere of about one ton, traveling at a speed of 40 miles per second, is subjected to a pressure of 50 pounds per square inch of cross-section, at a height of 50 miles: work is being done on it at the rate of 900,000 horsepower! When it has reached a level as low as 30 miles altitude, the increased density of the air has raised the rate of work to 500 million horsepower."

Such pressures generate tremendous heat, some 3,000° C., half the surface temperature of the sun.

The heat melts the meteoroid's surface and the air rasps it back over the sides to form the fiery tail. This process continues until friction slows the meteoroid down and the speed is insufficient to ablate it, and it strikes the earth. The vast majority of meteoroids completely disintegrate in the air; probably less than one in a million reaches the earth.

A large shower of meteors, such as occurs in some parts of the world in mid-August and mid-November in the years when a swarm is carried into the earth's path, is one of the most beautiful and awe-inspiring sights in Nature. The great shower in historic times occurred on the night of November 12, 1833. Spreading out like the spokes of an umbrella from a point in the constellation of Leo, a rain of celestial rockets poured into the earth's atmosphere.

Referring to the United States, Olivier says:

> Meteoric astronomy really began with this shower. [It] was so remarkable that the impress upon the popular mind has never been obliterated and the interest then aroused in meteors has never died out. . . . The writer has often had the old Negro cook of his family give him a vivid account of how she saw "the stars fall" when a girl of ten. Though the shower occurred 60 or 70 years before, the impression never left her which had been made on her mind when a child, and she vividly described the terror of the Negroes as "the stars fell, and fell, thick as snow coming down in a snowstorm," and of how all thought "the Day of Jedgment had sho' come."

The following (slightly abbreviated) account of this shower is by Denison Olmsted of Yale, who witnessed it from Boston (quoted by Olivier):

> About daybreak this morning our sky presented a remarkable exhibition of fireballs, commonly called Shooting Stars. The attention of the writer was

first called to this phenomenon about five o'clock, from which time until nearly sunrise, the appearance of these was striking and splendid, beyond anything of the kind he has ever witnessed.

To form some idea of the phenomenon, the reader may imagine a constant succession of fireballs, resembling rockets, radiating in all directions from a point in the heavens. They commenced their progress at different distances from the radiating point, but the lines they described, if produced upwards would all have met in the same part of the heavens. The balls, just before they disappeared, exploded. No report or noise of any kind was observed.

There were meteors of various sizes and degrees of splendour; some mere points, but others were larger and brighter than Jupiter or Venus; and one was nearly as large as the moon. The flashes of light were so bright as to awaken people in their beds.

How many meteors were there in this spectacular display? Olmsted likened their frequency to "half the number of flakes that one sees in the air during a snow shower." And the next evening one lay observer said he wanted to look at the darkening sky to see if there were any stars left! It was claimed at the time that 35,000 meteors could be seen each hour.

Thirty-three years later the swarm was again carried into the earth's path. Sir Robert Ball, the distinguished Victorian astronomer, thus describes this shower:

For the next three or four hours we witnessed a spectacle which can never fade from my memory. The shooting stars gradually increased in number until sometimes several were seen at once. Sometimes they swept over our heads, sometimes to the right, sometimes to the left, but they all diverged from the east.

Sometimes a meteor appeared to come almost directly towards us, and then its path was so foreshortened that it had hardly any appreciable length, and looked like an ordinary fixed star swelling into brilliancy and then as rapidly vanishing. Occasionally luminous trains would linger on for many minutes after the meteor had flashed across, but the great majority of the trains in this shower were evanescent. It would be impossible to say how many thousands of meteors were seen, each one of which was bright enough to have elicited a note of admiration on any ordinary night.

No showers to equal these brilliant displays have been seen since. But the great fireball procession which passed over part of the American continent on the evening of February 9, 1913, was, in some ways, even more impressive. It was first seen over Saskatchewan, sighted by ships beyond Bermuda, and last seen off Brazil a path of some 6,000 miles. Its speed was close to five miles per second. Eyewitness accounts vary about the number of meteors; a man who used opera glasses said that there were about ten groups, each consisting of 20 to 40 meteors. As they passed southeast over Ontario they grew more brilliant and great explosions were heard. Detonations and earth tremors were caused along the path of the procession to distances of 20 to 70 miles on either side.[3]

This tremendous spectacle passed out into the Atlantic and the crews of ships in the vicinity of the Bahamas saw it. According to the later witnesses, it seems to have grown ever more bright as it progressed. There were no witnesses of the end of this spectacular display. Probably after burning up much of their mass and exploding into smaller fragments, the whole procession was eventually engulfed by the waters of the deep Atlantic, far from any human eyes. (The references are collected in Willy Ley. See also Donald H. Menzel and L. G. Boyd.)

In the early morning of March 24, 1933, one of the most brilliant fireballs ever seen in the United States blazed erratically across nine Southern states, being seen for distances of over 100 miles from its line of flight. It was described as "the largest ever seen" and as "terrifying" by people who were many miles away. Nininger (1936) says that seasoned cattlemen, accustomed to facing the vicissitudes of life and who ordinarily knew no such thing as fear, told him they despaired of their lives during these "terrible moments." Yet they were 75 miles from the fireball's nearest approach!

Nininger, who investigated the passage of this meteoroid—named Pasamonte—and the material it dropped, says of the photograph which was taken near Clayton, New Mexico, by a farmer who hastily snatched a camera and snapped as the fireball blazed past: "The great luminous sphere which forms the center of the picture was six miles in diameter, while the column stretching behind it was a mile in width." Most of this, of course, was incandescent gas.

This meteoroid left a cloud of dust which filled 1,000 cubic miles. People in the vicinity of its lower passage through the air said that they noticed a peculiar sulphurous odor for some hours, and that they suffered from a throat irritation for several days. The passage of such a body sometimes affects radio and television reception, blacking them out completely for several minutes (LaPaz, 1958).

The vast majority of meteorites fall in the sea, or on uninhabited or sparsely populated areas—necessarily so, because towns and cities cover a

---

[3] "To listen to the sound effects produced by a large meteorite fall is a unique and awe-inspiring experience. Neither a hedge-hopping jet nor a keyholing rocket gives rise to the sky-filling reverberations set up by a falling meteorite." The powerful shock waves generated by its passage cause the earth tremors (LaPaz, 1958).

relatively small area of the earth's total surface. Some meteorites have been picked up on mountaintops and one was drawn up in a fish net from the bottom of a shallow lake. Many of the meteorites which fall in populated areas are so small, and so like ordinary debris in appearance, that the chances of their being recognized are extremely slight.

As there are meteor showers so, more rarely, are there showers of meteorites. These occur when a large meteoroid breaks up at a great height. Frequently, smaller pieces further disintegrate before reaching the earth. In large showers many stones are the size of a pea or smaller. The most numerous shower recorded as actually reaching the earth occurred on January 30, 1868, at Pultusk, near Warsaw, Poland. It is estimated that 100,000 stones fell. The weight of those recovered was 440 pounds, the heaviest being 20 pounds.

Each year a few falls are discovered, although in some of these there are hundreds of individual meteorites. However many stones or pieces of metal are shed from the original meteoroid, only one fall is recorded. Some 16,000 stones were recovered from a single fall at Holbrook, Arizona, after the meteoroid of July 19, 1912 (W. M. Foote). An average of about five falls per year are recorded in the continental United States.

Nininger (1933) says that from 1800 to 1925, 470 falls were studied and approximately 130,000 individual meteorites recovered, or an average of just over 277 per fall. Incidentally, Nininger is probably the world's greatest meteorite hunter. Writing in 1941, Watson says: "At present Nininger is accounting for half of all the discoveries in the world."

Mason, writing in 1962, says that about 1,700 falls have been recorded, by far the greatest number being in the United States. This does not mean, of course, that most falls occurred in the United States, but only that of those which did fall a relatively high proportion were reported. Area of a country, terrain, accessibility, density of population, and general education and other factors affect the reporting of meteorite falls.

Nininger (1963) gives an interesting example of the relation between education and meteorite reporting. Residents of an American agricultural area of some 22,000 square miles were made "meteorite conscious" by lectures, local press reports, and radio talks. In its previous 60 years of settlement this area had not yielded a single meteorite: the seven years following the indoctrination yielded 200, all from old unwitnessed falls.

Far more meteorites are found in Kansas than in any other state, probably because (a) Kansas has very few hard rock outcrops and therefore meteorites are more easily recognized and (b) it is well-known in the state that good money is paid for the "black rocks" which are occasionally turned up by the farmer's plow.

Known meteorites range in weight from a dust particle to many tons. The heaviest meteorite known is Hoba West, which lies near Grootfontein,

Southwest Africa. This meteorite is a roughly rectangular block, about 9 feet by 8 feet, estimated to weigh between 60 and 70 metric tons.[4] It is believed to have fallen over a million years ago and weathering has greatly reduced its original weight, which was probably in the region of 100 tons (L. J. Spencer, 1932). Unless they fall on very soft ground meteorites weighing more than 100 tons or so are unlikely to survive intact, the tremendous shock of the impact usually shattering them.

The heaviest "in captivity" is the 11-foot-long nickel-iron meteorite known as Ahnighito (Eskimo for "The Tent"), which weighs 30.4 tons. It was discovered in Greenland and was brought to the United States by Robert E. Peary. It took him three Arctic seasons to wrest the dense black mass from its bed on the shore of Cape York. Once in the hold of Peary's ship, the *Hope,* the meteorite put all the compasses out of action, making a hazardous voyage even more dangerous. It took 30 horses to drag it through the streets of New York to its resting place in the Hayden Planetarium in the American Museum of Natural History.

The heaviest meteorite known to have fallen in the British Isles weighs 65 pounds. It fell among a shower of stones in County Limerick in Ireland on the morning of September 10, 1813. The heaviest known English meteorite is the Wold Cottage stone, weighing 56 pounds. It fell within ten yards of a man working in a field near Scarborough on the afternoon of December 13, 1795, and is now preserved in the Natural History Museum in London.

The largest meteorite found in the United States, and the fourth largest in the world, was discovered in 1902 near Willamette, Oregon. It is a conical mass of iron weighing 15.5 tons, but deep erosion has eaten much of it away, and it is believed that originally it must have weighed between 20 and 25 tons.

This meteorite was discovered, by a man who lived near by, on property belonging to the Oregon Iron and Steel Company. He spent three months secretly at work in the forest where the meteorite lay, moving it to his own property. Shortly after he began to exhibit it, however, the company filed a suit to regain possession. The Supreme Court of Oregon ruled that it belonged to the owners of the land where it was found. In some countries meteorites belong to the government, and in others to the finder.

It may be imagined that the possibility of actually seeing a meteorite fall is remote indeed. Nininger (1933) says: "To witness the actual impact of one of these extramundane visitors may be considered the rarest of human experiences." There are, however, eyewitness accounts of about 500

---

[4] The weights of large meteorites are usually given in metric tons, *i.e.,* 1,000 kilograms or 2,204.6 pounds. They are named after the town or landmark nearest to their fall.

such impacts, although many more unrecorded falls must, of course, have been seen. There is no known photograph of a meteorite hitting the earth. In Czechoslovakia, however, Zdenek Ceplecha observed a meteor, photographed it on his two-station cameras, and estimated the fall so accurately that some meteorites were recovered.

The oldest meteorite still preserved, whose fall appears to have been witnessed, was a 280-pound stone which fell between eleven and twelve o'clock on the morning of November 16, 1492, at Ensisheim, Alsace. It was described as falling in a wheat field and penetrating five or six feet into the ground. Its fall was accompanied by a "loud clap of thunder" and reverberations were heard many miles away. The Emperor Maximilian ordered that two pieces should be broken off the stone, presumably for examination, and the rest put in the local church.

It was not until the 19th century, when people had become more meteoroid conscious, that the most detailed and accurate accounts of falls were recorded. One of the best accounts is of a fall of about 100 stones totaling 500 pounds at 10:15 P.M. on February 12, 1875, at Homestead, Iowa. Nininger (1933) quotes the following contemporary record of an eyewitness:

From the first the light of the meteor could hardly be tolerated by the naked eye turned full upon it. Several observers who were facing south at the first flash say that upon looking full at the meteor it appeared to them round, and almost motionless in the air, and as bright as the sun. Its light was not steady, but sparkled and quivered like the exaggerated twinklings of a large fixed star, with now and then a vivid flash. To these observers, all of whom stood near the meteor's line of flight, its size seemed gradually to increase, also its motion, until it reached a point almost overhead, or in a direction to the east or west of the zenith, when it seemed to start suddenly and dart away on its course with lightning-like rapidity.

The observers who stood near to the line of the meteor's flight were quite overcome with fear, as it seemed to come down upon them with a rapid increase of size and brilliancy, many of them wishing for a place of safety, but not having time to seek one. In this fright animals took part, horses shying, rearing and plunging to get away, and dogs retreating and barking with signs of fear. The meteor gave out marked flashes in its course, one more noticeable than the rest, when it had completed about two-thirds of its visible flight. All observers who stood within twelve miles of the meteor's path say that from the time they first saw it, to its end, the meteor threw down "coals" and "sparks."

Thin clouds of smoke or vapor followed in the track of the meteor and seemed to overtake it at times and then were lost. These clouds or masses of smoke gave evidence of a rush of air with great velocity into the space behind the meteoric mass. The vapor would seem to burst out from the body of the meteor like puffs of steam from the funnel of a locomotive or smoke from a cannon's mouth, and then as suddenly be drawn into the space behind it. The light of the meteor's train was principally white, edged with yellowish green throughout the greater part of its length, but near to the body of the meteor the light had a strong red tinge. The length of the train was variously estimated, but was probably about nine degrees, or from seven to twelve miles, as seen from Iowa City. The light about the head of the meteor at the forward part of it was a bright, deep red, with flashes of green-yellow, and other prismatic colours. The deep red blended with, and shaded off into, the colors of the train following; but the whole head was enclosed in a pear-shaped mass of vivid white light next to the body of the meteor, and the red light fringed the white light on the edges of the figure and blended with it on the side presented to the eye.

From three to five minutes after the meteor had flashed out of sight, observers near the south end of its path heard an intensely loud and crashing explosion, that seemed to come from the point in the sky where they first saw it. This deafening explosion was mingled with, and followed by, a rushing, rumbling and crashing sound that seemed to follow up the meteor's path, and at intervals, as it rolled away northward.

A story is told of a farmer who was plowing when a shower of meteoroids began falling round him. He rushed into town and called on the sheriff to protect him from his enemies, who he believed were pelting him from ambush! Such a story is reminiscent of the other man who, during the First World War, observed a shower and concluded that the Germans had opened long-range artillery fire on the United States. . . .

In medieval annals there are several accounts of people being killed by what may have been direct hits from meteorites. But there does not appear to be any reliable modern record of anybody being killed in this manner.

It has been suggested that some unsolved mysteries of death by violence may in fact have been death by meteorite. In Michael Innes's *The Weight of the Evidence* (1944) a fictional meteorite plays a prominent part in the plot, although it is not suggested that it fell directly on the victim from outside the atmosphere.

Rare though they are, there are some quite authentic records of people and animals struck or near-missed by meteorites. LaPaz (1951 and 1958) lists 20, ranging from prehistoric times to 1954, with a credibility rating varying from "doubtful" to "certain." The prehistoric (doubtful) entry is of a stony-iron meteorite found below the remains of a megatherium (giant South American sloth) which may have been killed by it. Only five of the entries are rated "certain." Among these are a 40-pound meteorite that hit a house in Braunau, Bohemia, on July 14, 1847, some parts falling on a bed where three children were sleeping; part of the Chicora, Pennsylvania, meteorite of June 24, 1938 (see p. 193) which tore the hide of a cow in a field; and the Sylacauga, Alabama, meteorite of November 30, 1954, which struck a woman on her left hand and arm and, to quote the medical report, on the "upper thigh." LaPaz calculates that the probability of a meteorite striking a human being is once in 300 years. The chances will greatly increase, of course, with the population "explosion"!

LaPaz also lists 27 buildings that have been struck by meteorites between 1790 and 1954. None was seriously damaged. In the Philippine Islands, on June 16, 1938, there was a rain of rice-grain-sized meteorites which fell on galvanized iron roofs like hail.

There are several records of airmen seeing meteoroids plunging earthward. The best account I have read of such an incident is by a civil airlines pilot, Bill Coyle (see Hubert J. Bernhard, and Nininger, 1952). Coyle was cruising during the night of March 23, 1933, two miles above Adrian, Texas, when he was surprised by what he took to be a giant floodlight turned on in the sky. He soon realized it was a brilliant meteorite "big as the Wichita hangar," flashing across the sky.

> In a second or two it became too bright for me. We were at about the same altitude. In a moment I caught sight of its tail and could tell it was going north of me. Its line of flight was probably 40 or 50 miles distant; at any rate it was so close I could see fragments of the [meteoroid] whirling away from it and dropping back into the tail. It left a deep red trail with a bluish tint which hung in the sky until daylight.

It disappeared with a thunderous rumble that was heard in several states.

Nininger informs me that he made a most careful survey of this meteoroid and proved that the fireball ended 17 miles above the earth, although some material reached the ground. As he points out, very few meteoroids approach nearer to the earth than four miles; they are very much farther away than most pilots who see them think they are. One pilot dipped a wing to "avoid" one that was about 100 miles away!

There are various kinds of meteorites, each with its own name. *Aerolites* are composed almost entirely of stone, and constitute about 90 per cent of all known falls.[5] The stone is quite different in texture and composition from most of the rocks of the earth's crust. *Siderites* are composed chiefly of iron with about 10 per cent nickel. *Siderolites* are a mixture of metal and stone and are the rarest type of meteorite. All the largest meteorites are siderites, as the other kinds are more easily crushed. These three main groups are subdivided into numerous classes; the Rose-Tschermak-Brezina system lists no fewer than 76 (A. Brezina). The much smaller classification of G. T. Prior is now widely used.

Probably no meteoritic subject has caused so much controversy as the smooth, curiously shaped, glassy lumps known as *tektites*. Some scientists are doubtful whether they are meteorites at all. They have never been seen to

---

[5] But not of *finds* because they break up easily and they are not easily recognized, often being mistaken for rocks. Siderites (nickel-iron) are found most frequently.

fall and they differ from all other known meteorites in composition, shape, and distribution. The large majority of all known tektites are found in Australia, the East Indies, and the Philippines (John O'Keefe).

There are various theories of their origin: chips blasted from the surface of the moon by large meteorites; parts of a planet which exploded and pelted the solar system with its debris; parts of the rocky crust of the earth when it was hit millions of years ago by a comet; and, finally, that they have nothing to do with astronomy but were formed by lightning striking sandy sediments.

Some people believe that there are ice meteorites. There is evidence that there is ice in the solar system (some astronomers believe that the satellites of Jupiter consist largely of ice), and it is possible—allowing for part of the mass to be ablated—that pieces of ice may land on the earth (Donald H. Robey, and John D. Buddhue).

Meteorites are of great value to scientists. They are the only direct evidence we have of some of the material of the universe beyond our planet. Apart from them, all our knowledge of the universe has to be interpreted from secondary sources, such as radar echoes and the characteristics of star light. It is meteorites alone which provide the astronomer with some of the actual matter of which the universe is made.

When meteoroids enter the atmosphere their behavior gives information about air resistance at high altitudes; density and composition of the air; speed and direction of winds many miles above the earth; and other aspects of the higher atmosphere. Students of ballistics learn from the behavior and condition of meteoroids something of how projectiles are likely to act when their speed approaches that of these cosmic bullets (Nininger, August 1940). Today, of course, satellites supply information on some of these subjects.

Meteorites are also of commercial value, both direct and indirect. They can be sold for money, the actual price depending on several factors, chiefly rarity. Pieces from a very rare meteorite were bought for seven dollars a gram, more than the price for platinum. But such a price is exceptional. Platinum, diamonds and gold have been found in meteorites, but only in minutes quantities. More valuable from a commercial point of view is the nickel-iron in siderites.

Although no element unknown on earth has been found in meteorites, unknown minerals and alloys have been discovered. It was a siderite which first gave industry nickel alloys. An engineering shop had the task of slicing a siderite for a museum. It was found difficult to cut, and somebody asked: "Why wouldn't nickel-iron be equally tough if made in a furnace?"[6] Experiments were carried out and the whole range of alloy steels was the result.

---

[6] An iron meteorite, about two feet high, wore out 82 bandsaw blades before it was cut in half.

Meteoroids   [185]

Meteoritic iron, which is both durable and malleable (it can be fashioned by hammer), has been used by man for many thousands of years. Long before he learned to smelt iron he used meteorites to manufacture tools. In many languages the name for iron contains a reference to the sky—in Sumerian it is *an-bar*, "fire from heaven." Fragments of a dagger unearthed at Ur of the Chaldees dating from before 3,000 B.C. are of meteoritic nickel-iron. Swords, daggers, arrowheads, and spurs from Mongolia to Greenland and Mexico were made of the same metal that fell from the skies. Attila possessed a "sword from heaven" and even in the 19th century Alexander, Emperor of Russia, had a sword made from meteoritic iron. Not surprisingly, there are representations in ancient rock carvings and other illustrations of meteor showers and falling meteoroids (G. F. Zimmer, T. A. Rickard, and LaPaz, 1958).

From prehistory to the Space Age, meteoroids have been Nature's own satellites, and their behavior, especially when entering the atmosphere, has provided valuable information to scientists concerned with the intricate problems of space travel. When John Glenn's capsule started its return to earth its speed approached that of a "slow" meteoroid. At this speed (about five miles per second) the protective heat shield glowed white-hot at a temperature of $1,500°$ C., while less than a foot ahead—just before the shock wave—it was $26,000°$ C., over four times the surface temperature of the sun.

Before satellites and space capsules began to girdle the earth it was thought that collisions with meteoroids was a major hazard. Experience has proved that this fear was greatly exaggerated, although a space capsule *could* be destroyed by such a collision. Owing to its enormous speed a meteoroid is, weight for weight, vastly more destructive than TNT. A pinhead-sized iron meteoroid could blast a hole in a capsule; one the size of a grape could destroy it. And astronauts clambering about the outside of their capsules, clad only in their space suits, are vulnerable even to dust-sized particles.

A very rare form of meteorite was responsible for great interest and excitement among scientists in 1961. In *Nature* for November 18, 1961, George Claus and Bartholomew Nagy announced that they had found microscopic-sized particles resembling fossil algae in carbonaceous meteorites. The implication, of course, was that here was clear evidence of life—albeit of a low order—that had existed on an object in outer space. This announcement caused considerable controversy, which will probably continue for some time. (See, for example, Harold C. Urey, Egon T. Degens, and Brian Mason.)

Every day meteoritic "dust" enters the atmosphere. Part of this comes from the ablation of meteoroids, the rest from micrometeorites, tiny particles of matter too slight to ablate with friction when they encounter the earth's atmosphere. This dust helps to make the sky blue and the sunsets glorious. It also adds to the weight of the earth—estimates vary from tens of thousands to five million tons a year.

The most spectacular effects of meteoritic falls are the "meteor craters" which are found in a few places on the earth's surface, and mark the fall of very large meteorites. How these are formed has been graphically described by Fletcher G. Watson:

A body several hundred meters in diameter, having a mass of many million tons, will pierce the earth's atmosphere without being appreciably checked, and crash into the ground while moving 15 to 70 kilometers a second [10 to 45 m.p.s.]. The holocaust that follows is difficult to describe in detail, but some effects are self-evident in the form of meteor craters.

As the mass plunges into the ground its forward motion is checked in a minute fraction of a second. Through this braking action the outer parts of the meteorite and the contacting ground are tremendously compressed, heated and partly turned to vapor. This gas, with steam from the omnipresent ground water, expands in a terrific explosion, blowing much of the meteorite back out of the ground, tearing a gaping crater. The meteorite is shattered and widely scattered over the surrounding area: at best a fraction of the original body remains in the crater. An intensely hot air blast spreads out burning and destroying the nearby vegetation and life. Simultaneously strong earth-waves spread from the crater, warping and shattering the surrounding rock strata.

The main characteristics of a meteor crater are its nearly circular shape: tilted rims sloping away from the center; the bending and warping of material beneath and surrounding the crater, and the presence of meteoritic material near by. The best view of a meteor crater is obtained from an airplane and several new groups of craters have been discovered by this means.

By far the best-known and most thoroughly investigated meteor crater lies near Winslow, Arizona. It is certainly the biggest hole I have ever seen. It is variously called Barringer Crater (after the man who spent a quarter of a century investigating it) and Meteor Crater.

Meteor Crater is almost circular—four-fifths of a mile across. Its circumference is nearly three miles. Around the edge is a parapet which was forced up by the enormous pressure of the explosion when the meteorite, or dense mass of meteorites, struck. The same phenomenon can be seen on a small scale round a bomb crater. This parapet varies from 130 to 160 feet in height. The depth from the parapet to the floor of the crater is now about 550 feet, but originally it was deeper—weather action having partially filled it in. If the Washington Monument were placed on the bottom, about six feet would protrude above the crater's rim.

Scattered about the crater's rim and the surrounding plain is the debris

Meteor (or Barringer) Crater, the imprint of a colossal meteorite that slammed into the Arizona desert thousands of years ago. *Spence Air Photos*

thrown out by the tremendous explosion which occurred when the meteorite struck. One slab of rock 10 feet thick was tossed fully half a mile. Some rock fragments and meteorites have been found six miles away. There are millions of tons of "rock flour," the powdery mass resulting from the pulverization of rock caused by the immense crushing effect of the meteorite's impact. Altogether it is estimated that 300 million tons of rock were displaced by the mass which gouged out Meteor Crater. In other words, in a flash of time a third of the total amount excavated in digging the Panama Canal was exploded from the earth when this giant meteorite struck.

In addition to the rock debris, thousands of fragments of the original meteoritic mass were scattered round the crater. The largest of these weighed over 1,000 pounds, but many smaller pieces, some weighing only a few grams, have been found.

As the original meteor mass would be worth many thousands of dollars several attempts have been made to find it. Drill holes have been sunk for many hundreds of feet in different parts of the floor. In 1919 a drill was driven down through the southern rim of the crater. After penetrating 1,100 feet of shattered rock it passed through a region increasingly rich in meteoritic material and, at about 1,340 feet, it struck a stratum containing 75 per cent nickel-iron. Such material is very tough and proved so resistant

The Elements Rage   [188]

to boring that after churning through another 30 feet the drill finally stuck—and has remained immovable to this day!

The results of these drilling operations, together with other evidence, have enabled geologists and meteoricists to obtain a fairly accurate picture of what happened on that Arizona plain when the meteorite struck many thousands of years ago—estimates of the time vary between 5,000 and 50,000 years.

How big was the meteoroid that blasted out Meteor Crater? Various estimates have been given; George P. Merrill considered that it was 500 feet in diameter, traveling at five miles per second. A body of nickel-iron this size would weigh some ten million tons. But Eugene M. Shoemaker (1960), using the knowledge of craters formed by nuclear explosions, considers that a meteorite with a diameter of about 80 feet, weighing 63,000 tons and traveling at 15 kilometers per second (about 10 m.p.s.) would be sufficient.

Imagine a body of this size hurtling through the air and approaching Winslow from the northwest. Friction with the air makes the surface incandescent as the oxygen in the atmosphere blow-torches the iron. From this great flying mass sputtering chunks, large as houses, fly off as the meteoroid, traveling at a low angle, nears the ground. A huge cylinder of superheated air is forced along by the meteoroid and, as it strikes, this air is forced across the surrounding countryside in a fiery blast that instantaneously scorches every living thing for a hundred miles in every direction.

When the meteorite strikes, the whole earth is jolted. The meteorite tears its way through *a quarter of a mile* of solid rock. A wall of flame shoots 20 miles high and the thunder of the colossal impact goes round the world.

Although the most famous, Meteor Crater is not the only imprint on earth of the fall of a giant meteorite. Meteor Crater was not officially recognized until the 1920's; previously it had been explained as a result of a volcanic explosion.[7] Today, exploration in remote areas, aerial photography, and advances in chemical analysis of rock structures have revealed other craters dotted over the earth's surface. But some of these are so old that they are barely discernible from the ground (that is where aerial photography helps) and are called "fossil" craters.

There are at least ten meteor craters, proved to be such by the presence of meteorites. In addition, there are 30 or so other scars on the earth's surface which have been ascribed to meteoritic impact. These range from depressions, 65 yards in diameter, at Amak in the Aleutian Islands, to the Vredefort Ring, South Africa, which is some 30 miles wide.

The existence of meteor craters has been recognized for only a few decades—previously they had been ascribed to various geologic processes. Several probably still await discovery. Moreover, many old craters have been

---

[7] Although it had been described as such in 1905 by D. M. Barringer.

New Quebec crater, Canada. Formerly called Chubb Crater, after its discoverer, this hole is claimed to be the largest meteor crater on earth. Some scientists, however, think it may have been caused by geophysical processes.   *Robert C. Hermes*

obliterated by erosion, sedimentation, and other factors. It is estimated that meteorites capable of producing craters 30 feet or more in diameter strike the earth, on average, once every 100 years, and meteorites of Meteor Crater standard—cosmic H-bombs—once every 100,000 years.

By far the largest of the alleged meteor craters for which serious evidence has been offered is the Vredefort Ring, some 70 miles southwest of Johannesburg, South Africa. Robert S. Dietz suggests that it was formed by the impact of an asteroid with a diameter of over a mile.

But Walter H. Bucher, Professor Emeritus of Geology at Columbia University, has challenged this theory. He points out that meteorites are random phenomena, both in time and space. If, therefore, the Vredefort Ring and similar structures were caused by meteoritic impact these structures must be characterized by randomness. Bucher maintains this is not so, and that Vredefort and similar features were all formed during roughly the same geological period and at sites where volcanic activity is known to have occurred.

New Quebec Crater (Chubb Crater) in the subarctic region of Quebec Province, Canada, has been regarded as the largest crater on earth, but

The Elements Rage

many meteoricists now question it. V. Ben Meen's expedition of August 1951 thoroughly explored the crater, which is about two miles across, 800 feet deep, has a circumference of 6.8 miles and a parapet with a maximum height of some 500 feet. A number of larger features of the same type are at present (1965) being investigated in Canada.

And what of the surface features of the moon? One view is that many of these are the result of movements within the moon itself (Patrick Moore).

Ralph B. Baldwin, however, believes that all lunar features, including the mountain ranges, can be explained by meteoritic impacts and resultant explosions.

Although the chances are slight than an astronomer would be viewing the moon at the exact moment, a few have seen meteoroids strike (Walter Haas). On April 15, 1948, British astronomer Francis H. Thornton was studying the Plato plain with a nine-inch reflector, power 220, when he saw "a minute but brilliant flash of light." He says that it looked like an anti-aircraft shell exploding in the air with an orange-yellow flash about ten miles away.

The moon's surface suffers much less change than the earth's (it has virtually no atmosphere). Thus moon craters formed many millions of years ago are still visible. Equally ancient ones on earth have long since been obliterated. Lunar astronomy therefore enables meteoritic impacts to be studied in a way impossible on earth.

No one knows the total number of craters on the moon—little more than half the surface is visible from earth—but in 1878 J. F. J. Schmidt published a book in which he described 32,856. Modern estimates vary, but the lowest recent figure I have seen is 200,000, or one crater for every 40 square miles.

The photographs taken at close range by the United States satellite Ranger 7 show that this figure is much too low. The moon's surface is so pock-marked that even its craters have craters. The last Ranger photograph, taken from about 1,600 feet, shows about 20 in an area of 1,700 square yards. Some of these craters are pinhead size in the photograph. The craters are of two kinds: primary from meteoritic impact; secondary from chunks of rock exploded by the primary impact, which form their own craters. The same secondary craters have been seen to form after a nuclear test explosion in the Nevada desert (Shoemaker 1964). Some of the moon's craters are vast, greatly exceeding any on earth, but they are not deep compared with their diameter.

The famous Tycho crater is 54 miles in diameter and about $2\frac{1}{4}$ miles deep. Larger still is Copernicus with a diameter of 56 miles. Both these huge craters are dwarfed by Clavius, 146 miles wide, 3 miles deep. Yet even Clavius is only half the diameter of Mare Imbrium.

What were the sizes of the bodies which caused the greatest of the

Meteoroids

moon craters? Baldwin (1949) considers Clavius could have been made by a body between one and two miles in diameter. A nickel-iron asteroid about one mile in diameter, with an impact velocity of 10 miles per second, would have an energy of some 1.5×10^{28} ergs.

Baldwin believes that Mare Imbrium was probably formed by the impact of a nickel-iron asteroid (minor planet), some ten miles in diameter, striking with a velocity of about 20 m.p.s. The energy released by such a titanic impact would be of the order of 6×10^{31} ergs.

As this is a book about extreme violence in Nature it is appropriate, in the only chapter on astronomy, to mention the greatest known violence in the universe. It used to be thought that this was a supernova, a star which blows itself up in a paroxysm of celestial energy radiated at a rate hundreds of millions times greater than the energy output of the sun, estimated to be 3.8×10^{33} ergs per second (M. A. Ellison). There are definite records of very few supernovae in our galaxy[8]—the Milky Way—and the frequency is believed to be of the order of one every 500 years.

But there is now evidence that there are super-supernovae, or hyper-novae, vastly more powerful than anything yet known: the so-called quasars, quasi-stellar objects. They have been described as perhaps the most remarkable objects yet discovered by man. As I write (1965), astronomers are still discussing them, but already enough facts have emerged to establish them as the source of the greatest violence known.

Quasars are about 10,000 times smaller but 100 times brighter than the brightest known galaxy. Some are five thousand million light years away and are receding into the abyss of space at the fantastic speed of half the speed of light—some 90,000 miles per *second*. It is estimated that quasars consume energy at the rate of 100 of our suns per year, one sun for fuel every 3½ days: an energy output about a million times greater than that of a super-nova! Nuclear processes are probably too weak for such energies; it is possible that they come from a source of which earth has neither measure nor faintest parallel.

Such are the quasars. How has man learned about them? From the electric pulses they emit, picked up by radio telescopes; and their light, photographed by the camera and analyzed by the spectroscope. It is a fascinating commentary on modern science, and the power of the human mind, that we have learned about the universe's vastest energies from its tiniest. The total amount of the quasars' radiated energy so far collected by telescopes on earth is not sufficient to raise the temperature of a gram of water by one millionth of a degree Centigrade (D. W. Sciama, and H. P. Palmer).

After that brief excursion into violence for which man has no con-

---

[8] Most astronomers say three but there is some evidence for more (C. M. Cade).

ceivable measure, the largest meteorite ever to blast this earth is, in comparison, less than the pop of a Christmas firecracker. Nevertheless, in view of the tremendous (by human standards) effects of large meteoritic impacts and their occurrence in past millennia, the question arises: What are the possibilities of an asteroid or giant meteoroid striking the earth today? The answer is that they are very real: *this century* has witnessed the passing fairly near us, astronomically speaking, of a dangerously large mass, the near escape of Pittsburgh from a 500-ton meteoroid, and a direct hit from a mass weighing thousands of tons.

On October 30, 1937, the asteroid Hermes came uncomfortably close to the earth. It was estimated to be about a mile in diameter and its weight would thus be vastly greater than the mass which gouged Meteor Crater.

Hermes came to within about 500,000 miles of the earth. Judged by standards of terrestrial measurement that may seem to be a comfortable enough distance away, but it isn't in terms of the astronomical yardstick. This is the light-year, or the distance which light, traveling at over 11 million miles a *minute,* will cover in a year. It takes eight minutes for the light from the sun to reach us, but four *years* for the light from the nearest star to travel across the vast distances of interstellar space and reach this planet. Judged by that standard (*i.e.,* the light-year and not, of course, its actual speed), Hermes missed this earth by only three seconds! Put another way it means that a mass, capable of blasting Los Angeles off the face of the earth, missed us only by one or two degrees in the inclination of its orbit and a slight difference in its speed relative to the earth.

And Hermes is only one of over 40,000 asteroids, with diameters between a half and more than 400 miles, traveling round the sun. These flying mountains normally have elliptical orbits but the attraction of other planets affects their course, thus sometimes bringing them near to the earth.

Asteroids are of special interest to the spaceman: while collisions must obviously be avoided, it may be possible to land on them and use them as en route stations for interplanetary travel.

What of Pittsburgh's near escape? On the evening of June 24, 1938, a brilliant light flashed across the Pennsylvania sky, and a few seconds later the northern part of Pittsburgh was rocked by a terrific explosion, like long drawn-out thunder. The noise was so great that a rumor spread that the powder magazine at nearby West Winfield had exploded. Actually the light and noise were both caused by a meteorite. Had it fallen at a different angle it could have destroyed Pittsburgh and killed half a million people.

The phenomena connected with the fall of this Chicora meteorite, as it was named, have been thoroughly investigated, by F. W. Preston, E. P. Henderson and James R. Randolph. The authors consider that at a height of 12 miles above the earth this meteoroid weighed some 500 tons.

Meteoroids

If this big meteorite had come straight down instead of at this long slant, it would have reached the earth with a lot of its structure still intact and a lot of its energy still in it. And if it had landed on Pittsburgh there would have been few survivors. Its kinetic energy of 31,400,000 foot-pounds per pound is more than 20 times as great as the explosive energy of TNT. At least its capacity for destruction would have compared favorably with that of the shipload of TNT that blew up in Halifax Harbor in 1917. And such a catastrophe, or even a very much larger one, can happen at any time, with no more warning than the observers of the Chicora meteorite had. But fortunately the energy of this meteorite had all been absorbed by the air before it reached the ground.

As about three-quarters of the earth's surface is covered by water, and the fall of meteorites is completely random, it is a statistical certainty that most meteorites fall ino the oceans. It is also certain that some of these have been large enough to send vast waves sweeping across the seas to inundate far distant shores. Some alleged seismic sea waves (tsunami) have almost certainly been caused in this way; although, as far as I know, there is no historical record of one. And such a catastrophe could happen anywhere at any time.

At the meeting of the British Association in 1908 W. N. Shaw (later Sir Napier Shaw), the distinguished British meteorologist, drew attention to some unexplained oscillations in the microbarograph record. These showed that powerful air waves had passed across England from north to south on June 30, 1908. The scientists at the meeting could find no satisfactory explanation of these mysterious "kicks."

On the same day some seismographs in Germany and Russia registered mild earthquake shocks. Calculations located the focus of the earth tremor in Siberia, a region where earthquakes were virtually unknown.

Another series of unusual phenomena was noticed at the same time. On June 30, 1908, near Gothenburg in Sweden "an extraordinarily strong light" appeared in the sky about an hour after sunset and lasted until after two in the morning. A book could easily be read by it.

At ten o'clock on the same night at Aberdeen, Scotland, the light, instead of continuing to fade from the sky, suddenly grew brighter, "almost as bright as daylight." A similar lengthening of the hours of daylight was noticed in other parts of the country. Moreover, there was no auroral display at the time to account for this strange light phenomenon. A photograph taken at night by the light was published in the *Quarterly Journal of the Royal Meteorological Society* for October 1938.

Closely associated with the increase of light were the spectacular sunsets. The evening skies for several days were a blaze of bright green, golden-red, and pure yellow.

These four things—the strange kicks in the microbarograph record; the disturbance of the seismograph record, apparently from a non-earthquake region; the lengthening of daylight; and the brilliantly colored sunsets—were duly noted and then filed. Natural science was not yet sufficiently integrated to notice any relationship between disturbed air pressure, ground shocks, a lengthening of the hours of daylight, and brilliant sunsets.

The years passed and then came the First World War. Men had other things to think about than unexplained records buried in scientific archives. Then, early in the 1920's, reports began to filter out from a remote part of Russia, to which access was very difficult, that a tremendous explosion had occurred some years before the outbreak of the war. Later these reports became more definite. The explosion had occurred in Siberia sometime during the summer of 1908. And then the forgotten records were remembered. . . .

Most of the information concerning what happened is due to the researches of L. A. Kulik and his assistants of the Academy of Sciences of the U.S.S.R. In addition to collecting all the information he could from eye-witnesses, Kulik conducted five expeditions over a period of ten years to the site of the explosion (references in Barbara Middlehurst and Gerard Kuiper).

In the first expedition in 1921 he failed to reach the exact spot, because the marshy forests were almost impassable. The ground is frozen during the winter and swampy for the rest of the year. In March 1927 another expedition set out and made slow headway poling a raft along the small rivers intersecting the marshes. In three months the expedition covered little more than 40 miles.

Other expeditions followed, including an aerial survey, and during 1930–31 Kulik explored the area for 13 months. There was another aerial survey in 1938 and for the first time photographs of the area were taken. From the information thus collected it is now possible to construct a fairly accurate picture of what happened to cause the four unexplained phenomena recorded so many years before.

At about 7 A.M. on June 30, 1908, over the Central Siberian forest near Vanavara, out of the clear southwestern sky a great incandescent mass flew through the air. Just before it struck there was a terrific explosion. A moment later the earth was shaken as the fragments buried themselves in the ground. At the site of the fall flames and what appeared to be smoke were seen.

Fortunately we have the statements of some of the witnesses of this unique event in the history of modern man. From their simple records a vivid impression can be gained of what it was like to be within a hundred miles of that lonely Siberian landscape in the early morning of that historic day.

A man who was at Vanavara, 40 miles south of the point of the cataclysm, said:

> There was a fiery flame in the northwest, which gave off such heat that my shirt nearly caught fire. I felt as if I were enveloped in flame. I noticed that this miracle covered a space of not less than two kilometers [a little over a mile]. . . . I only had time to note the extent and the flame disappeared. After the flame disappeared there was an explosion which threw me off my feet a distance of seven feet or more. . . . The glass and frames of the house broke and clods of earth were spit up from the square in front of my hut.[9]

A man who was at Kansk, about 300 miles from where the meteorite fell, said:

> I was washing wool with my workmen on the banks of the Kan River when all of a sudden I heard a noise like the whir of the wings of frightened birds, and downstream the waters of the river took on an undulatory movement. This was followed by one sharp thud, then dull noises like an underground roaring. The thud was so severe that one of the workmen fell into the water.

So much for the actual statements of witnesses. Additional facts about this great cataclysm were gathered by the various investigators. At the time the body struck, observers at three widely separated places, three or four hundred miles distant from the actual site, saw in the bright sunlight a huge column of fire rise to an estimated height of 12 miles. At Vanavara, 40 miles away, this fiery column appeared to be a mile across.

Kulik (1939) says that this "pillar of fire" was caused by the burning of the *taiga* (coniferous forest) over an area some 20 miles wide. The cylinder of incandescent gas (estimated temperature above 1,000° C.) accompanying the meteoroid spread out for miles in all directions at tremendous speed when it hit the earth, and almost instantaneously burned the more inflammable parts of the trees and undergrowth. This great mass of red-hot air caused far more destruction that the impact of the meteoritic mass itself.

Following the fiery column, a great pillar of smoke rose into the air at least as high as the flames.

The sound effects were as impressive as the spectacle. On a river over 100 miles away there was such a cannonade that the crew on a ship rushed to the cabin for safety. The blasts grew in intensity and lasted for over three minutes. Six hundred miles away, near Turokhansk, an observer said:

---

[9] There appears to have been a pressure wave followed by a suction wave.

A few of the millions of trees felled by the comet which fell in Central Siberia on June 30, 1908.   *Fotokhronika Tass*

"Away to the east I heard three or four dull thuds in succession, like distant artillery fire."

Some of the mechanical effects of the fall have already been described in the accounts of witnesses. But there were others. Within a radius of 20 miles from the center of the fall the destruction was enormous. There were reports of whole families being wiped out. Certainly if they had been within 20 miles they would have been instantly killed by the searing heat and tremendous concussion. Three hundred miles from where the meteorite struck, men and horses were flung off their feet.

But it was not until many years later, when Kulik and his companions explored the immediate area of the fall (lat.61° N., long.102° E.), that the most spectacular evidence of destruction was seen—the wreckage of 80 million trees over an area of nearly 2,000 square miles!

Within a central area of about 80 square miles the scorched skeletons of numerous trees were still standing. This indicates that the trees were blasted simultaneously from all directions by shock waves from the explosion, especially as farther out from this central area felled trees lay like matchsticks—all their heads pointing away from the central area. Here the tremendous shock waves did not neutralize each other and trees went down wholesale.

In an area of over some 400 square miles not a tree was left standing. Toward the perimeter of this area trees were found uprooted, broken and stripped of their branches. There must have been an instant obliteration of life throughout the whole of this area.

Progressively outward from this central area fewer trees were blown down, but some were felled as far as 40 miles out. The most distant trees to be felled were those on high ground, where the destructive blast of air had free passage.

A puzzling feature was the absence of any crater at all comparable to the vast destruction it caused. At the center of the area of destruction the ground was shattered and the rocks were "folded into small wrinkles," but there is nothing resembling a meteor crater.

According to Kulik (1939) witnesses declared that:

> Where the meteorite fell "it twisted and turned the ground," and "water gushed from the earth." The evidence about water gushing from the ground is confirmed by traces of a great inundation, when the level of the water in many of the explored places rose above the level of the hillocky peat marshes.

The explanation of these facts, including the absence of a crater, is probably that the violent midair explosion of the meteoroid broke it up so much that only comparatively small fragments fell, and that these exploded again on striking the ground. This second explosion explains why the lateral effects of the impact were so much greater than the vertical, *i.e.*, the shattering and wrinkling of the rocky ground, but no crater. No meteorites have ever been recovered from the area.

How much did the meteoroid weigh? No one, of course, knows its original weight, but it is possible to estimate its weight when it struck the earth. The Russians have exploded nuclear test devices roughly the same distance from microbarographs as the Siberian meteorite. When a 30-megaton bomb was exploded near Novaya Zemlya on October 23, 1961, it created about the same disturbance on the microbarograph records as the meteorite. From this and other information it is believed that the Siberian meteorite weighed not less than 30,000 tons (R. V. Jones). One ton of meteorite is equivalent, in energy expenditure, to many tons of TNT. The actual figure varies with the speed; at 44.7 miles per second the impact of a one-ton meteorite would be equal to 600 tons of TNT.

Various estimates have been made of the energy released by this great meteorite ranging from 3.2×10^{20} ergs (F. J. W. Whipple) to 10^{24} ergs (R. V. Jones). Probably the most authoritative estimate is that of the Russian experts, 10^{23} ergs (K. P. Florensky, *et. al.*).

Throughout this chapter I have referred to a meteorite having caused the explosion but there are other opinions. One is that it was the nucleus of a comet. This theory was first propounded by Whipple in 1930 and has since been put forward by Russian scientists (see references in E. L. Krinov, 1963). Robey suggests that it was a cometoid—a mass of frozen substances at a very low temperature.

Whatever is the truth about the cause of the Siberian catastrophe, the answers to the quesetions which puzzled the scientists at the meeting of the British Association in 1908 will now be fairly obvious. The disturbances of the seismograph records were due to the ground wave set up by the impact and explosion of the fragments crashing into the earth. The seismograph at Irkutsk, about 550 miles from the fall, was agitated for an hour and a half.

The lengthening of the hours of daylight and the brilliant sunsets were caused by the vast cloud of meteoritic dust and smoke which was flung miles high into the air—and, on the other theory, also by the comet's tail. Kulik (1939) says:

> At dusk, that same day, enormous silver clouds were seen at an altitude of 83 km. [about 50 miles], which almost turned the night into day throughout the continent, from the basin of the Yenissei to the Atlantic and even the Black Sea.

A vast dust cloud high in the atmosphere catches the sun's rays and reflects them downward, for a time even when the sun has sunk below the horizon.

The kicks in the microbarograph records were caused by the great atmospheric wave set up by the explosions of the meteorite. It took five hours for this wave to reach Britain, 3,500 miles away. The microbarograph records in Batavia (Djakarta)—4,410 miles—and Washington, D. C.—5,570 miles—were also disturbed when the wave reached them.

It is a sobering thought that this great meteorite fell in exactly the same latitude as Leningrad. Had it fallen about five hours later the rotation of the earth would have caused this great city to be immediately beneath it. Leningrad would have been razed to the ground, every one of its inhabitants killed.

Nearly 40 years later another meteorite crashed in Siberia. On February 12, 1947, a mass believed to weigh about 70 tons flamed through the atmosphere and disintegrated above the Sikhote Alin Gory mountain range, some 200 miles north of Vladivostok. The explosion was heard 125 miles away. Unlike the earlier fall there is no doubt that this was caused by a meteorite as many pieces were subsequently recovered (Krinov, 1963).

The first British edition of this book was published in April, 1945, four months before the atomic bomb was dropped on Hiroshima. Someone drew it to the attention of the director of intelligence of the British Air Staff remarking that one of the photographs indicated that someone had exploded an atomic bomb before. That was not the explanation of the photograph, of course, but the remark has disturbing implications. Suppose a similar explosion were reported today. There is the possibility that it would be mistaken for a nuclear explosion. Fortunately the danger has been foreseen. It was the subject of a letter from W. E. Le Gros Clark and Kenneth P. Oakley in the London *Times* for September 25, 1961. I hope the warning has been heeded.

chapter 9

Earthquakes ⟩⟩

Although not so spectacular as a volcano, a great earthquake makes an ineffaceable impression on the mind of man. We are so accustomed to living on solid earth, that when *that* begins to shake the mind is overwhelmed.

Throughout the world there are over a million earthquakes every year —an average of two a minute. The vast majority are extremely slight, about 20 are serious but do not occur in built-up areas, about five kill and destroy. The British Isles have an average of three newsworthy earth tremors each year; the United States averages 700.

The ancients had various theories to account for earthquakes. The Algonquin Indians believed that the earth was supported by a great tortoise and that when the earth shook he was shuffling his feet. In Mongolia the earth-shaker was a pig, and in India a mole.[1] The early Japanese believed the quakings of the earth were caused by the movements of an underground spider. Later Japanese theorists thought the troublesome creature was a catfish; a rock rested on its head to keep it quiet, but presumably the fish occasionally wriggled free to set the world a-shaking. The people of Kamchatka, Siberia, thought that earthquakes were caused by the dogs of their god Tuil. The dogs were believed to be infested with fleas, and when their master took them for a walk they occasionally stopped to scratch. When they did the earth shook.

One of the earliest "scientific" theories was that of Aristotle, who believed that powerful subterranean winds caused earthquakes. This theory is referred to by Shakespeare in *Henry IV*, Part I, where Hotspur declaims:

> Diseased Nature oftentimes breaks forth
> In strange eruptions; oft the teeming earth
> Is with a kind of colic pinch'd and vex'd
> By the imprisoning of unruly wind
> Within her womb; which, for enlargement striving,
> Shakes the old beldam earth, and topples down
> Steeples and moss-grown towers.

---

[1] It is easy to understand the choice of this animal as the responsible earth-shaker. Writing of the California earthquake of April 18, 1906, Charles Davison (1936) says: "In most places the surface formed a ridge from three to 10 feet wide and from a few inches to 1½ feet high, as if it had been raised by a gigantic mole-creeping underground."

Today, the immediate causes of earthquakes are fairly well-known, but the ultimate causes are still shrouded in controversy and uncertainty, and will not be discussed here. (See Charles F. Richter and John H. Hodgson for a discussion of the various theories.)

There are several types of earthquakes. Some are caused by the underground movements of the magma, or liquid rock, in volcanoes; others by the collapse of subterranean spaces beneath extinct volcanoes; and some appear to be due to rockfalls. But these three causes never produce an earthquake which is felt or even recorded outside a small area, although it may be severe locally.

Some earthquakes are caused by movements in that skin of rocks, some 30 miles thick, which encloses the body of the earth.[2] Others originate 400 to 450 miles down.

Miles below the surface a strain develops inside vast masses of rock. Suddenly something gives way, generally along a fault, or weak line, and the sudden adjustment of these immeasurable masses of the earth causes a shiver to pulse through the entire globe. A shift of an inch by a hundred-mile-long section of rock is enough to cause an earthquake. The shock in the immediate area rarely lasts for more than a minute, and generally only for several seconds, but milder aftershocks may continue intermittently for a long time, very rarely for years.

The "Elastic rebound" theory of earthquakes, propounded by Harry Fielding Reid, is the one most generally accepted by geologists today. It is thus summarized by Heck:

> Rock will rupture when it is submitted to elastic strains greater than it can endure. Such strains may be the result of sudden explosion, but ordinarily they are due to slow displacement of the earth's crust. This displacement sets up stresses between adjacent portions of the crust that grow slowly until the point of rupture is reached. The strained rock rebounds under its own elastic stresses until the strain is wholly or partially relieved.
>
> In the 1906 California earthquake measurement by triangulation showed that the portion of the earth affected by the rebound extended only a few miles on either side of the fracture. In general, though not necessarily, the rebounds are in opposite directions on opposite sides of the fault plane. The directions of the slow relative displacements and of the elastic rebound, which are practically parallel with each other, may be horizontal, vertical or inclined.

---

[2] Manmade structures can, by disturbing the loading on thee arth's crust, cause dangerous tremors. Manmade lakes, such as Kariba and Aswan in Africa, by concentrating many millions of tons of water over a small area *could* cause a tremor capable of cracking the dam wall itself. Remember the Fréjus dam disaster in France on December 3, 1959.

Regions containing high mountains, especially if they are near deep seas, are particularly prone to earthquakes.

The great earthquake regions of the world bear out the above assertion. Nearly all earthquakes—some 95 per cent—occur in one or the other of the two great belts which together encircle the earth. The first belt runs round the margins of the Pacific (with branches into the West Indies and the Southern Antilles), and the other passes through the East Indies, the Himalayas, the Caucasus and the Alps. Roughly this is the same course as that followed by the earth's major volcanic belts. In the United States the most active earthquake regions are in Alaska and California. The San Andreas fault runs some 700 miles from northern California to the Mexican border, its west side grinding northward at an average rate of nearly two inches a year.

There is an elaborate chain of instruments throughout the world for recording earthquakes. They are called seismographs and have a long history. The first earthquake recorder appears to have been made about 130 A.D., by the Chinese astronomer Chang Heng. It consisted of a copper dome fixed to the ground, inside which was a delicately balanced inverted pendulum. Set equidistantly round the rim were eight dragons' heads, each with a copper ball balanced on the tongue of its open mouth. Below each dragon was a bronze toad with its mouth agape—dragons and toads are Chinese symbols for heaven and earth.

The slightest jarring of this contraption shot the balls nearest in line with the path of the earthquake wave out of the mouth of the dragon into that of the toad waiting below. The occurrence and approximate direction of earthquakes were thus recorded long before news arrived by messengers from the stricken areas.

A duplicate of this father of all seismographs is in the National Science Museum, Ueno, Tokyo. The dragons' heads regularly shoot their copper balls into the toads' mouths whenever Japanese earthquakes are near enough and violent enough to shake the copper dome.

Other simple seismographs were used for hundreds of years before the modern highly sensitive instruments came into general use. Even today valuable "on-the-spot" information can be obtained about the strength and direction of earthquakes by observing the direction in which tombstones fall, the way ornaments are rotated on mantelpieces, and the direction of swing of hanging objects such as chandeliers.

Most modern seismographs work on the basis of the inertia principle. When the earth moves, heavy bodies which are not rigidly fastened to it, have sufficient inertia to prevent an immediate response.

In seismographs a heavy weight, as much as 20 tons, is suspended on a pendulum from a framework connected directly to the earth. When a quake occurs it sends a shudder through the earth. On reaching a seismograph the shudder agitates its framework, but the pendulum, because it is hanging free, does not move. In most modern instruments the weight is linked to an electromagnetic system which conveys the movements to the recording device.

The movement of the earth is recorded in various ways as a series of agitated lines. In early models a needle, attached to the pendulum, recorded on a continuously running band of smoked paper. In modern seismographs the recording is mostly done photographically (a beam of light—the "pen" —on sensitized paper), or electronically (magnetized tape). But smoked paper seismographs still give the sharpest line.

There are various types of seismographs. Some record slight sub-earthquake tremors, others distant quakes. Throughout the world there are over 1,000 seismograph stations, some of which can record an earthquake of magnitude 4 or greater occurring anywhere in the world.

The actual movement of the earth at places many miles distant from the place where the earthquake occurs is naturally extremely slight. Sometimes the ground movement at the seismograph station is about one forty-millionth of an inch. But when big earthquakes are near, the over-all movement is measured in inches, or even feet.

By electrical and mechanical means the movement is magnified by the seismograph; in the most delicate instruments over a million times. If a seismograph's heavy weight is touched by a feather the needle agitates violently. Spiders crawling about a seismograph vault have produced oscillations on the record, and children dancing have shaken the earth sufficiently to leave their mark. Even the beating of the surf against the shore may be recorded as a continuous flicker. In siting seismograph stations the interference caused by traffic must be considered.

When an earthquake occurs, it sends out various waves which travel faster than the swiftest bullet. The first wave is called P (for primary), and it travels through the earth at speeds of the order of a few miles per second. Then follows the S (for secondary) wave, which rocks from side to side. It moves at little more than half the speed of the P-wave. Some writers call P and S waves "Push" and "Shake" respectively, as these terms describe their behavior more graphically. Other waves follow, and by studying the seismograph record seismologists are able to tell with tolerable accuracy where and when an earthquake occurred, and its probable magnitude.

Throughout the world seismographs are agitated about once every hour. Widely recorded earthquakes occur at the rate of just under two a day, major earthquakes once a week. These figures are not so alarming as they sound, because about two-thirds of all earthquakes occur under the sea and of the remainder many occur in uninhabited or sparsely inhabited areas.

Seismologists have compiled scales to measure (a) the intensity of shocks and (b) the magnitude of the earthquake causing them. The two types of scale are often confused in popular accounts of earthquakes, but

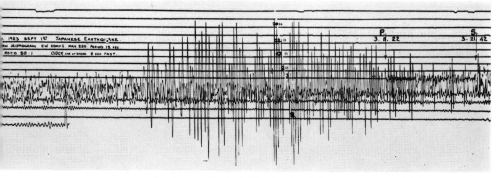

Seismograph record taken at Oxford, England, of the earthquake which wrecked Tokyo and Yokohama on September 1, 1923.   *Science Museum, London*

they are quite distinct. There are many shock intensities in an earthquake, but only one magnitude, which is related to the total amount of energy released.

Like the Beaufort wind scale, earthquake intensity scales are based on the effects produced, which vary with the distance from the epicenter. Practice varies from country to country. One of the most widely used is the Modified Mercalli Scale, based on the one originally propounded in 1902 by the Italian seismologist, Giuseppe Mercalli, and modified by the American seismologists, Harry O. Wood and Frank Neumann. Versions of the scale—some abbreviated, others with additional comments—are published in various books on earthquakes.

The MM (as the scale is often referred to) has 12 intensities. The first is so slight that the shocks do little more than cause some trees to sway and a few doors to swing. Most people do not realize there has been a shock at all. The twelfth intensity begins "Damage is total" (see Appendix 2).

It will be obvious from the greatest intensities on the scale that the forces involved in a severe earthquake are enormous. Where an earthquake is concerned there is no such thing as an immovable object, even mountains are moved. The only comparable release of energy is in the most powerful volcanic eruption, an exceptionally heavy meteoritic impact—or a multi-megaton nuclear explosion.

The best-known earthquake magnitude scale is Richter's. It is based on the maximum reading-deviation from the horizontal—on a standard type seismograph. The scale starts at 0 and the highest figure is 8.9. Each increase of a whole number on the scale represents a tenfold increase in the magnitude of the earthquake.[3] Thus an earthquake of 8.0 magnitude is not twice,

---

[3] Strictly, in the wave amplitude produced by the earthquake at any given distance.

but *10,000* times greater than one of 4.0. But—to complicate matters even further!—the actual energy release rises even more steeply with each increase in magnitude number.

It must be emphasized that the figure given for the magnitude of any earthquake is only approximate. Different seismologists often give different figures for the same earthquake. This is easily understandable when it is realized that (*a*) seismograph readings vary according to place and other factors and (*b*) seismologists don't all use seismographs with the same response. Estimates for the magnitude of the main shock of the great Chilean earthquake of May 22, 1960, varied between 8.25 and 8.9—that is, some seismologists said it was $6\frac{1}{2}$ *times* greater than the estimate of other seismologists (Haroun Tazieff).

Strange as it may sound, nuclear test explosions have added another complication. The Bikini test of July 24, 1946, was originally assigned the equivalent of an earthquake magnitude rating of 5.5, implying a total energy release of 8×10^{21} ergs. But from other information it was known that the energy from the explosion which went into seismic waves was less than one-thousandth of this value. Partly as a result of this knowledge seismologists have had to revise the earthquake magnitude—energy relation which they use for the estimation of the total energy release.

K. E. Bullen, an authority on the physics and mathematics of earthquakes, says that the probable maximum energy released in the greatest earthquakes is about 10^{25} ergs, which is one-hundredth of the figure given in prenuclear days. The smaller figure is still over 1,000 times greater than that for the energy release of the Bikini explosion. And the largest hydrogen bomb explosion for which figures are available—the equivalent of 15 million tons of TNT—released 6×10^{23} ergs, or between one-tenth and one-hundredth of the energy released in the greatest earthquake. These figures should be borne in mind when considering their effects.

The actual place in the earth where the quake originates is called the focus, and the point on the surface immediately above is called the epicenter. The length of the fracture which causes a big earthquake varies greatly. The longest measured on land appears to be that of the April 18, 1906, California quake, in which faulting occurred along a line of some 270 miles. The breadth of any individual fracture is often only a few inches, but, again, it is sometimes measured in feet. In a large earthquake the vibrations are felt over hundreds of thousands of square miles.

This fact was well illustrated in the great Lisbon earthquake of November 1, 1755. The shock was felt over an area of some 1,300,000 square miles, or more than one-third of Europe. Inland waters, such as Loch Lomond, Scotland, over 1,000 miles distant from Lisbon, were oscillated as the earthquake waves raced through the earth.

At Amsterdam, over 1,000 miles away, water in canals was agitated so violently that several boats broke loose from their moorings. At nearby Rotterdam the oscillations of the water in canals and rivers were so great that buoys were broken from their chains and even large vessels snapped their cables. The River Dal in Sweden, 1,800 miles away, overflowed. There is some evidence that this great earthquake agitated the waters of Lake Ontario in Canada, over 3,000 miles away.

Another remarkable feature of this earthquake was that in many Continental churches, a thousand miles or more from Lisbon, chandeliers vibrated or swung. They acted as primitive seismographs recording the passage of the earthquake waves.

The total loss of life in this earthquake was about 15,000. In Lisbon itself 17,000 houses out of a total of 20,000 were either totally destroyed or rendered uninhabitable by the combined effects of earthquake, fire and sea waves. According to an eyewitness who visited the city three weeks after the earthquake there were then "no signs of streets, lanes, squares etc., but hills and mountains of rubbish still smoking." (Quoted in Davison) It is hardly surprising that this earthquake had a profound effect on 18th-century philosophy (see Sir Thomas Kendrick, and Theodore Besterman).

One of the best-known stories of this cruel day is that a newly built quay at the mouth of the Tagus, on which a number of people were standing, sank out of sight and all the people were drowned. Sir Charles Lyell says "perhaps a narrow chasm opened and closed again in the bed of the Tagus, after swallowing up some incumbent buildings and vessels." Yet the story was disproved as soon as Portuguese engineers examined the site shortly after the earthquake (Moreira de Mendonça, and Reid).

It was stories like this which made people believe that in severe quakes the earth opened and swallowed people. It is easy to understand such a belief —many earthquake photographs show what appear to be yawning chasms. Fissures do appear in the upper surface but there is no evidence that these are more than a few feet deep.

In the great New Madrid, Missouri, earthquakes of December 1811 to February 1812 numerous fissures were caused, some of them running parallel for miles. The greatest were 5 miles long, 10 feet wide—but only 4½ feet deep.

L. Don Leet, an American authority on earthquakes, points out that most accounts of people, animals and buildings disappearing into the ground belong to the earlier records of earthquakes.[4] Thus, in the great Calabrian earthquakes in Italy in February and March of 1783, it was reported that houses sunk into great fissures and the ground closed over them. During the

---

[4] The official report of the 1906 California earthquake records that a crevice opened on a ranch and engulfed a cow, head first. Before it could struggle free the fissure closed, leaving only the cow's tail visible above ground.

Concrete bridge wrecked by the earthquake which hit the Fukui district of Japan on June 28, 1948.   *International News Photos*

same earthquake some men were said to have fallen into the earth, only to be thrown out again—alive (Lyell).

Against such anecdotes Leet puts the following quotation from Akitsune Imamura, one of Japan's greatest seismologists: "As no authentic record exists in this country of an open fissure having closed up and engulfed men and animals, this dread of fissures finds no justification so far as records of Japanese earthquakes are concerned." Japan, of course, is one of the most earthquake-prone countries in the world, where virtually every seismic effect has been experienced many times. It must be added, however, that in the great Fukui earthquake of June 28, 1948, there was definite evidence of a woman falling into a fissure and being found dead, buried up to her chin. It was believed that she was crushed to death (H. Tsuya).

In addition to surface fissuring, several other movements of the ground occur during an earthquake. Frequently the ground moves horizontally. One part of a road sometimes moves several feet in relation to another part, and fences are likewise displaced. During the 1906 California earthquake the Farallon Islands (Point) Lighthouse was moved nearly six feet. Elsewhere there was a movement of 20 feet. Vertical displacement also occurs; part of the ground sinks or is pushed up. In the Alaskan earthquake of September 10, 1899, a beach became a cliff overnight (see p. 217).

In the New Madrid quakes an area of some 30,000 square miles sank

The Elements Rage   [208]

between 5 and 15 feet. Reelfoot Lake, Tennessee, was formed during this period.

Displacement also takes place under the sea, probably by secondary effects, such as seaslides (see p. 229). A fortnight after the Hawke's Bay, New Zealand, earthquake of February 3, 1931, men collecting stones on the beach at Tuamotu Island, South Pacific, saw a two-acre bank, covered with large boulders, rise seven feet "out of the sea without warning" (Sydney W. S. Strong). It is often said that the greatest displacement known occurred in Sagami Bay, Japan, during the earthquake of September 1, 1923. But many seismologists, including those in Japan, dispute the claim because they think the measurements are questionable (see Hodgson).

Among the most spectacular movements are the visible waves which accompany the greatest earthquakes. They have been described as the earth's clumsy efforts to imitate the ocean. Some seismologists consider these waves to be an optical illusion: the combination of the shaking earth, clouds of dust, and general terror causing eyewitnesses to imagine that the surface of the earth itself is rippling. But there are a number of detailed descriptions which make it hard to dismiss the waves as an illusion.

Writing of the Californian earthquake of 1906, Davison says:

> It is clear, from the descriptions given, that the waves resembled undulations in water. The estimates of their size may be exaggerated, but several observers agree in stating that they were two or three feet in height. At San Jose many persons saw waves in the ground more than a foot in height, and, according to one careful estimate, about 60 feet from crest to crest. Near the same place waves were seen traveling from the south, but, about the middle of the shock, they were met by others, the whole surface resembled hillocks or cross seas, and the tree tops waved wildly.

Similar waves were witnessed in the great Assam earthquake of June 12, 1897. R. D. Oldham says that the speed of these waves was faster than a man could walk, but slower than he could run. He thus quotes A. E. Shuttleworth, the District Superintendent of Police:

> We saw the earth all round heaving in a most frightful manner. The earth resembled waves coming from opposite directions and meeting in a great heap and then falling back; each time the waves seemed to fall back the ground opened slightly, and each time they met, water and sand were thrown up to a height of about 18 inches or so. . . . The shock was strong enough to knock over a couple of elephants I had in camp with me. My horse, too, in the stable was knocked off his legs and my dogs could not stand up in the veranda of the bungalow.

Oldham also quotes a young woman cyclist:

A department store leans drunkenly after the Fukui earthquake.
International News Photos

When we had gone about 300 yards up the hill I suddenly heard a dreadful roar. I couldn't make out what it was. It sounded like a train, thunder, landslip all together, and it came nearer and nearer, and then the ground began to heave and shake and rock. I stayed on my bicycle for a second, and then fell off, and got up and tried to run, staggering about from side to side of the road. To my left I saw great clouds of dust, which I afterwards discovered to be houses falling and the earth slipping from the sides of the hills. To my right I saw the embankment at the end of the lake torn asunder and the water rushing out, the wooden bridge across the lake break in two, and the sides of the lake falling in; and at my feet the ground cracking and opening. I was wild with fear, and didn't know which way to run.

Masonry boundary pillars, two or three feet high, were shaken to pieces by the violent agitation of the ground. Arthur Holmes says the ground vibrated rapidly, "each to and fro movement being more than a foot in range." Buildings are wrecked by very much smaller movements than this.

The effect of all the various movements and accompaniments of an earthquake is to induce a feeling akin to sea sickness, and sometimes hallucinations.[5] During the Lisbon earthquake priests in the great church of

---

[5] Was it this which gave the idea to some old-time charlatans to peddle "earthquake pills"?

São Vicente de Fora said they saw it suddenly rock and sway like a wave-tossed ship. But John Harpum tells me that such reports of rocking are probably the result of disturbance of the balancing mechanism of the ear due to shock waves. "I have experienced the same from near bomb misses."[6]

The Assam earthquake of August 15, 1950, was one of the greatest earthquakes ever recorded, registering 8.6 on the Richter scale. Rivers were dammed; major floods drowned the countryside; mountains and hills split open and square miles of their surface covering were stripped off; rain came down as mud owing to the dust-choked air; and the geography of the region was permanently changed.

This earthquake was experienced by the British botanist, Frank Kingdon-Ward, and his wife Jean. They were in a valley at Rima, Tibet, about 25 miles from the epicenter. They have recorded what happened, and seismology is the richer for the vivid accounts of their terrifying experiences.

The first shock came early in the night. They went out of their tent, Frank Kingdon-Ward carrying a lantern.

> Two paces more and we were thrown violently to the ground, which was now shuddering like a mad thing beneath our feet. The lamp also fell with a crash and went out instantly, leaving us in darkness. Bewildered and annoyed, we tried to pick ourselves up and behave with a little dignity, only to find that it was impossible to stand, or indeed even to sit, while the world broke up all round us. With the first big shock there came a deep rumbling noise from the earth itself, full of menace, which quickly swelled in volume to a deafening roar that filled all the valley. Mixed with it was a terrifying clatter, as though a hundred rods were being rapidly drawn over sheets of corrugated iron. The noise was unbelievable, agonizing. Never before had our ears been subjected to such an onslaught of sound [Jean Kingdon-Ward].

Their two servants managed to fight their way to them across the heaving earth. All four lay face downward, gripping hands.

> We waited in indescribable terror for the enraged earth to open beneath us and swallow us whole. It seemed impossible that any of us could escape that fate, for the convulsions beneath us never ceased for minutes on end; and how long, I wondered, could the tortured sand bear our weight upon it? Helpless as we were in the grip of the earthquake, every one of us, I think, experienced that night the uttermost depths of human fear.
>
> Incredibly, after an interval that can only be measured in terms of eternity, we found ourselves back in the more familiar dimensions of space and time. The deep rumbling gradually died away, and only then was it possible

---

[6] But George Plafker, who made a study of the great Alaskan earthquake of March 27, 1964, tells me: "It took two minutes of hard shaking for one six-story building in Anchorage to collapse. Many others were not even seriously damaged."

to distinguish which elements of the confusion and uproar had been earthquake noises and which the thunder of landslides. We got up and looked around us in the darkness.

Throughout the night the ground shook every few seconds, and an endless barrage of rocks and earth cascaded down the mountains. The stars were blotted out by an immense pall of dust. It began to rain.

At dawn they looked out. The earth was still trembling, but the shocks were neither so strong nor so frequent. Dust was everywhere, blotting out the rising sun. A stream had dried up, there were fissures in the ground, and a rope bridge across a river had snapped like cotton. But the birds still sang. "No eggs though, for with one accord every hen in the valley ceased to lay."

The Kingdon-Wards and their servants joined with others to escape to India, about 100 perilous miles away. They did so after a terrifying journey lasting more than two weeks. One of the hazards of the journey was rock avalanches which continued for months after the earthquake.

Jean Kingdon-Ward, describing one avalanche, says:

A wedge of granite broke away with a savage roar from the cliffs above the river, toppled over very, very slowly, then crashed hundreds of feet in one bound till it hit a projecting spur. There it exploded into smaller blocks, which fell hundreds of feet again down the sheer mountain wall, breaking into still smaller fragments as they bounced off the cliff once more and plunged headlong into the muddy waters of the Lohit. After the barrage ceased, the whole cliff smoked with clouds of pulverized rock, white and brown and yellow. No sooner was it clear again than the awful performance was repeated. The noise alone was terrifying.

Earthquake movements cause local compression of the soil. Daly says that after the Mino-Owari, Japan, earthquake of October 28, 1891, plots of ground which before were 48 feet long, measured only 30 feet. After some earthquakes there are numerous sand and water geysers. Sometimes they erupt with explosive force, sand and water shooting 40 feet into the air. In the California earthquake of 1906 sand was brought up from 80 feet below the surface and shot 20 feet above it. Sometimes gases force the sand upwards, and these geysers are known as "sand blows." Earthquakes also cause landslides (see page 225).

Earthquakes sometimes cause rivers to flow backward. In the New Madrid earthquakes of 1811 and 1812, the uplift of the bed and caving in of the banks caused a temporary rise in the water level of about six feet and a reversal of the current. According to Victor Hugo Boesen, some panic-stricken men, who took to their boat to escape the violence of the quake, found themselves "carried upstream with the speed of a galloping horse"!

It was in this great series of earthquakes that parts of a forest were

The Elements Rage   [212]

seen to fall, the trees dropping "like soldiers grounding their arms at the word of command." The shaking is so violent in some earthquakes that the soil round the roots loosens and trees fall down. Trees over fissures are sometimes split in half. In the New Madrid quakes, large oak trees were split for 40 feet up the center of the trunk, the halves standing on either side of the fissure.

In a violent earthquake the vertical motion shoots objects into the air. Large stones bounce up and down like peas on a drum and potatoes have been seen jumping out of the ground. During the Calabrian earthquake of March 5, 1783, a stone well shot eight feet above the ground. In the Japanese earthquake of September 1, 1923, wells jumped out of the ground, some of them rising 10 feet before breaking into fragments. Even more remarkable was the appearance, three feet above the surface, of some two-foot-wide wooden pillars. They had been submerged well below the surface, and proved to be supports for a bridge built in 1182 whose existence had been completely forgotten. During the Valdivia, Chile, earthquake of November 7, 1837, a great mast, which had been sunk over 30 feet, was lifted by the earthquake out of the ground so cleanly that the socket remained as round and regular as it was before. Some of these effects, however, may have been due to the differential settling of the ground.

During an earthquake at the seaport of Niigata, Japan, on June 16, 1964, part of a nearby island rose about five feet. Observers said it rose in a series of jolts, as though Neptune were cranking it up with a giant car jack!

It was the jolting action of an earthquake which was responsible for one of the most macabre incidents I have ever read. During the earthquake at Arica, Chile, on August 8, 1868, a cemetery on a mountainside was disturbed. The dead had been buried upright in concentric ranks, as in an amphitheater, all facing the same way. The nitre-impregnated soil had so preserved the bodies that awe-struck watchers suddenly saw uncovered on the mountainside a close-packed army of the dead—rank on rank of mummified corpses. Coupled with the appalling effects of the earthquake this was the last touch of horror to convince them that it was the end of the world (Tazieff).

A variety of sounds accompanies an earthquake—"the cracking and twisting of all creation." Davison (1921 and 1924) has classified these sounds in a scale ranging from intensities of one (the loudest) to seven, the sounds being likened to well-known noises. The first is: "Wagons, carriages, traction engines or trains passing, generally very rapidly, on hard ground, over a bridge or through a tunnel; the dragging of heavy boxes or furniture over the floor." The seventh point in the scale is of miscellaneous sounds which have been heard and likened to: "The trampling of many animals, an immense covey of partridges on the wing, the roar of a waterfall, a low pedal

Japanese quake lays one building on its side, tilts others. The earthquake occurred in northwest Japan on June 16, 1964. At Niigata, where this photograph was taken, nearly one-third of the buildings were either destroyed or damaged. *United Press International*

note on the organ, and the rending or settling together of huge masses of rock."

In some earthquakes the "awful rumblings" of the straining earth have been so deafening that the individual crashings of buildings and trees have not been heard as separate noises. But while most earthquakes are definitely noisy, others perform their deadly work in near silence.

Davison lists under the sixth intensity "the boom of a distant heavy gun." This is a mysterious earthquake sound which has been commented on by several observers. Jean Kingdon-Ward, in her account of the 1950 Assam earthquake, says that *after* the main earthquake shocks were over and all was quiet "from the northwest came the sound of heavy gunfire. It was as though a salvo of shells had been fired, and were bursting in quick succession somewhere up the valley of the Rong Thö Chu." The sounds were consecutive and occurred at regular intervals. The same "gunfire" was heard on the Assam plains, 200 miles from the epicenter.

As far as I know there is no explanation of these mysterious post-earthquake bangs, although Harpum tells me: "The boom of guns is very characteristic of earth tremors of the rock-fall type encountered in the collapse of underground workings. I have heard these and the gunfire description fits perfectly."

Strange noises and strange lights. These lights have been reported before, during, or after the earthquakes themselves: they include lightninglike flashes; luminous spots and narrow bands; diffuse lights in the air; globes, streamers and columns of fire; and numerous sparks and luminous vapors. The color of these lights varies, but the most common are red, blue, and white.

This is how Davison (1936) describes the lights which were seen during the Idu earthquake in Japan on November 26, 1930:

> In a few cases the lights were seen before 4:30 A.M., when the earthquake occurred. Near the epicenter they continued for at least an hour after that time. There is no doubt, however, that the lights were most conspicuous about the middle of the shock. As a rule the duration of each light seemed longer than that of lightning, and, according to some careful observers, more than a minute.
>
> Their form and color varied. Most of the lights were radiated like the rays of the rising sun, some were shaped like searchlights, others like fireballs. According to one observer, ball-shaped lights of great brilliancy were arranged in a straight row. In most cases the color was described as bluish, but reddish-yellow, yellow and reddish-blue lights were also seen. The lights were evidently brilliant. At one place, 30 miles from the epicenter, they were brighter than moonlight, and even in Tokyo a number of observers state that objects illuminated by them could be discerned.

The lights observed during this earthquake finally overcame the scepticism of seismologists. Two members of the Earthquake Research Institute of Japan saw the lights, and one of them, Kinkiti Musya, was so impressed that he made extensive inquiries and later published the results of his findings. He received nearly 1,500 accounts from eyewitnesses, including many sketches and outlines of the various lights. Some lights were observed 70 miles from the epicenter of the earthquake (see also Torahiko Terada).

The lights are not confined to the land. During the Sanriku earthquake in Japan on June 15, 1896, the sea partly receded and the bed of the ocean was seen to glow with a bluish-white luminescence. When another earthquake occurred in the same area on March 3, 1933, the same lights were seen. In addition, the crest of the waves emitted a dim continuous light, and the whole surface of the sea glittered. When the waves broke over the shore, the coastline was faintly illumined by bluish light.

What is the explanation of the lights? The sea lights are the most easily explained. They are almost certainly due to the violent agitation of the sea and ocean bed which disturbs tiny, luminescent organisms.

Earthquakes   [*215*]

What the Alaskan quake did to 4th Avenue, Anchorage. Part of the area dropped thirty feet. Notice sign of photographer's wrecked shop near center of photograph.   *Mac's Foto, Anchorage, Alaska*

The lights over the land are not susceptible of such a simple explanation. Some of them, no doubt, can be explained by causes having no connection with earthquakes, and others by secondary earthquake action. In the first series are lightning and meteors. In the second, disturbance of electricity supply lines, and earthquake-induced fires. Earthquakes generate considerable heat—trees overhanging a fault have been scorched. But when all these, and other suggestions, have been considered, there remain a number of light phenomena which still defy explanation. So, as one seismologist put it: "Earthquake lights constitute the darkest chapter in the history of seismology."

The most severe American earthquake since the magnitude scale was invented occurred in Alaska on Good Friday, March 27, 1964, when an intensity of about 8.5 was reached: an energy release of some 10^{23} ergs.[7] With an epicenter near Prince William Sound in eastern Alaska, the earthquake affected an area of some 100,000 square miles, caused damage of 750 million dollars and killed 115 people.

A notable aspect of this great earthquake was the tectonic warping. An area of more than 50,000 square miles was affected. In the northern half of the area, including Kenai Peninsula and Kodiak Island, the ground sank as much as eight feet. In the south, including most of Prince William Sound, it rose generally four to eight feet and in some places as much as 33 feet.

In Alaska's largest city, Anchorage, buildings and pavements dropped in places as much as 30 feet. The 470-mile-long Alaska Railroad was so buckled and twisted that it was estimated it would cost 25 million dollars to repair it.

Offshore there were submarine slides and giant waves (tsunami). These waves inundated shorelines to nearly 40 feet, causing loss of life and property along the southwest coastline of the Gulf of Alaska. Submarine landslides carried away the port facilities of Seward and Valdez. "Local violent surges of water, some of which were generated by submarine slides during the earthquake, left trimlines and swash marks [nearly] 175 feet above lower low water" (Arthur Grantz, et al., and William P. E. Graves).

Earthquakes are by no means unknown in Great Britain; there are records of at least 1,500. Davison (1924) wrote a book about them. I experienced one in Altrincham, Cheshire, on the night of December 29, 1944. The earthquake was extremely mild where I was, but elsewhere people were bounced out of bed, crockery was smashed, and ceilings cracked. But in all British earthquakes only two deaths have been reported: In the earthquake of April 6, 1580, which shook the whole of England and was particularly

---

[7] Another of about the same intensity occurred in Alaska on September 10, 1899. It was this earthquake which caused the greatest vertical displacement known. The most careful investigations proved that in one place the shores of Disenchantment Bay rose 47 feet 4 inches.

severe in London, stones fell from the top of a church and killed two apprentices. London earthquakes average about three a century (Ellis S. Hillman).

The most severe earthquake Britain has known within historic times occurred on April 22, 1884, and was felt over half of England. The shock lasted about ten seconds, and was accompanied by the noise of "thunder," "loads of stones falling," "wind," and "explosions." Small fissures appeared in the ground and water rose in wells. In Colchester, Essex, over 400 buildings were damaged and chimney pots were tumbled down for miles around. Within an area of 150 square miles of Colchester 1,213 buildings were damaged, many severely. Yet no one was hurt (Raphael Meldola).

Earthquakes have occurred in both Washington, D. C., and New York City. The U. S. Coast and Geodetic Survey tells me that during the last 230 years nine earthquakes have originated in the vicinity of Washington, and six distant earthquakes have been felt there. During the same time comparable figures for New York City are eight and seven. The most severe Washington quake was on August 31, 1886, when an intensity of 5 was recorded but little, if any, damage was done. The worst New York quake was on August 10, 1884, with an intensity of 7. Some damage to houses occurred in the Jamaica and Amityville districts.

But throughout the world, earthquakes, with their accompanying fires and floods, are the greatest of all natural destroyers of human life and property. Their only rivals are hurricanes and volcanoes, but neither of these has taken the same toll throughout the centuries as earthquakes, which, on average, kill some 15,000 people every year. The estimate of lives lost in the greatest earthquakes must be approximate (tallies don't always agree) but the following figures are approximately correct.

Greatest Earthquakes

Date	Location	Deaths	Remarks
January 23, 1556	Shensi, China	800,000	
October 11, 1737	Calcutta, India	300,000	
December 16, 1920	Kansu, China	180,000	
September 1, 1923	Kwanto, Japan (Tokyo & Yokohama)	140,000	Subsequent fires accounted for most of the casualties.

Despite these terrible facts people still live in potential earthquake areas. Concepción, Chile, has been razed by earthquakes five times in its history. After each devastation a new city has been built on the rubble of the old. Messina, Sicily, has had a similar history. After the initial terror people disregard the earthquake and carry on with their lives as before—as far as possible.

Trees and houses lean crazily against each other after the great Alaskan earthquake of Good Friday, 1964. *Mac's Foto, Anchorage, Alaska*

Some interesting observations on the psychological effects of an earthquake were made by William James, a pioneer psychologist. In 1906, when he was 64, he was visiting professor at Stanford University, California. Before leaving Harvard a friend said to him: "I hope they'll give you a touch of earthquake while you're there." At 5:30 A.M. on April 18, 1906, the wish was granted; the most famous earthquake in American history struck San Francisco, 35 miles from where James was staying.

[When] I felt the bed begin to waggle, my first consciousness was one of gleeful recognition of the nature of the movement. "By Jove," I said to myself, "here's B.'s old earthquake, after all!" And then, as it went *crescendo,* "And a jolly good one it is, too!" I said.

Sitting up involuntarily, and taking a kneeling position, I was thrown down on my face as it went *fortior* shaking the room exactly as a terrier shakes a rat. Then everything that was on anything else slid off to the floor, over went bureau and chiffonier with a crash, as the *fortissimo* was reached, plaster cracked, an awful roaring noise seemed to fill the outer air, and in an instant all was still again, save the soft babble of human voices from far and near that soon began to make itself heard, as the inhabitants in costumes *negligés* in various degrees sought the greater safety of the street and yielded to the passionate desire for sympathetic communication.

The thing was over, as I understand the Lick Observatory to have declared, in 48 seconds. To me it felt as if about that length of time, although

I have heard others say that it seemed to them longer. In my case, sensation and emotion were so strong that little thought, and no reflection or volition, were possible in the short time consumed by the phenomenon.

The emotion consisted wholly of glee and admiration; glee at the vividness which such an abstract idea or verbal term as "earthquake" could put on when translated into sensible reality and verified concretely; and admiration at the way in which the frail little wooden house could hold itself together in spite of such a shaking. I felt no trace whatever of fear; it was pure delight and welcome.

"Go it," I almost cried aloud, "and go it stronger!"

James went to San Francisco to observe how the catastrophe affected the victims. What impressed him most was (a) the rapid way people improvised to bring order out of the tremendous and unprecedented chaos and (b) "the universal equanimity. . . . Not a single whine or plaintive word did I hear from the hundred losers whom I spoke to. Instead of that there was a temper of helpfulness beyond the counting."

At Stanford University the prevailing emotion seems to have been gaiety.

Everybody was excited, but the excitement at first, at any rate, seemed to be almost joyous. Here at last was a *real* earthquake after so many years of harmless waggle! Above all, there was an irresistible desire to talk about it, and exchange experiences.

Most people slept outdoors for several subsequent nights, partly to be safer in case of a recurrence, but also to work off their emotion, and get the full unusualness out of the experience. The vocal babble of early-waking girls and boys from the gardens of the campus, mingling with the birds' songs and the exquisite weather, was for three or four days a delightful sunrise phenomenon.

Earthquake time on the campus. . . .

It seems difficult to find a single practical blessing for which most of us are indebted to earthquakes. Yet, strange as it sounds, an earthquake may be regarded as a safety measure, saving us from far worse disasters. Earthquakes release the stresses and strains of the rocks before they build up even more titanic forces, wreak even more devastation. As it is, Gutenberg and Richter say that the energy released every year by earthquakes averages between 10^{26} and 10^{27} ergs.

Earthquakes provide knowledge of the deep interior of the earth; the conduits of volcanoes reach only a comparatively short way. The quiverings of the thin-skinned earth alone reveal something, small though that is, of those vast depths that no man can reach. Philip M. Morse thus describes how this knowledge is gained:

The Elements Rage

Several hundred seismographs, set up over the world, listen to the earthquake wave as it echoes and re-echoes in the earth's interior. Since the earth is formed in onionlike layers above the core, and since each layer reflects and re-reflects the wave, unscrambling the recorded seismic record is a complicated procedure. . . . However, since we cannot see the interior, we must content ourselves with hearing, and, as a matter of fact, the calculated results show a surprising amount of detail.

The nearest approach to an immediate benefit from earthquakes comes from this kind of investigation, by which scientists seek to locate valuable minerals and other deposits beneath the earth's surface. In this geophysical prospecting, charges of dynamite are exploded in the earth and the waves from the miniature quake are studied with the help of portable seismographs. The speed of the waves varies. Passing through sand they travel at about one mile per second, through granite at nearly four. S-waves do not pass through molten rock, P-waves do. By studying the records, and with knowledge of the terrain and existing data, it is thus possible to learn something of what lies below the surface (Bullen).

These methods have led to the discovery of salt deposits in Texas, a success which showed that seismic prospecting was commercially worth while. Today it is used throughout the world, from tracing likely accumulations of oil and coal, to investigating dam sites and the polar icecaps. The oil companies alone spend about 400 million dollars a year on geophysical prospecting.

In the Nuclear Age every seismologist has a politician breathing down his neck. Why? The detection of underground tests is bedeviled by their similarity to earthquakes—both send similar waves pulsing through the earth. But improvements in detecting apparatus, and greater experience in interpreting the seismograph records will make distinction easier. In particular, arrays of seismographs facilitate detection and interpretation of earth movements. An array in Montana has 525 instruments deployed over a circle 120 miles in diameter.

A useful byproduct of all this activity will be an increase in knowledge of the earth and earthquakes, and a possible improvement in their prediction (Peter Stubbs).

Seismologists have given much attention to lessening the danger from earthquakes. Attempts have been made to forecast them, but the results so far have been unsatisfactory. The Japanese have given much study to preliminary tiltings of the ground, but it is still tragically true that one of the most impressive things about an earthquake is its unexpectedness.

Some people who have experienced several earthquakes say that the atmosphere seems unnaturally still shortly before the quake. On the evening before the Quetta earthquake of May 30, 1935, Betty Montgomery drew the attention of her husband—now Field Marshal Lord Montgomery—to a

Earthquakes   [*221*]

The Saada Hotel, Agadir, Morocco, before the earthquake of February
29, 1960.   *American Iron and Steel Institute*

skein of silk in her hand. Every strand stood out separately, stiff as wire. Coincidence? (Robert Jackson)

A brief warning of a coming earthquake is often given by animals.
They show unusual signs of alarm seconds, and sometimes minutes, before
the main shock occurs. Pheasants, particularly, have frequently been heard
to call before an earthquake was felt by humans. In the Second World War
pheasants called at the fall of distant bombs of which the birds' human
neighbors were unaware.

About half an hour before the earthquake at Sofiadhes, Greece, on
April 30, 1954, storks were seen to take to the air in an agitated manner.
Many villagers, noticing this, feared a catastrophe was coming and took to
the open, thus saving their lives.

Although it appears contradictory to the above, some people have
claimed that before a quake a marked hush descends on the animal kingdom,
birds and insects in particular ceasing their normal activities. One suggestion
is that they are alerted by long-distance vibrations.

Although seismologists have so far failed to devise any accurate means
of forecasting earthquakes, they at least point out areas where earthquakes
are likely. But what if it is impossible to avoid living in an earthquake area?
Japan, for example, is exceptionally earthquake-prone, and nothing less than
a mass evacuation could ensure immunity from the disastrous quakes which
periodically devastate the country. In such regions the architect, in col-

The Saada Hotel—After.   *American Iron and Steel Institute*

laboration with the seismologist, can do much to reduce the danger. The best foundation on which to build in order to resist earthquakes is hard rock; the worst is soft ground or "made" land—filled-in shallow land alongside rivers, lakes or sea.

No building is completely proof against earthquakes.[8] If one were sited immediately over the epicenter, and the earth fissured widely beneath, it would probably be torn apart as a man breaks an orange. Some types of buildings are particularly vulnerable, others are very resistant to earthquake damage. Model buildings are tested on "shaking platforms" where, as far as possible, conditions in an earthquake are simulated. From such tests, and actual experiences in earthquakes, the most earthquake-resistant types of structure have been evolved. The result? If you live in an earthquake zone choose either a tent or a skyscraper! Wood-frame structures are also recommended, as they have a good record in earthquakes.

Buildings with thick and heavy walls are bad because it is difficult to give them the necessary strength to resist the lateral stresses induced by an earthquake. In violent quakes such buildings are shaken down and bury those living within. Brick buildings, especially if not very well built, often collapse. Heavily tiled roofs are a menace; the shaking sends the tiles crashing down on the heads of the people below.

---

[8] If money were no object, however, a virtually earthquake-proof building could be built: a steel boxlike structure (C. R. Enock).

Earthquakes   [223]

Well-built simple structures often come through earthquakes unscathed. During the Charleston, South Carolina, earthquake of August 31, 1886, a Negro family in a log cabin slept unharmed right through the quake. But wooden buildings in thickly populated areas can be very dangerous because of the fires which break out after nearly all severe earthquakes.

The conditions governing the building of earthquake-resistant structures vary according to the geology of the area. It is estimated that to erect an earthquake-resistant building instead of a normal one of good quality adds, at most, 7 per cent to the cost. In many earthquake-prone countries the building codes make some protection obligatory. And the town planners should see that the streets are wide enough to allow buildings to collapse outward without crashing into those opposite.

Both Concepción and Messina have been rebuilt as earthquake-resistant cities with remarkable results. Concepción had five major shocks in May 1960, yet suffered extremely little damage. Messina has not again undergone trial by earthquake but in November 1943 about 4,000 tons of Allied high explosive rained down on the city. Inevitably, many people were killed, but the structural damage was astonishingly light. Not a single building was condemned as beyond repair.

Modern American skyscrapers are good examples of earthquake-resistant buildings; they are safe unless close to the epicenter of one of the highest magnitude. What happens then may be judged from an eyewitness description of the 1923 Japanese earthquake by Henry W. Kinney, an experienced American journalist and editor. He was in a train approaching Yokohama.

> I glanced out just as the stone face of an embankment shot down over the tracks. It did not slide or tumble down: it literally shot down, as if compelled by a sudden, gigantic pressure from the top, the stones spreading in a twinkling over the wide right-of-way. A four-story concrete building vanished, disintegrated in the flash of an eye. Tiles cascaded with precipitate speed from the roofs. The one predominating idea that struck the mind was the almost incredible rapidity of the destruction.

It was this earthquake which tested the famous Imperial Hotel in Tokyo, designed by Frank Lloyd Wright during the First World War. It came through this terrible earthquake practically unscathed—as did the vast majority of modern buildings. It was the subsequent fires which caused the havoc (Noel F. Busch). But not to the Imperial. Wright had insisted that the hotel should have a large ornamental pool. When the earthquake destroyed the city's water services this provided the water which saved the hotel.

What to do in an earthquake? First turn off all naked lights. Then get under something that will protect you from falling debris and count to 40—although occasionally earthquakes last much longer than this. Then come out and get into open ground—fast. Jean Kingdon-Ward says: "There is a powerful instinct that urges one to get out of doors in an earthquake." Incidentally, Leet says that in an earthquake there is a curious psychological twist which makes each person think that he's at the center of the disturbance.

Landslides are often started by earthquakes.[9] During the Calabria, Italy, earthquake of February 5, 1783, acres of land moved half a mile across a ravine. Yet flowers and corn, large oak and olive trees were unharmed. They continued to flourish as well at the bottom of the ravine as their companions—from which the landslide had separated them—500 feet above and half a mile away. Thus the answer to Macbeth's question (on hearing the Apparition say that he would never be vanquished until Birnam Wood came to Dunsinane Hill): "Who can impress the forest, bid the tree unfix his earthbound root?" is "A landslide."

The Japanese earthquake of 1923 caused severe landslides on steep slopes. Part of the forest reserves on Mt. Hakone and Mt. Tanzawa slid away, and one tremendous landslide swept down a mountain valley at 60 m.p.h., obliterating a village and wrecking a railway line. Elsewhere a mass of red loam swept into a mountain stream, forming an avalanche of mud 200 yards wide and some 50 feet deep which carried all before it. Houses, railway tracks, and bridges were swept away and, together with a train carrying over 200 passengers, were sunk in Sagami Bay. The water for six miles out to sea was colored red and brown (David Niddrie, and Davison, 1931).

The greatest landslide in North America within historic times occurred on June 23, 1925, in Wyoming's Gros Ventre Mountains, near the southern boundary of the Yellowstone National Park.[10] Heavy spring rains moistened the clay in an underlying section on the side of a valley. Eventually, the section slipped and an enormous mass of sandstone rock covered with forest—an estimated 50 million cubic yards—slid across the valley and rammed against the opposite side to a height of 350 feet. This, in turn, dammed the Gros Ventre River, which then formed a huge lake three miles long. Nearly two years later part of the dam burst and a great flood, 15 feet high, swept down the valley, drowning the little village of Kelly. There is still a

---

[9] Landslides are a separate subject, although closely linked with other geological sciences. Technically, landslides range from almost imperceptible earth movements to the most violent rock falls. I have written about the latter in the Avalanches chapter; other violent landslide movements are dealt with here. For a detailed discussion on landslides, see Edwin B. Eckel.

[10] A severe earthquake occurred in the Park itself on August 17, 1959. It shook some 40 million cubic yards of rock from Madison Canyon, damaged Hebgen Lake, destroyed property and killed 28 people (see U. S. Geological Survey Professional Paper No. 435).

Eighty million tons of rock dam Madison River and state highway after Montana earthquake of August 17, 1959.   *U. S. Forest Service*

lake at Gros Ventre, a permanent memorial to America's greatest landslide (William C. Alden).

Slides, or flows, of various kinds occur in special conditions. Sudden heavy rain falling on mud on a steep gradient sometimes causes a mudflow— a huge mud river with tremendous carrying power. Heavy rain sometimes bursts bogs, unleashing a flow of half-liquid peat. Such bog bursts occur in Ireland, as may be expected, but one of the worst was in Stanley, Falkland Islands. Following heavy rains in June 1886, a peat river, four to five feet deep, flowed through the town. Streets were blocked, houses wrecked, and people killed (references in C. F. Stewart Sharpe).

One of the most curious—and dangerous—slides occurs with quick clay, which can change quickly from a solid to a liquid. It is composed of very fine mineral particles and water. If a small cube of quick clay is held in the open hand and shaken, it becomes moist and loses its shape. If a lump that has been supporting 20 or so pounds is put in a perfectly dry beaker and stirred, it will turn liquid and can be poured out. (This property of thixotropy is used in nondrip paints.)

So in nature. Normally, quick clay is as firm and solid as earth, supporting houses, offices, factories—a whole township. But, on rare occasions, an earthquake shock or other disturbance will turn sloping ground that has been solid for thousands of years into a soupy lake which slides away, carrying everything with it.

The Elements Rage   [226]

Result of a quick clay slide at Surte, Sweden, on September 29, 1950.
Swedish Geotechnical Institute

On November 12, 1955, part of the center of Nicolet, Quebec, slid away into the Nicolet River. Another quick-clay disaster occurred at Vaerdalen near Trondheim, Norway, during the night of May 19, 1893. About one square mile, involving about 60 million cubic yards, slid into a valley. The earth was turned into a heavy liquid that washed down the valley toward the fjord below. A score of farms were destroyed and 111 people killed. Some farmers were rescued after sailing 3½ miles down the clay river perched on the roof of their house (Per Holmsen, H. Reusch, and Paul F. Kerr and Richard S. Liebling).

In Norway during the Second World War, several quick-clay slides were triggered by bombing. In southern Norway, British bombers, trying to hit a nitrogen factory, started a slide over an area of some 50,000 square yards which carried away ten houses. And near Petsamo, in the north, Russian bombers set off a huge slide which swept down a valley, destroying a bridge, some military depots and artillery positions.

I. Th. Rosenqvist, Professor of Geology in the University of Oslo, who tells me this, adds: "These two incidents are all I know about bomb-triggered slides, and in many cases heavy blasting of bedrock has taken place in the neighbourhood of quick clays without any slides being caused."

The greatest landslides in recorded history were those of December 16, 1920, in Kansu, central China, near the Tibetan border. Following severe earthquakes, landslides occurred on a monumental scale over an area of 30,000 square miles comprising ten cities and numerous villages. In one area there were 17 immense landslides within a 20-mile semicircle.

The nature of the soil and the terrain explains what happened. Loose earth carpeted hills which, shaken by the earthquake, sent billions (British) of cubic yards of soil cascading into valleys and plains. The scars left by some of the slides were so clean that they appeared to have been scooped out by a gigantic trowel.

The Chinese coined the phrase *Shan tso-liao,* meaning "The mountains walked," to describe the fantastic results of this greatest of all known landslides. The phrase was almost literally true in some areas. Upton Close and Elsie McCormick, in their firsthand report in *The National Geographic Magazine,* say: "One astonished peasant looked out of his window in the morning to find that a high hill had moved onto the homestead, stopping its line of march within a few feet of his hut." Elsewhere a mountain slid into a valley—complete with the temple which had been erected on the mountain-top!

But the monstrous avalanches of soil which slid into the village-dotted valley were the real destroyers. Some villages were blotted out entirely: men, women, children, livestock, and dwellings buried forever under an immense blanket of earth. Sometimes those on the outskirts of inhabited areas escaped the deadly brown flood, and a handful owed their lives to happenings as fantastic as any in the whole record of Nature's violence.

Seven great landslides fell into the three-mile-long Valley of the Dead, wiping out the entire population—except three men and two dogs. They were carried on the crest of one slide, whirled in the giant maelstrom which formed when several slides met, and landed on the slope of a hill—together with their house, orchard, and threshing floor. In another valley a farmer and his two sons, together with their farmstead, were carried on top of the landslide for about three-quarters of a mile.

The force of these landslides was colossal. Whole sections of roadway were transported bodily across country. In the Valley of the Dead two sections of an ancient, well-packed highway, including the bordering trees, were swept across a stream and set intact on top of a mass of loose earth. Elsewhere a slide plowed deep beneath a roadway and deposited it virtually intact nearly a mile away, complete with trees and the birds' nests in their branches!

So much for the effects of earthquakes on land, but more occur beneath the sea (seaquake) than the land. This is not surprising as the sea covers about 70 per cent of the earth's surface. These seaquakes do little direct damage beyond breaking submarine cables and disturbing bottom-feeding fish. Sometimes the fish migrate to more equable surroundings, thus affecting fisheries. Davison (1938) says:

The Elements Rage

On fish, the results of a strong earthquake are . . . generally fatal, for fish receive the blow, as of a dynamite shock, over the whole surface of their bodies at once. . . . For several days after the Assam earthquake of 1897 the rivers of the Garo Hills were choked with thousands of dead fish brought down from the upper reaches.

Seaquakes have two indirect, or secondary, effects. Such quakes, as well as some earthquakes occurring near the sea, displace unconsolidated material on steep slopes. One result of such displacement is to cause "turbidity currents." The term is misleading, but it refers to the avalanches of mud, sand, and sludge which occasionally cascade down the slopes of the continental shelves, and other submarine prominences. It is believed that in some of these submarine slides the initial speed is 50 m.p.h. Such a speed, although held for only a fraction of the total path, is maintained against the tremendous braking power of water. Seaslides have been proved to travel as much as 300 miles along the ocean floor.

Paul F. Kerr suggests that marine quick clay is responsible for some submarine slides. One on November 18, 1929, south of Newfoundland, was 230 miles wide and flowed for some 400 miles, much of the distance along the comparatively flat ocean floor.

Submarine slides are one of the chief hazards of submarine cables; the Newfoundland slide cut 12 cables. Cables raised after a breakdown are sometimes found to be twisted into a shapeless mass—the result of being turned over and over in the slide. Seaslides can also, of course, be a fatal hazard to submarines. (See Bruce C. Heezen, and Francis P. Sheppard for a discussion of submarine slides.)

The second, and much more dangerous, effect of a displacement of the ocean bed is that it may generate large sea waves that race across the oceans at enormous speed. They are often called tidal waves, although they have nothing to do with tides. To avoid confusion oceanographers call them by the Japanese word *tsunami,* whether the waves are caused by quakes or volcanoes (see p. 265).

Strangely enough, tsunami (the word is plural) are virtually undetectable at sea. Although from crest to crest they sometimes measure 600 miles, their height from trough to crest is only one or two feet. But it is the tsunami's speed which is remarkable, and the greater the depth of water the greater the speed. A wave driven by the strongest wind rarely travels more than 60 m.p.h. Tsunami have traveled across the ocean at 500 m.p.h., or even faster. As the tsunami approaches land the speed is greatly reduced.

The tsunami following the Sanriku, Japan, earthquake of June 15, 1896, was recorded on tide gauges at San Francisco, nearly 5,000 miles away, 10½ hours later. Its average speed across the Pacific was therefore nearly 480 m.p.h. Tsunami from other seaquakes have been recorded 10,000 miles away.

Kamehameha Avenue, Hilo, Hawaii, before the "Big Wave" (tsunami) of May 23, 1960.   *The Hilo Tribune-Herald*

Unlike wave-driven winds, tsunami do not affect ships at sea. When the Sanriku tsunami struck, fishermen 20 or so miles offshore noticed nothing strange, not even unusual swells, and were quite unprepared for the devastation that met their eyes at the end of the day when they sailed into offshore waters strewn with bodies and the wreckage of houses. This tsunami swept away 10,000 houses and left 27,000 dead.

Often, strange as it sounds, the first sign of an approaching tsunami is the sea going out. Why? Because there is an abrupt collapse of part of the ocean bed which, in turn, causes the sea above it to drop, leaving a de-

After the wave, high as a two-story building, swept across the town. An eyewitness said: "The roar of the massive wall of water blended with the crashing of dozens of stores and apartments and theatres and restaurants— and with the screams of dozens of persons for whom the final noisy warning came in the same moment with death." About sixty people died, but the bodies of some were never found.   *The Hilo Tribune-Herald*

pression on the surface. The surrounding seas rush to fill the depression, there is a wild turmoil of waters and then the seas flow back again, but higher and faster than they went out. Often this process is repeated several times following a seaquake. The first return wave generally appears within 15 minutes although Heck (1947) says that two hours have elapsed before its return. Many people have died because the return wave came before they expected it.

A tsunami's effect on reaching shore varies according to its violence (speed) and the nature of the coast. A medium tsunami crashing against high cliffs will probably damage nothing but objects—and people—on the beach. The same tsunami crashing against a shallow shore will sweep inland and, in built-up areas, cause great destruction.

But the greatest violence occurs when a tsunami, traveling "as fast as a galloping horse," sweeps into a funnel-shaped bay and the sea piles up to crash inland as a vast wall of water. If the tsunami is already of exceptional violence the resulting disaster is unimaginable. Heck (1936) says of such a tsunami "it is the most spectacular and appalling of all earthquake phenomena."

The sea defense does not exist which can repel a great tsunami: a vast wall of water 50, 100, even 200 feet high, weighing untold millions of tons, crashing inland at 100 or even 150 m.p.h. A tsunami of 210 feet was recorded at Cape Lopatka on the southern tip of Kamchatka, Siberia, in 1737. The height of the vast majority of tsunami, however, is much less than this.

In 1947 Heck published a list of tsunami. From the earliest in 479 B.C. there were 270 which were sufficiently violent to have left their mark on history. It is suggested that a Mediterranean tsunami may have contributed to Noah's Flood (see p. 166).

By far the highest waves occur in bays and enclosed bodies of water, when a vast mass suddenly plunges down. These waves are not strictly tsunami, although earthquakes often cause the fall of material. On September 13, 1936, at Loen Lake, Norway, about a million and a quarter cubic yards of rock fell into the water, sending a wave to a maximum height of 230 feet crashing onto the opposite shore (Gunnar Holmsen).

But this and all other known records for giant waves is surpassed by those which sometimes race across Lituya Bay; a T-shaped, ice-scoured, nearly landlocked bay on the northeast shore of the Alaskan Panhandle. Deep water, precipitous topography at the head of the bay, plus ice and rock slides, appear to be the reasons. At least four times in 100 years these great waves have swept high into the forests lining the bay, felling thousands of large trees, sweeping the fjordlike sides clear to the bare rock.

The greatest wave of all, and by far the highest in the recorded history of man, occurred here on July 9, 1958. An earthquake shook 40 million cubic yards of rock, weighing 90 million tons and falling from a maximum height of about 3,000 feet, into Gilbert Inlet at the head of the bay. This is roughly equal to the simultaneous launching of 2,000 large battleships from a slipway half a mile high.

The tremendous rockfall sent a vast wave racing across the bay at a

The result of the greatest wave in the recorded history of man. On July 9, 1958, ninety million tons of rock fell from a height of about half a mile into Lituya Bay, Alaska. A wall of water shot a third of a mile up the opposite slope, stripping it to the bare rock. Four square miles of forest were detroyed; some trees were four feet in diameter.   *U. S. Coast and Geodetic Survey*

speed of about 100 m.p.h., and caused water to surge over the opposite wall of the inlet to a maximum height of 1,740 feet—a third of a mile, nearly twice the height of the Eiffel Tower, over three times the height of the Washington Monument! Four square miles of forest, extending inland for 3,600 feet from the high-tide shoreline, were destroyed. Large trees with diameters of four feet were either washed out or snapped off near the ground (Don J. Miller).

Ships caught in a big tsunami near shore are helpless. During the great earthquake which destroyed Port Royal, Jamaica, on June 7, 1692, immense waves swept over the town. They lifted a large English frigate, the *Swan*, which was lying on her side in the careening slipway, and carried her across the town. Many people struggling in the water above the housetops were able to grab the *Swan's* cables and rigging and were hauled aboard. Eventually the frigate reached the sea on the other side of the sandspit on which Port Royal was built, having miraculously survived a sea journey over a town while picking up passengers on the way (Niddrie).

A vivid description of what it is like to be caught on a ship in a tsunami

Earthquakes   [233]

has been given by Rear Admiral L. G. Billings. At the time he was a lieutenant aboard the flat-bottomed U. S. Navy steamship *Wateree* when she was off Arica, Chile, on August 8, 1868.

> We were startled by a terrific noise on shore, as of a tremendous roar of musketry, lasting several minutes. Again the trembling earth waved to and fro, and this time the sea receded until the shipping was left stranded, while as far to seaward as our vision could reach we saw the rocky bottom of the sea, never before exposed to human gaze, with struggling fish and monsters of the deep left high and dry.
> The round-bottomed ships keeled over on their beam ends, while the *Wateree* rested easily on her floor-like bottom; and when the returning sea, not like a wave, but rather like an enormous tide, came sweeping back, rolling our unfortunate companion ships over and over, leaving some bottom up and others masses of wreckage, the *Wateree* rose easily over the tossing waters, unharmed.

The main return wave did not strike until the evening. The *Wateree* was overwhelmed, but struggled through to the surface. She was carried by the immense waters like a matchbox on a fast-flowing stream.

The wave carried her three miles up the coast and nearly two miles inland. She was lifted over sand dunes, a valley and a railroad track, and finally deposited high in a little cove. Billings says that they found near them the wreck of another ship with her anchor chains wound round her as many times as they would go, indicating that she had been rolled over and over by the force of the water. Had the *Wateree* not been a flat-bottomed ship she would almost certainly have perished.

chapter 10

Volcanoes 💥

An erupting volcano is Nature's greatest spectacle. The vast display of energies; the violent uprush of liquid rock and gases from deep below the surface to miles above it; the shake and tremble of the earth; the flash of lightning and the roar of thunder; the brilliant firework display of the glowing and exploding lava; and the multitudinous sounds of the belching crater—these make an ineffaceable impression upon the mind of the beholder.

Frank A. Perret, after witnessing an eruption of one of the most famous volcanoes in the world, Vesuvius in 1906, wrote: "Strongest of impressions was . . . that of an infinite dignity in every manifestation of this stupendous releasing of energy. No words can describe the majesty of its unfolding."

Perret was present before, during, and after the eruption and was thus able to study it in detail. His monograph (1924) is one of the classics of geological literature.

Vesuvius was almost ready to go in May 1905, but then part of the side of the main cone fissured, releasing some of the pent-up lava. But 11 months later, in April 1906, she literally blew her top. Molten lava issued from the crater on April 4, and thereafter there were continuous eruptions for days.

After midnight on April 7 there were violent earthquake shocks, and terrific explosions in the crater. It was impossible for observers to stand still. The whole of Vesuvius was humming and vibrating like a gigantic boiler under a colossal head of steam.

Millions of tons of lava, ash, and dust-charged gas were exploding from the crater, accompanied by violent electrical discharges: "flashing arcs," St. Elmo's fire, and other forms of lightning. The lightning flashes forking through the dark volcanic clouds added greatly to the impressiveness of the scene.[1]

---

[1] "Flashing arcs" sometimes occur when a powerful explosion propagates a spherical sound wave which reflects the light falling on it. The cause of volcanic lightning is obscure. It was thought friction in the dust cloud caused it, but C. B. Moore tells me: "Our observations at Surtsey [see p. 253] clearly show that the electrification is not generated in the dust clouds above the volcano; the particles are already charged when they are ejected from the crater."

A cauliflower-shaped dust-cloud towers miles above Vesuvius during the eruption in March, 1944.   *U. S. Navy*

After two days of violent eruption, during which the upper portion of the cone unfolded in all directions, the throat of Vesuvius appeared to be clear. Then, from unknown depths, there rushed up a tremendous blast of volcanic gas which shot seven miles into the sky, where it formed a gigantic cauliflower-shaped cloud. The compression of the gas while imprisoned in the earth, and its acceleration within the shaft of the volcano, must have been colossal. This enormous blow-off lasted throughout the daylight hours of April 8, accompanied by a Niagara-like roar.

At times the dust clouds were lighted by incandescent jets of molten lava and vivid lightning flashes, so that they formed a gigantic torch, miles high, which illuminated the Gulf of Naples from Capri to Cape Miseno.

The next stage in this grand display was the emission of jet-black clouds. Near the volcano it was pitch dark; Perret says that it was impossible to see a compass held in the hand. Fine dust penetrated everywhere.[2]

---

[2] During the 1822 eruption of Vesuvius the dust particles became progressively finer with each ejection. At the end they were so fine that they penetrated the finest cracks and found their way into locked boxes, drawers and similar receptacles (G. J. Symons).

A gigantic pall hung over Naples and the surrounding country for a fortnight, and men might well have thought "the last eternal night of story had settled on the world"—the words used by Pliny the Younger to describe the Vesuvian eruption of his day. Lightning forked through the darkness, ash rained down upon the landscape, and hot dust avalanches plunged down the mountainsides.

Water vapor condensed in the cloud over the crater and formed soft mud balls, some as large as hens' eggs. Finally, rain fell in torrents, and streams of mud flowed across the surrounding country, causing great damage and some loss of life. Then, on April 30, after $3\frac{1}{2}$ weeks of almost ceaseless activity, Vesuvius was quiet.

Before dealing with the mechanism of volcanic eruptions it is necessary to have a general picture of the nature of the earth's interior which is as follows.

Broadly, the composition of the continental part of the earth's surface is: first, a thin covering of earth, sand and clay which averages less than $\frac{1}{10}$ of a mile thick. Next there is a layer of various kinds of rock which have an average density and composition similar to that of granite. This granitic layer grades into another which has the density and composition of basalt—the common dark volcanic lava. The Giant's Causeway, Northern Ireland, and Fingal's Cave, western Scotland, are composed of basalt. Much of the north of the British Isles shows the results of ancient volcanic action. The islands of Skye and Mull were covered with great sheets of molten lava. The granite masses of the Isle of Arran and of the Mourne Mountains belong to the same volcanic episode.

The average depth of the combined granitic and basaltic layers of the continents is about 20 miles, but is deeper under mountain ranges. Between the basaltic layer and the next great section of the earth's interior, is a surface known as the Mohorovicic discontinuity (Moho for short). Andrija Mohorovicic was a Yugoslav seismologist who, on examining the records of the Croatian earthquake of October 8, 1909, discovered that as the shock waves passed through the earth, they suddenly changed direction and speed. This change occurred when the shock waves hit the bottom of the basaltic layer. It has since been discovered that there are similar discontinuities at deeper levels.

Beneath the Moho is the mantle, a great section of heavy rocks extending some 1,800 miles. Then there is an outer core of molten nickel-iron 1,300 miles thick, surrounding the earth's inner core which is a huge solid nickel-iron sphere with a diameter of 850 miles.

Beneath the oceans there is no granitic layer, only sediment some half-mile thick. As I write (1965) an attempt is being made to drill through the sediment at the ocean bottom into the basalt—Project Mohole (William E. Benson). The basaltic layer below this is three to six miles thick. Incidentally, the land area of the earth is about 58 million, and that of the sea 139 million square miles.

Temperature increases steadily with depth, but there are wide variations in different places. Generally, a temperature of 100° C., the boiling point of water, is reached at some 10,000 feet, about two miles down. A temperature of 177° C. was recorded nearly five miles down. This was in a fruitless search for oil by the Phillips Petroleum Company in Pecos County, Texas. On October 12, 1958, after drilling for 732 days, the drill bit 4.8 miles into the earth—the deepest hole ever made by man and still only a thousandth of the distance to the center—the equivalent of a mosquito stinging an elephant!

Despite the extremely high temperatures of the earth's interior, the popular conception of a liquid mass of fire at the heart of the earth is no longer held by geologists. They point out that with increase in depth there is also increase in pressure, and this is so great in the center that it must keep the potentially molten rocks in a solid state. The pressure at the earth's center is estimated to be about 26,000 tons to the square inch, and the temperature about that of the sun's surface, some 6,000° C.

Although the pressures deep in the earth are, of course, beyond anything man can achieve mechanically, pressures equal to those existing hundreds of miles down have been duplicated in presses in engineering laboratories. Pressures have been exerted hydraulically equal to those reached from 20 to nearly 600 miles deep in the earth—about a maximum of 3,000 tons to the square inch.[3] Sometimes the presses themselves cannot stand the strain and parts fly off with explosive violence. Not surprisingly, the operators are protected by heavy steel shields.

Immense pressures have queer effects on familiar substances, and happenings in the laboratory give some idea of what happens deep in the earth. Steel stretches to 300 times its original length; marble flows like tar; ice becomes so dense that it will not float; and water, usually regarded as incompressible, is squeezed to half its normal volume—quart into pint pot at last! (F. Barrows Colton)

Although, in general, the earth is believed to be solid rock for nearly 2,000 miles, there are pockets, known as magma chambers, much nearer the surface. The conduits of volcanoes reach down to these chambers which lie from about 3 to 100 miles below the surface.

By processes which are still not fully understood the movement of the magma—a mixture of gases and molten rock—occasionally increases, probably as a result of earth movements. The magma expands, forces it way to the surface through conduits and there is another volcanic eruption. As

---

[3] Momentarily, pressures up to about 30,000 tons to the square inch can be attained (George A. W. Boehm).

far back in geological time as it is possible to go, volcanoes have lived and died, leaving their lava-strewn monuments across the face of the earth.

With few exceptions the deep fractures in the crust which give rise to volcanoes (and many earthquakes) are found today in two great belts. The first is the Pacific Girdle of Fire (the margins of the Pacific), where some two-thirds of all the world's active volcanoes are found. The other belt runs from Central America to the East Indies. Most volcanic regions are near the sea, especially where there are great variations in altitude; high mountains alongside deep ocean.

Estimates vary, but probably not fewer than 500 volcanoes have been active in historic times. They may be dormant for hundreds of years, then erupt. The volcanic island of Tristan da Cunha was dormant from its discovery in 1506, yet erupted in 1961 after an interval of over 450 years.

As about three-quarters of the earth's surface is beneath the sea it is virtually certain that there are many more volcanoes on the ocean floor. Of these, about 60 are known to have erupted within the last 200 years or so. Authorities differ about the exact number of both land and sea volcanoes.

Today, active land volcanoes range from cones about the size of a haystack to some of the loftiest mountains in the world. Their mode of activity differs considerably, but they all have one feature in common—a conduit which connects with the magma chamber. The matter ejected from a volcano consists of gas and either dust, liquid (lava), or solid rock, or a combination of these, varying with the volcano and type of eruption. Gas is always present and some 20 different kinds have been detected. Steam is the most abundant.

Incidentally, it has been suggested that volcanic gases and temperatures may have played a part in helping to create the conditions for the origin of life on this planet (Sidney W. Fox).

The word volcano comes from Vulcan, the blacksmith of the gods. The ancients believed that he had his forge deep in the earth and sometimes its fire and flames broke through the surface. The entrance to the forge was believed to be on the island of Vulcano off northern Sicily in the Mediterranean.

The main force in a volcanic eruption is gas, especially steam. Underground water is heated by hot rocks and red-hot magma. The physics of water explain the rest; when it turns to steam its volume increases about one thousand times. It is as if vast stores of dynamite were suddenly exploded inside the volcano. Most of the lava breaks through fissures at the sides of the volcanic cone rather than by flowing over the top.

Volcanoes erupt in different ways, from a comparatively mild outflow of lava to tremendous violence. Some volcanoes exhibit several of these types during the course of one eruption. The main types of eruption are as follows:

A seething lake of lava in Kilauea's four square mile crater.
U. S. Information Service

Hawaiian: the discharge of streams of liquid lava but with no explosive liberation of gases or ejection of fragmentary material. The action is sometimes extremely rapid, with lava cascading down the sides of the crater at 25 m.p.h.

The name for this phase derives from Hawaii, with its two volcanoes, Mauna Loa and Kilauea. Mauna Loa is the greatest volcano in the world. Rising from a base over 70 miles wide on the ocean floor, it towers nearly 29,000 feet, 13,675 feet being above sea level. Its crater is not funnel-shaped like most volcanoes, but is a vast flat-floored cauldron (caldera) with vertical sides. When Mauna Loa erupts, great fountains of molten lava shoot upward, sometimes reaching a height of 1,000 feet. When the crater overflows a torrent of lava pours down the volcano's sides in the typical Hawaiian phase of volcanic activity.

J. D. Dana wrote of an eruption of Mauna Loa which he witnessed: "Its deep unearthly roar waxed louder and louder as we drew nearer the action, until it resembled the roar of the ocean's billows when driven by the force of a hurricane against a rock-bound coast, or like the deafening roar of Niagara." He says that the intense heat (over 1,000° C.) created miniature tornadoes which "stalked about like so many sentinels, bidding defiance to the daring visitor."

The immense temperatures of molten rock and other volcanic materials

The Elements Rage [240]

cannot, of course, be measured by ordinary thermometers. An approximate temperature, however, can be obtained by an optical pyrometer, used in steel furnaces to determine the heat of molten metal. By matching the color of the object, *e.g.*, steel or lava, against a scale on the pyrometer a temperature reading is obtained. The greatest known temperature for lava is about 1,400° C., recorded at Vesuvius. The temperature is retained for years in a big lava flow. Perret (1935) says that he once broke open a lava block which was dead black outside. Inside it was "brightly incandescent, a full cherry red in sunlight, causing wood to ignite at a distance of six inches."

Strombolian: a continuous but comparatively mild volcanic discharge. The name derives from Stromboli, in the Lipari Islands north of Sicily, which is known as "The Lighthouse of the Mediterranean." It has been continuously in action at least since before the dawn of human history. Mild explosions occur at the rate of one to 30 per hour, lava and gas being thrown into the air. John Harpum tells me: "Volcanic bombs [lumps of lava] are very common on Stromboli. I have counted ten bombs in the space of two minutes, rolling down the side of the cone and hissing into the sea."

Vulcanian: a much more explosive type of volcanic action. Magma gradually accumulates in the heart of the volcano over a period of years, the exposed lava at the top of the conduit acting as a plug which prevents it from erupting. When sufficient magma has accumulated at the base, the explosive gases and boiling lava burst the rocky plug and the volcano erupts. Masses of solid and liquid rock burst out and great cauliflower-shaped clouds of vapor and dust form over the crater.

During the Second World War there was considerable speculation on the efficacy of volcano bombing, especially Vesuvius and the Japanese volcanoes.

There is a moment in every Vulcanian phase when the resistance of the plug of exposed lava at the top of the conduit, and the force exerted by the accumulated gases at the base of the volcano, are about equal. It is possible that a very heavy bomb or bombs dropped on the plug at this time might precipitate an eruption. But volcanologists are sceptical about the military value of such operations (see L. Don Leet).

Bombing volcanoes is, of course, not new; lava flows have been bombed to prevent them from engulfing buildings (Jagger, 1945).

Vesuvian: combines features of the Strombolian and Vulcanian types but is more explosive. There is a violent outburst of magma highly charged with gas. This chapter opened with a description of a typical Vesuvian eruption.

Plinian: violent Vesuvian eruptions sometimes culminate in a stupen-

Kilauea spouts molten lava like a gigantic firework display.   *Süddeuts-*
cher Verlag

dous blast of gas which shoots miles into the stratosphere (see p. 236). The
name comes from Pliny the Younger, who first recorded such an outburst
during the eruption of Vesuvius in A.D. 79. The material from such eruptions reaches the jet streams and is often carried great distances.

Icelandic: the discharge from fissures of great volumes of fluid basaltic
lava which spread over the adjacent countryside, for thousands of square
miles in some eruptions. The only examples of such flows in historic times
have been in Iceland, which consists entirely of volcanic material, mostly
basaltic lava.

One of the greatest Icelandic eruptions began on June 8, 1783. Tremendous explosions came from the area near Mount Laki in southern
Iceland and great ash clouds spread over thousands of square miles. The ash
damaged crops as far away as Scotland and Norway.

The explosive initial phase was followed by an enormous outpouring
of lava from many vents along a fissure ten miles long. Further flows continued until the middle of July. Eventually the largest flow was 50 miles
long and 12 to 15 miles wide, with an average thickness of about 100 feet,
but in some places 600 feet. The total flow of lava was estimated to be about
three cubic miles (Th. Thoroddsen). This is the greatest ejection of lava
in historic times.

The effects of this colossal lava flow were disastrous. Most serious was a noxious haze which lay over the country during the summer, spoiling the grass and causing famine. The toll to Iceland of this eruption was one-half of its cattle, three-fourths of its sheep and horses, and one-fifth (about 9,500) of its population.

During the great ice age, some half million years ago, Iceland was almost completely covered with an ice sheet over half a mile thick—and sometimes volcanoes erupted underneath.

A faint idea of the shattering paroxysms which then occurred can be gathered from what happens today when there is an eruption beneath a glacier—a rare example of the meeting of fire and ice. These are known by their Icelandic name, *jökulhlaup* ("glacier burst"). The hot lava melts the ice for hundreds of feet and causes tremendous floods: floods composed of ice and icebergs (some as big as a three-story house), volcanic debris, rocks, mud, and countless millions of tons of water. During the tremendous eruption of Mt. Katla in 1918, water from melted glaciers reached a maximum flow of some 100,000 cubic yards per *second*. The maximum discharge of the Amazon, greatest waterway in the world, with a mouth 50 miles across and some 150 feet deep, is not much more than this (130,000

> We do not know the total amount of water released by a jökulhlaup from Katla. We only know that it is considerably less than that of a glacier burst from Grímsvötn. A normal Grímsvötn jökulhlaup releases about two cubic miles of water. My estimate is that Katla releases not more than half a cubic mile, or two thousand million tons of water. But because of the suddenness of the Katla jökulhlaup the maximum flow is much higher than that of Grímsvötn. A Grímsvötn flood lasts about a week, a Katla flood about one day.

Solfataric: the final phase of an eruption when only gases appear. The name derives from Solfatara in Italy which last ejected solid matter in 1198 and since then has erupted only gases.

Peléean, or nuées ardentes: a highly dangerous form of eruption, in which enormous clouds of superheated steam, charged with molten rock, are ejected at high speed, often from the side of the volcano because the upward conduit is blocked—hence the danger. Peléean-type eruptions often mark the final phase of volcanic activities—a "last fling" before years of rest or extinction. The names come from Mont Pelée, and the French description of what happens—a "glowing cloud" rushes down the side of the volcano, although the cloud does not always glow.

St. Pierre was a prosperous town on the northwest coast of Martinique

c.y.p.s.) (Tom F. W. Barth, and Sigurdur Thorarinsson).

Thorarinsson comments:

Volcanoes

in the Caribbean. About five miles away was Mont Pelée, a volcano which had been quiet for 50 years, but whose previous eruptions had clothed the countryside with rich volcanic ash, making the soil fertile for valuable sugar cane plantations.

But in April 1902 Pelée awakened. There were some earthquake shocks and mild eruptions which dusted the streets. The activity increased and by the end of the month Pelée had cleared its throat and was raining noxious ash on the town. Then, on May 5, a cataract of boiling mud coursed down the mountain at express-train speed, overwhelmed a sugar mill and killed 30 workmen.

Panic spread in St. Pierre; some people left, more prepared to go. The local newspaper published soothing editorials and the authorities tried to stem the exodus, even posting soldiers to block the roads. Then, during the night of May 7, Pelée gave its final warning and the darkness was cleft by a magnificent display of natural fireworks. People stared in wonder. Some were frightened and again prepared to leave St. Pierre, but others were thrilled by the brilliant spectacle and stayed.

The next morning dawned bright and sunny, and the only sign of activity on Mont Pelée was a huge vapor column rising high into the heavens. Awake early, Fernard Clerc, one of the leading planters on Martinique, looked at his barometer. The needle was in constant agitation. He didn't waste a moment. He ordered his carriage at once, piled his family into it and soon after 7 A.M. drove out of the city. His friends laughed at his fears and waved as his carriage sped away. He made for Mont Parnasse, a mile from St. Pierre. On arriving there he and his family got out of the carriage and looked back. It was 7:50 A.M. on May 8—zero hour for one of the world's greatest tragedies.

As Clerc watched he saw an eruption burst from the main crater on Pelée, and at the same instant the volcano's side opened with a roaring explosion. A vast black cloud shot out horizontally at enormous speed. It was as if the other three rocky sides of Pelée formed the mouth of a gigantic cannon from which shot a bolt of superheated vapor, gas, and white-hot fragments of molten rock.

This tremendous blast rushed down the slopes of Pelée like a hurricane of black fog. There was a continuous roar of staccato explosions like a gun battery in nonstop action. This was probably caused by the continuous lightning flashes playing about the descending cloud, and the exploding (rapidly expanding) gases.

Clerc, watching from the safety of Mont Parnasse, said the blast covered the five miles to St. Pierre in two to three minutes. Two other observers, one watching from the same vantage point as Clerc and the other from the deck of a vessel in the harbor, said the blast swept across St. Pierre itself in two to three *seconds*. It then fanned out to sea.

St. Pierre was hit by a hurricane-force barrage of red-hot sand and stones. It was set ablaze from end to end almost instantaneously. At this moment the ship *Pouyer-Quertier* was lying some six miles out to sea west of St. Pierre. The crew saw two giant flashes from Pelée; then "light appeared in the direction of St. Pierre, and 30 seconds later the binoculars showed the town to be in flames. The whole flank of the mountain on the side towards St. Pierre was glowing red" (quoted by Perret, 1935, who thinks the phrase "glowing red" refers to a flashing arc).

With the exception of one who miraculously escaped, most of St. Pierre's 30,000 inhabitants were wiped out before they knew what hit them.[4] One breath of that fiery cloud and a man's lungs shriveled away. But some bodies were found in positions indicating that an attempt had been made to flee.

After devastating St. Pierre the blast swept across the harbor. With the exception of two steamships, every craft in the harbor capsized and was totally wrecked. Their crews quickly perished in the now boiling water. The steel masts of the steamer *Roraima* broke across their bases two feet above the deck, snapping off perfectly clean, like clay pipe stems struck with a stick (Ellery S. Scott). Her funnel, bridge and boats were swept away and tons of ash were deposited on her decks. She was set ablaze fore and aft. Most of her crew, and all but two of her passengers, were killed. The other ship to survive, the *Roddam,* staggered out of the harbor with 120 tons of volcanic ash on her decks. Submarine cables offshore broke under the weight of ash that fell on them. Dust fell on ships hundreds of miles out at sea and on Barbados, 150 miles to the south of Pelée, an estimated *two million* tons of dust rained down.

This vivid eyewitness account has been left by Assistant Purser Thompson of the *Roraima.*

I saw St. Pierre destroyed. It was blotted out by one great flash of fire. Of 18 vessels lying in the Roads, only one, the British steamship *Roddam,* escaped, and she, I hear, lost more than half on board. It was a dying crew that took her out. Our boat arrived at St. Pierre early Thursday morning. For hours before we entered the roadstead, we could see flames and smoke rising from Mt. Pelée. No one on board had any idea of danger. Captain G. T. Muggah was on the bridge, and all hands got on deck to see the show. The spectacle was magnificent. As we approached St. Pierre, we could distinguish the rolling and leaping of the red flames that belched from the mountain in huge volumes and gushed high in the sky.

Enormous cloud of black smoke hung over the volcano. The flames were then spurting straight up in the air, now and then waving to one side

---

[4] See p. 249. Some accounts say that more than one survived in the town but the others soon died of their injuries. After the blast of volcanic air, there was a return wind from the sea of hurricane force.

or the other a moment, and again leaping suddenly higher up. There was a constant muffled roar. It was like the biggest oil refinery in the world burning up on the mountain top.

There was a tremendous explosion about 7:45, soon after we got in. The mountain was blown to pieces. There was no warning. The side of the volcano was ripped out, and there hurled straight toward us a solid wall of flame. It sounded like thousands of cannon. The wave of fire was on us and over us like a lightning flash. It was like a hurricane of fire, which rolled straight down upon St. Pierre and the shipping.

The town vanished before our eyes, and then the air grew stifling hot and we were in the thick of it. Wherever the mass of fire struck the sea, the water boiled and sent up vast clouds of steam. I saved my life by running to my stateroom and burying myself in the bedding. The blast of fire from the volcano lasted only a few minutes. It shriveled and set fire to everything it touched. Burning rum ran in streams down every street and out into the sea. Before the volcano burst, the landings of St. Pierre were crowded with people. After the explosion not one living was seen on land. Only 25 of those on the *Roraima*, out of 68, were left after the first flash. The fire wave swept off the ship's masts and smokestack as if they were cut with a knife [quoted by Leet].

When it reached the sea this Peléean blast had spread a distance of four miles. The small town of St. Philomène was destroyed even more completely than St. Pierre; not a single wall was left standing.

In the whole of the area encompassed by the volcano's fiery breath 30,000 to 31,000 people had been living. As far as could be ascertained, only 30 of these escaped death, and of these only 4 were uninjured. With one blast Pelée killed over 30,000 people, wrecked 2 towns, sunk 14 ships and incinerated ten square miles of country.

Immediately following the blast, the dust it liberated and the vapor column which was simultaneously ejected out of the main crater threw a dense pall over St. Pierre and the surrounding countryside. It was so dark that Clerc, on Mont Parnasse, said that he could not see his children who were within arm's reach, and men on the two surviving ships in the harbor could not see halfway across the deck. This almost total darkness lasted for half an hour.

Yet another horror was to come. Torrential rain swept tens of thousands of tons of volcanic ash down Pelée's slopes. A deluge of soft pasty mud cascaded into St. Pierre, burying many houses to the rooftops. Rushing into the sea it produced a small tidal wave which was felt at Fort de France, about 12 miles away.

Writing of this mud, Chief Officer Ellery S. Scott of the *Roraima* says:

After the stones came a rain of hot mud, lava apparently mixed with water, of the consistency of very thin cement. Wherever it fell it formed a coating, clinging like glue, so that those who wore no caps it coated, making a complete cement mask right over their heads.

The shock waves of this great blast encircled the earth and the noise was audible for at least 300 miles. It may have been heard at a much greater distance than this because the U. S. Consul at Maracaibo, 800 miles from Martinique, reported that at about the time Pelée exploded he heard a sound like "cannonading with heavy siege guns; it was neither thunder, nor the strange, unpleasant subterranean sounds of convulsions of the earth; it was as if immense explosions were fired high up in the clouds" (quoted by Angelo Heilprin, 1908).

When the rescue ship *Marin* from Fort de France arrived at St. Pierre 3½ hours after the disaster, the heat from the still burning town prevented her from approaching the shore. So great had been the conflagration that neither torrential rain nor the avalanche of mud had been sufficient to damp the fires.

When the first rescue party eventually entered the city a scene of unparalleled devastation met their eyes. The white town of St. Pierre was a heap of dirty blackened rubble.

There were some remarkable examples of the effect of the volcanic whirlwind.[5] Three-foot-thick walls of stone and cement blown down and torn to pieces as though they had been children's bricks. Century-old trees plucked from the ground, roots and all; heavy siege guns, ten feet long, blown from their mountings; and a statue of the Virgin Mary, weighing three tons, flung some 50 feet from its pedestal. Alfred Lacroix (quoted in Heilprin) considers a wind speed of some 300 m.p.h. would have been required to accomplish this last feat.

When the blast first shot from the volcano it was probably traveling at this speed. Peléean blasts are propelled by continuously expanding and exploding gas previously dissolved under pressure in the magma they carry with them.

The temperature of the blast, according to Heilprin, was not less than 450° C. Some of the particles of molten rock swept along by it would have had an initial temperature of about 1,000° C. Such temperatures are feasible when it is remembered that this blast carbonized green juicy fruits, softened glass objects in places where there was no conflagration, and set fire to the wooden decks of ships in the harbor well offshore.

Yet, as in cases of tornadic destruction, some of the frailest objects escape damage. George Kennan, who was among the first to explore the town, says that he found a thin plaster bas-relief of "Christ before Pilate." Although the building in which it had been housed had been completely

---

[5] The damage was not all done by one blast; the one on May 20 was extremely violent (Perret, 1937, and Bullard).

Furrowed cone of Boquerón puffs smoke on the west side of San Bene-
dicto Island. The island, three hundred and fifty miles off Mexico's west
coast, was the birthplace of this volcano in August, 1952.   *U. S. Navy*

demolished, this frail object, which a light blow would have shattered, was
hanging uninjured and undisturbed from a fragment of one of the walls.

The condition of some of the corpses gave a vivid impression of how
death had come. Here was a clerk bending over a ledger, pen still in hand,
frozen in the immobility of death. There was a man bent over a washbasin
from which the water had evaporated. Here a family sat around a restaurant
table. Some had evidently staggered a few steps and lay with contorted
bodies, hands clutching at scalded mouths and throats. Scott says of one of
the passengers on his ship "the man's tongue was literally burnt out of his
head."

Numerous bodies were found without a vestige of clothing. Many others had burst abdomens and split skulls, but with no other signs of injury. Such wounds indicate that a sudden reduction in the surrounding air pressure had caused their bodies literally to explode. Two of the survivors on the *Roraima* said: "While the blast lasted it was too hot to breathe much, and immediately afterward there seemed to be nothing we *could* breathe. We gasped as if in a vacuum, without being able to get anything that satisfied the lungs."

A short while after the disaster a young traveler, A. L. Koster, visited St. Pierre to take the first photographs of the dead city.[6] He was particularly impressed by the complete silence, and the carpet of fine talcumlike powder that was almost everywhere. The ground was still so hot it was uncomfortable to walk about.

> Evidence of terrific heat was everywhere. The bodies of victims strewn among the ruins were greatly reduced in size. It was as if most of the moisture had suddenly been extracted from them. But as they were not burned, and as trees and other pieces of wood were barely charred, I concluded that either the duration of the heat had been extremely brief or that the heat had failed to ignite anything because of an absence of oxygen. . . . A tidal wave attending the blast drove sailing vessels ashore. Their masts had shrunk to a mere fraction of their original diameter inside the protective iron collars at deck level.

St. Pierre's sole survivor was a prisoner, a 25-year-old Negro named Auguste Ciparis who was trapped in the dungeon of the jail. The tiny window of his cell faced away from the volcano, and the massive stone walls of the prison resisted the heat and blast so effectively that he learned of the catastrophe only when he was rescued. Four days he waited, starving and terrified in his tiny underground cell. At last his cries for help were heard; he was rescued and lived to recount the story of his amazing escape. History contains none more marvelous. This fact did not escape the famous American showman, P. T. Barnum; he exhibited Ciparis as one of his circus curiosities (Kennan).

Mont Pelée was not exhausted even by this monstrous eruption. She spoke again at least five more times, wiping out several villages near St. Pierre and claiming 2,000 more victims.

One final drama was still to come—Vulcan's own memorial to the town he smote. In October, from Pelée's crater, a vast mass of solidified lava slowly rose until it formed a gigantic rock obelisk. Eventually this "Tower of Pelée," with a diameter at the base between 350 and 500 feet, stood 1,000 feet above the crater floor. It gradually disintegrated and

---

[6] No date is given but it was probably shortly after the second blast on May 20.

disappeared as a result of weathering toward the end of 1904 (Heilprin, 1904).

The tragedy of St. Pierre had one good result. It shocked the world into awareness of the importance of volcanology, and the importance of having trained watchers at dangerous volcanoes.

A Peléean blast occurred in the United States on May 22, 1915, when Lassen Peak, California, erupted. Fortunately it was in a relative wilderness and no one was killed. The blast melted a mass of ice and snow estimated to be 40 feet deep, and cleared a valley of great trees and every movable object for a distance of over four miles. A. L. Day and E. T. Allen say "before the blast the valley is reported to have contained five million feet of standing timber (original forest), much of which reached the diameter of three to five feet. After that date the bottom of the valley was swept like a floor, and was left without stumps or roots to indicate its previous forest cover. It was hard to find even a pebble in that area greater than a few inches in diameter."

Although a Peléean eruption is highly dangerous, some volcanologists believe that there are others even worse. Possibly, however, the difference is only one of degree.

Haroun Tazieff tells me he considers that a more dangerous type of eruption than the Peléean is the *ignimbritic,* when dense clouds of frothy red-hot lava (ignimbrites[7]) and exploding gases shoot from groups of fissures. He believes that such an eruption caused The Valley of Ten Thousand Smokes in Alaska. There, in June 1912, Katmai erupted for several days.

There appears to have been more than one type of eruption. First a column of ash and pumice was hurled 25 miles into the stratosphere. Then from a single fissure, or narrow set of fissures, on the western foot of the volcano there issued millions of tons of red-hot lava particles suspended in hot gases, which poured down the 15-mile-long valley. Liquid rock hundreds of feet deep covered an area of 42 square miles. The surrounding country was barren and unpopulated.

The tremendous hot blanket vaporized ground water so that shortly after the eruption the whole floor of the valley was smoking with thousands of steam jets (fumaroles)—hence its name. The superheated steam from some fumaroles reached nearly 500° C.—hot enough to melt zinc and ignite a stick held in the steam. Today the valley is part of Katmai National Monument, the largest national park in the United States, comprising 4,215 square miles (Robert F. Griggs, and P. Bordet, *et al.*).

The greatest volume of matter ejected from a volcano within historic times is believed to be about 36 cubic miles—from the eruption of Tambora,

---

[7] From *ignis,* "fire" and *imbris,* "rain."

Billowing clouds of dust rise from an erupting volcano on the island of
Fayal in the Azores, North Atlantic, in October, 1957. The height of the clouds
may be gauged from the lighthouse which is one hundred and fifteen feet
high.   *Servicos Geológicos de Portugal*

Indonesia, in April 1815. It has also been estimated that internal pressure
during this eruption rose to some 20,000 tons per square inch. During the
tremendous explosions the volcano lost 4,100 feet in height, and a crater
seven miles in diameter was formed. A vast dust cloud turned day into
night for hundreds of miles around the volcano, darkness which lasted for
three days, as on the island of Madura, 310 miles away.

It is difficult to appreciate the stupendous volume of 36 cubic miles.
Perhaps the two following comparisons will help. Up to the year 1964 the
total world consumption of oil was about six cubic miles. The other comparison is from a striking illustration of Hendrik Willem Van Loon's.
Imagine if you can every one of earth's 3,300 million inhabitants heaped
together in one place. Their total volume—allowing 40 cubic feet per person
—would be less than a cubic mile, so that if a giant box, roughly ¾ mile
in each dimension, could be constructed, the whole human race could be
packed into it! Incidentally, the whole human race could find standing room
on Hong Kong (400 square miles, current population 3,600,000). But if the
population continues to expand at the rate it has during recent years, by the
year 2665 the entire land mass of the earth will be packed with standing
people. . . .

Volcanoes   [*251*]

So that in the Tambora eruption a total mass was thrown out of the crater equal to about six times the total volume of the oil so far used by the human race, and some 36 times the total space taken up by all the human beings on earth.

What energies are involved to project such colossal masses miles above the earth? If (a) the exact weight of the mass ejected were known, and (b) the height to which it traveled, the energies involved could be worked out by arithmetic. But as both (a) and (b) are obviously only rough estimates, so must be estimates of the energy. Moreover, different volcanologists give varying figures for the same eruption. However, there would, I think, be general agreement that the following table gives, in order of magnitude, a fair idea of the energies involved in some famous eruptions.

Approximate Energies Involved

Volcano	Date	Ergs		Megaton explosions
Tambora		8.4×10^{26}		25,000
Krakatoa	Aug. 26–29, 1883	10^{25}		500
Krakatoa	Aug. 27, 1883	7.2×10^{22}	different	$1\frac{1}{2}$
	(Single eruption)	8.6×10^{23}	estimates	25
Pelée		4.7×10^{21}		$\frac{1}{7}$

Although the large majority of active volcanoes are on land, some erupt beneath the sea. These volcanoes often discharge huge masses of pumice—rock with so many air spaces that it floats. Sometimes great drifts of pumice accumulate in bays and form floating rafts on which it is possible to walk. The extensive Pacific archipelagoes of Hawaii, Samoa, and Tonga were all built by submarine volcanoes. So were the Azores in the Atlantic (Alexander R. McBirney).

But there is much volcanic action which neither reaches the surface, nor leaves permanent trace above the waves, as with Myojin. In September 1952 several vessels noticed violent explosions rising from the surface of the Pacific Ocean about 250 miles south of Tokyo. Sea water was mixing with red-hot lava from an ocean-bed volcano and, expanding with dynamic violence, was throwing rock, water, and gas thousands of feet into the air. Time and again a small island would form, only to be destroyed by wave action and further eruptions. One survey vessel, seeking the volcano on a day when Myojin's head was below the surface, apparently strayed directly over it. Just then Myojin threw another broadside into the sky. Neither the vessel nor the 31 men aboard were ever seen again; only lava-pitted wreckage (Robert S. Dietz).

Some of the explosions were so violent that they sent waves racing across the sea at 150 m.p.h. to dash, 20 feet high against Hachijo Island,

75 miles away. An island of hardened lava 600 feet long once rose 150 feet above sea level, only to disappear again a few months later.

The most recent example of a volcanic island is Surtsey, which rose from the sea some 20 miles off the south coast of Iceland near the Vestmann Islands, on November 15, 1963. Early in the morning on November 14, men on an Icelandic fishing vessel saw a red glow just above the sea surface and thought it was a ship on fire. Two days later Surtsey was about 120 feet high and 1,500 feet long. And ten days after its birth Surtsey was 300 feet high and half a mile long. It was belching out a great column of steam, rocks, ash, and smoke which rose five miles high and was capped with a mushroom-shaped cloud.[8] The Vestmann Islanders stopped work to stand and stare, and schoolchildren were given a holiday to see "a land on fire" rising newborn from the sea (Thorarinsson).

These volcanic islands are a cartographer's nightmare, for some of them appear, disappear, and then rise up again! Falcon Island, near Tonga in the Southwest Pacific, was known as a reef in the 18th century. In 1867 the sea became unexpectedly shallow in the area and seamen passing near saw "smoke" rising from the sea. Then in 1885 an island rose on the site, attaining a height of about 250 feet. But the sea gradually eroded it until, in 1899, Falcon Island was no more.

But in 1927 there was an eruption which built up a cone 300 feet high and three miles in circumference. Falcon Island was once more on the map. It stayed above the waves until March 1949. Since then it has not been seen again, but by the time this book is published the cartographers may once again be reaching for their pens.

These effects upon geography are typical of the practical importance of volcanoes. Volcanic eruptions have, at times, seriously affected world weather. Three eruptions took place in 1812, 1814, and 1815, the last being that of Tambora. The cloud of dust released by these three eruptions was so vast that it prevented an appreciable amount of the sun's heat from reaching the earth. Eighteen sixteen was known as "the year without a summer," or "Eighteen Hundred and Froze to Death." In some parts of the United States six inches of snow fell in June; people wore overcoats and gloves in July and a temperature of 37° F. was registered in August. The summer of that year was filled with freakish weather, 100° F. one day, snowstorms the next —almost! (See also Harry Wexler)

The weather in the immediate area of a volcano is largely created by the effects of the eruption: heat, gases, and the great volume of dust. In all

---

[8] The crew of an airplane that flew over the crater at about 6,000 feet saw rocks whiz past them, which indicates an initial speed of some 400 m.p.h. (Robert Anderson, *et al.*). At times during the first month half a million tons an hour were ejected. In February 1965 Surtsey was nearly a mile square. As I write (March 1965) it is still growing.

An explosive blast from Surtsey, the volcano which rose from the sea about twenty miles off the south coast of Iceland in 1963. *Sigurgeir Jónasson*

violent eruptions there are thunderstorms with brilliant lightning, hail, and heavy rain. The great heat in some eruptions also causes tornadoes.

Pough (1943), writing of an incident at Parícutin, Mexico, says "a tremendous outlet of gas, roared off in a spiraling clockwise tornado perhaps 20 feet in diameter and sounded as if it had irresistible force."

During the great eruption of Tambora in April 1815 the most violent tornadoes formed. They snatched up men, horses, cattle, and anything movable. The largest trees were torn out of the ground by the roots and whirled into the air. For days during the eruptions the surrounding seas were littered with trees and branches (C. E. Wurtzburg, and J. T. Ross).

Volcanic dust in the atmosphere is responsible for brilliant red sunsets and sunrises. As the sun's rays pass obliquely through the dusty upper air the shorter wavelengths of light are affected, and the consequent preponderance of the longer, reddish waves produces brilliant sunsets. Edward Whymper has given a remarkable account of this prism effect of volcanic dust. On July 3, 1880, he and his party were camped 16,000 feet above sea level on Chimborazo, about 60 miles from the Andean volcano Cotopaxi when it suddenly erupted.

Several hours elapsed before the ash commenced to intervene between the sun and ourselves, and when it did so we witnessed effects which simply amazed us. We saw a green sun, and such a green as we have never, either before or since, seen in the heavens. We saw smears or patches of something like verdigris-green in the sky, and they changed to equally extreme blood-red, or to coarse brick-dust reds, and they in an instant passed to the color of tarnished copper or shining brass [quoted by Symons].

Such enhancements of natural beauty are not the only benefit which accrues to humanity from volcanic action. Volcanic ash helps to replace topsoil lost by erosion, and the soil resulting from the decomposition of volcanic materials is extremely fertile. Some of the world's most beautiful and fertile areas, such as the Caribbean chain of islands and the Hawaiian area, have been built by volcanic action. Java is a volcanic island and, although only the size of New York State, is so fertile that it supports nearly 60 million people—about three times the population of New York.

Volcanic ash, because of its extreme fineness, makes an ideal polishing and cleansing agent. Because of its high porosity it has been used in the manufacture of dynamite (as an absorbent for nitroglycerine), and as a thermal insulator.

Valuable chemical products are obtained from volcanic substances; gold and silver are sometimes found in volcanic deposits. The rich gold and silver lodes of Cripple Creek, Colorado, are situated in the throat of an ancient volcano. Similarly, the Kimberley "pipe" in South Africa, which has produced such a wealth of diamonds, is the solidified conduit of another ancient volcano. Other African volcanoes contain niobium-bearing ore and other rare minerals.

Volcanoes have also helped to make men's collars—and birds' nests. The ash has been used to put the linen finish on celluloid collars. The passage of steam through a mass of molten glasslike lava produces large quantities of material resembling spun glass. Small particles of this material are carried into the air and birds sometimes seize on some of the finer strands to help make their nests.

The immense energies stored in volcanoes could, if harnessed, provide a virtually inexhaustible source of power. C. du Riche Preller calculated that

Fountaining lava from Kilauea blocks a road in Hawaii's Volcano National Park. Serviceman (bottom right) gives scale.   *U. S. Geological Survey*

a fairly mild eruption of Etna develops sufficient energy to supply the whole of Italy with electricity for three years (quoted by G. W. Tyrrell).

Several attempts have been made to harness volcanic forces. The observatory on Etna used to obtain its supply of warm water from a steam fumarole, or vent, on the volcano. Iceland, New Zealand and California have also made practical use of volcanic steam. One advantage is that the supply is practically inexhaustible; magma cools so slowly that it still supplies steam *thousands* of years after the original eruption. In Iceland, apart from other uses, 60 per cent of the houses in Reykjavik, the capital, are heated by natural steam. The first power plant in the United States to be operated by natural steam was opened in 1960 in Sonoma County, California. With the ever-growing need for power, volcanoes and their by-products may become increasingly valuable—especially in areas where conventional sources of power are lacking.

To the scientist, volcanoes provide firsthand evidence of the composition of the earth. Geographers and geologists learn much from the distribution and structure of volcanoes. Moreover, the advance of volcanology enables warnings to be given of impending eruptions. Small earth tremors,

The Elements Rage

easily detectable by seismographs, almost invariably precede an eruption. Perret (1935) says, "the warning which precedes a great eruption always gives ample time for escape." He might have added: Thanks to himself and other scientists who have devoted their time, and occasionally risked their lives, unraveling the secrets of Vulcan's tremendous forge. Many more people have been killed by earthquakes than by volcanoes.

And surely on the credit side must be put the terrible beauty of a volcano in action—the most tremendous natural spectacle of all. An erupting volcano in full blast is literally "the greatest show on earth" and adds immeasurably to our heritage of natural wonders. When watchers saw Parícutin shoot a spectacular display of volcanic fireworks into the sky they broke into an involuntary cheer. Parícutin is one of the few volcanoes to have been under almost constant observation from the day of its birth.

On February 5, 1943, earthquakes shook the State of Michoacán, Mexico, and continued for about two weeks. Then, about four o'clock in the afternoon of February 20, 1943, an Indian peasant, Dionisio Pulido, was plowing outside his mountain village of Parícutin in Michoacán in a field which contained a small pit from which subterranean rumblings were occasionally heard. On this afternoon Pulido noticed a fissure extending through the hole for some two feet. Soon his field trembled as though a giant hand deep in the earth had shaken it. Then sulphurous smoke arose accompanied by hissing, sparks came from the fissure, and pine trees 100 feet away began to burn. Pulido hurriedly left.

Soon watchers came from several miles away, attracted by the plume of smoke. The fissured hole was now a tiny pear-shaped crater which was erupting ash, sparks, and stones, while a choking odor pervaded the area. The ground was "jumping up and down." The incipient volcano's activity rapidly increased.

By midnight on its birthday the volcano was hurling huge incandescent rocks into the air with thunderous roars, and a heavy pillar of ash was lit with lightning flashes.

When Pulido arrived at eight o'clock the next morning the upstart, which had taken over his field, was a true volcanic cone, some 35 feet high. Smoke, incandescent rocks, and debris were belching out, causing the cone to grow to over 100 feet by midday. The first lava issued from the volcano the next day. Then on the evening of the third day, February 22, the first volcanologist—Ezequiel Ordonez—arrived and from then on Parícutin was under constant scientific observation until its activity ceased.[9] (There are varying accounts of its beginnings. The above is based on that by

---

[9] The new volcano was named Parícutin after the village it soon overwhelmed. So great was the rain of ash that a year later it was difficult to realize a village had ever been there.

Parícutin's dust plumes rise three thousand feet into the air. *T. Ifor Rees*

R. González and William F. Foshag, who conducted many interviews with eyewitnesses.)

Parícutin grew rapidly. In a week it was 550 feet high, and throwing up masses of viscous lava with a thunder that was heard over 200 miles away. During the first few months it was estimated to be ejecting solid material—lava, cinders, and ash—at the average rate of 2,700 tons a minute, or nearly four million tons every 24 hours. In addition an estimated 16,000 tons of steam was discharged every day. In the first seven months about two thousand million cubic yards of solid material had fallen on the surrounding countryside.

The great rain of volcanic material ejected from Parícutin ruined the countryside over an area some 35 miles in diameter, and depopulated 300 square miles. Everything within a radius of five miles of Parícutin's cone was blanketed with volcanic dust like black snow, varying from one to nine feet in thickness. Two hundred miles away in Mexico City ash fell on streets and rooftops, and in Uruapan, some 15 miles away, street lights had to be turned on in the dusty daylight, and tiled roofs of houses were cracked by the amount of ash that fell on them. Nearer to the volcano, buildings col-

The Elements Rage

lapsed under the weight of ash. This ash was quite cold to the touch after it had fallen from the chill upper air.

Throughout the ruined area grass disappeared entirely, but a few bulbous plants pushed their heads through one- and two-foot-thick ash beds. Many shrubs withered and the bare limbs of trees near the volcano testified to the searing action of volcanic gas and ash. Lois Mattox Miller, who flew over the area, says:

> I first noticed its devastating effects 75 miles away. Black ashes shroud once-green valleys and mountain sides. Gardens and orchards have vanished. Church spires stick up, half buried under a mountain of slag. Springs have gone dry and the river Cupatitzo is now a slow-moving stream of mud.
>
> Not a green thing, not a blade of grass, is alive in an area of 100 square miles. Fifty miles away, tender crops wither and only the hardier growth, the trees and shrubs, still lives. The disaster has brought complete desolation to seven villages and damage to many others. Vegetation on the fertile farmlands withers and dies wherever the shifting winds spread a blanket of ashes. Birds drop lifeless from the skies.[10] Water is scarce, for the springs have gone dry.

Although *El Monstruo,* as the Indian peasants call the "fire monster" in their midst, wrought great destruction, it also brought its compensations. Some of the peasants did a roaring tourist trade, and Pulido had at least one offer to buy Parícutin!

To the volcanologist, Parícutin presented the chance of a lifetime to study a volcano almost from the day of its birth. In July 1944, the "United States Committee for the Study of Parícutin Volcano" was formed to integrate the study of the eruption and its various effects. Parícutin's action was Strombolian of the most vigorous type. For about a year its activity was almost continuous.

Parícutin had a wide repertoire of sounds. In its milder phases it spoke with the roar of a heavy surf breaking on the shore. But when it cleared its throat by hurling molten rock 3,000 feet into the air it was as if a score of battleships had fired broadsides simultaneously. A few moments after each violent explosion there was the noise of sporadic riflefire—the spatter of the ejected rocks falling back onto the volcano's slopes.

Other sounds were caused by the flow of red-hot rocks down the cone. Frederick H. Pough (1943) describes these sound effects as "a steady tinkle from the sliding, falling rocks, accompanied by a loud crackling like that of

---

[10] Pough (1943) explains how such casualties occur. Writing of the rain of cinders, etc., near the cone, he says: "The stinging impact of the half- or one-inch particles was enough to explain the plight of a lone blue jay, fluttering along with a broken wing, and the otherwise total lack of life. What wasn't buried under nine feet of cinders was no doubt driven away or even killed by the falling masses."

a hot fire, as the cooling surfaces cracked open and the rocks broke up into smaller masses." Yet another note in the mighty orchestration was the short, sharp crack of thunder caused by the lightning flashes which forked through the billowing dust clouds.

These vast clouds poured from the crater and swirled upward like a giant cauliflower stuck in the volcano's mouth. Black, gray, steam-white; sometimes colored yellowish-red with the glow of molten lava and lightened by the darts of lightning and "flashing arcs," this immense smoke plume towered four miles above the volcano's summit.

There were at times massive flows of cherry-red lava, one started in January 1944 and continued until August, when it was about six miles long. A hail of volcanic bombs frequently shot thousands of feet into the air.[11] At first these bombs were liquid and solidified in the air, but later they were solid red-hot spheres. Trask says that they varied in size from that of a walnut to a big house. He saw one 50 feet in diameter. A bomb four feet in diameter landed 25 feet from where he was standing and buried itself in the ground, the top being a foot beneath the surface. Another small bomb broke a large oak limb before burying itself three feet in the ground.

Seen from a distance, these flying rocks looked like a "flock of black-birds escaping from an inferno" (James A. Green). They assumed all sorts of shapes while flying through the air and often solidified into them. Birds, fish, boomerangs, clubs, and hammers have all been represented. Once a 25 foot "fish" was found at the foot of the cone.

These volcanic missiles were the chief danger at Parícutin. Sometimes the force of an eruption tore solid rocks from the volcano's throat and then these were added to the hazards of volcanic exploration. Surprisingly, however, there was not one fatality. Apparently the worst accident was to a woman visitor who had some ribs broken when a shed in which she was sheltering collapsed during a rain of ash.

Parícutin finally blew itself out by March 4, 1952, after 9 years and 12 days of almost ceaseless activity. At that time it stood about 1,500 feet high, having ejected an estimated 3,500 million tons of solid matter, of which about a quarter was lava.

Finally, here are two descriptions by eyewitnesses of this "greatest show on earth." T. Ifor Rees says:

> Both by day and by night Parícutin is a magnificent spectacle. By day the dense volumes of smoke pour upward in rolling, swirling, revolving

[11] "Gas explosions send fragments of lava—which we call bombs—flying from the crater. Some of these fiery objects have been tossed up to a maximum of 4,120 feet. This measurement may be calculated fairly accurately by timing their descent. The longest fall, 16 seconds, when checked against the acceleration of gravity, gives the distance." (Foshag, quoted by Green.) Stromboli has flung 30-ton blocks two miles!

masses to a height of about 3,000 feet where they meet air currents which carry them away to the north and east. These billowy fleece-like masses, as they swirl powerfully out of the crater, range in color from white to black, with every shade of gray in between.

Occasionally there is an electrical discharge within the huge pillar of smoke, followed by a thunderclap. By night, when the columns of smoke are not visible, the volcano is like an enormous blast furnace, hurling into the air vast quantities of incandescent material which falls in a glowing shower on the slopes, covering them with a shimmering and ever-changing mantle of fire as the flaming rocks roll down.

The other eyewitness is Foshag.

> In my opinion Parícutin is the greatest show on earth. It is, I believe, just as spectacular as Vesuvius ever was, and in its more violent phases it is better.
>
> You should see Parícutin when gas bubbles burst in the lava high in the crater. Such an explosion sends out a fiery umbrella. Last June [1943] there were spectacular blasts, and the hills rolled with thunder. Houses and the ground shook. There was a cascade like Niagara's. People came from 20 miles away to see what was going on.
>
> On August 1 the fireworks became so spectacular that spectators burst into applause. Think of that: people applauding a volcano! [quoted by Green].

No reference to volcanoes would be complete without mention of the two greatest explosions within the recorded history of man—Santorin and Krakatoa. Although Santorin (now Thira) was such a tremendous eruption, very little is known about it. Angelos G. Galanopoulos, the Greek seismologist, has investigated this natural catastrophe of the eastern Mediterranean which, according to radio-carbon dating, occurred about 1450 B.C.

Santorin is a crescent-shaped island in the Aegean Sea, and lies north of Crete between Greece and Turkey. The hollow of the crescent is believed to have been formed by volcanic action and consequent collapse of the central part of the island.

From brief descriptions and allusions in ancient writings, the archaeology of the area, studies of the volcanic remains, and from knowledge of volcanic behavior, it is possible to reconstruct a little of that vast explosion in the dawn of Mediterranean civilization. Whole cubic miles of rock were blasted into the air. Dust and volcanic debris carpeted the earth for tens of thousands of square miles. A vast wall of water, hundreds of feet high at first, surged out from Santorin to swamp islands and all the shorelines of the eastern Mediterranean.

It is highly probable that it was this cataclysm which destroyed the

Parícutin lights up the night sky. The photographer, writing in 1943, said: "By night the volcano is like an enormous blast furnace, hurling into the air vast quantities of incandescent material which falls in a glowing shower on the slopes, covering them with a shimmering and everchanging mantle of fire as the flaming rocks roll down." *T. Ifor Rees*

centers of Minoan civilization, notably Knossos, which was about 80 miles away. It may also have been the cause of the disappearance of Plato's Atlantis (there is some evidence that this was an island in the eastern Mediterranean), and of the Flood of Deucalion that destroyed the part of Greece around Attica. The dates roughly agree.

And what of the plagues of Egypt? Various explanations of these have been given by commentators in terms of natural phenomena but, as far as I know, until Galanopoulos's researches on Santorin no one had suggested a volcanic explanation. Ruined crops, violence in the skies, blood-red waters, pestilence, and "thick darkness, even darkness which may be felt"—all these are likely results from a vast rain of volcanic dust (J. G. Bennett).

Little is known about Santorin, much about Krakatoa. Its eruption in 1883 was the subject of some of the most intensive scientific studies ever accorded a single natural phenomenon. R. D. M. Verbeek wrote a two-volume study in Dutch. The chief British contribution was the report of the Krakatoa Committee of the Royal Society, published in 1888. It was edited by G. J. Symons and has chapters by various experts, collating a vast mass of worldwide observations on every aspect of the subject. The report runs to over 500 pages and is replete with diagrams, charts, maps, and both black-and-white and colored illustrations.

The thoroughness with which the work was done can be gathered from the statement in the Preface: "We have not only collected the facts, but have done our utmost to enable everyone to verify them." To this fine monument, not only to the greatest explosion in 3,000 years, but also to Victorian science in Britain, all writers on Krakatoa are deeply indebted. Although there is no doubt about the fact of the eruption, there is controversy about some of the details. I shall deal only with the major features, which have been frequently described, as in Rupert Furneaux's detailed study, *Krakatoa*, published in 1964.

Krakatoa is a small volcanic island in the Sunda Strait midway between Java and Sumatra. When it exploded on August 27, 1883, it made its mark in one form or another on every one of earth's 197 million square miles.

Krakatoa is in the center of the area of the earth's greatest volcanic activity. At some unknown period, judging by the effects produced, Krakatoa had exploded with even greater violence than in 1883. Again, in May 1680, Krakatoa erupted and destroyed the rich tropical forests that covered the island. From then until 1883 Krakatoa was quiet.

On the morning of May 20, 1883, booming sounds, like heavy artillery fire, were heard in Batavia (now Djakarta) and Buitenzorg (now Bogor), 100 miles from Krakatoa. For many hours, doors and windows rattled in these towns and in neighboring villages. The commander of the German warship *Elizabeth* noticed a dust column rising from Krakatoa, which he estimated to be about seven miles high. Dust fell 300 miles from the vol-

Lightning flashes through the volcanic dust clouds above Surtsey. Lightning frequently accompanies volcanic eruptions but the mechanism is not fully understood. This photograph was taken on December 1, 1963, about ten miles from the volcano, the camera shutter being left open for two minutes.

Sigurgeir Jónasson

cano, and for miles around the air was heavy with sulphurous fumes which blackened the brasswork of ships passing through the Strait.

After these premonitory rumblings Krakatoa quieted down. But further rumblings and minor eruptions occurred in June and July; several new craters formed and fresh vents appeared in the main crater.

On August 26, 1883, there began the first of a series of explosions which, with short intervals, were to culminate in the final paroxysm when Krakatoa destroyed itself. Some of these explosions were heard over an area as large as Great Britain. Large waves struck nearby shores, one of them flinging the Dutch warship *Berouw* onto the Sumatran coast.

Various observations were made about this time by members of ships' crews in or near the Sunda Strait. At 2:00 P.M. Capt. Thomson of the *Medea*, then 76 miles from Krakatoa, saw "a black mass rising up like smoke" to an estimated height of 17 miles.

At sunset Capt. Wooldridge, of the *Sir Robert Sale,* described the sky as presenting "a most terrible appearance, the dense mass of clouds being covered with a murky tinge, with fierce flashes of lightning." At 7 P.M. the dense vapor and dust brought an inky darkness. For 100 miles around, midday was like midnight. Through the darkness flashed lightning caused by Krakatoa's eruptions. At this time the volcano presented "the appearance of an immense pine tree, with the stem and branches formed with violent lightning." Strong sulphurous fumes pervaded the whole area and from midnight until 4 A.M. there were continuous explosions: "The sky one second intense blackness, the next a blaze of fire." Wooldridge, viewing the spectacle from 40 miles away, said the great vapor cloud looked like "an immense wall with bursts of forked lightning at times like large serpents rushing through the air."

All the eyewitnesses refer to the splendor of the electrical phenomena during this "curtain raiser" to the grand finale. A ship lying some 45 miles from Krakatoa was struck by lightning five or six times on the mainmast conductor. A rain of phosphorescent mud covered masts, rigging, and the deck. Some of the crew tried to extinguish this phosphorescent fire because they thought it was the work of evil spirits trying to scuttle the ship!

Throughout the night Krakatoa rumbled and nobody in Batavia could sleep for the noise. But toward morning it quieted down.

The great discharge of magma had created a deep cavity beneath Krakatoa, and parts of the island collapsed into this abyss, causing the sea to rush in. There was a titanic battle—Vulcan's fires *versus* Neptune's waters—and more of the island fell. At about 10 A.M. on the 27th there was a further collapse—signal for the greatest explosion in the recorded history of man to burst upon the world.

Into the vast seething cauldron of red-hot magma, the sea poured in, to be instantly turned into steam which exploded with catastrophic violence. In a roaring cataclysm of noise which shook the earth, four cubic miles of rock and ash was hurled into the stratosphere, some of it shooting 40 to 50 miles high.[12]

The violence of the underwater explosion, coupled with the enormous masses of falling material, caused a vast wall of water, rising to several hundred feet, to shoot out in all directions from Krakatoa and sweep across the Sunda Strait at 350 m.p.h. It swept lighthouses away like matchsticks. It caught the *Berouw* and carried her 1.8 miles up a valley and left her stranded about 30 feet above sea level. She is still there today.

Bursting upon the nearby coasts of Sumatra and Java, this great wall of water, now about 100 feet high, caused immense damage and loss of life along a shoreline of hundreds of miles. Along the shallow shore at Merak, Java, the wave was estimated to be 125 feet high—as tall as a 12-story building. Altogether 295 villages and towns were inundated, 5,000 ships destroyed, and some 36,000 people killed.

---

[12] It is estimated that about 4.3 cubic miles of material were ejected and a further 1.8 cubic miles of rock were engulfed (Furneaux).

Racing across the Indian and Pacific Oceans with undiminished speed (judging by time and distance it must have been over 400 m.p.h. in some directions) the sea wave (*tsunami*) hit far distant shores. In the Strait of Surabaya, 500 miles from Krakatoa, tidal gauges were lifted ten inches. In Port Elizabeth, South Africa, 5,000 miles away, ships were rocked at anchor, and according to some reports the effects of the wave were noted in the English Channel, on the other side of the world, 11,000 miles away.

The blast of air from the explosion burst windows and cracked walls in Batavia and Buitenzorg. A gasometer, hit by a terrific gust of compressed air, jumped out of its well. At even greater distances cracks were made in walls by the impact of this great air wave.

Krakatoa caused the mightiest noise on record. The thunder was deafening in Java, Sumatra and Borneo, 500 and more miles away. In the Celebes, nearly 1,000 miles away, the noise was so loud that two ships were sent out to make a reconnaissance. At Daly Waters in Australia, 2,023 miles away, an observer reported: "On Sunday, the 26th, at midnight, we were awakened by an explosion resembling the blasting of a rock, which lasted for a few minutes."

On Rodriguez Island, nearly 3,000 miles from Krakatoa,[13] the chief of police recorded: "the distant roar of heavy guns, coming from the east-ward." A Rodriguez coast guard also noted the sound and his detailed note leaves no doubt that it came from Krakatoa. It had taken the sound waves four hours to reach the island!

Sound travels much better over sea than over land, but it is interesting to envisage such distances in more familiar terms. If Krakatoa had been Pike's Peak, Colorado, the sound would have been heard throughout the continental United States, from Alaska to Florida. If Krakatoa had been Vesuvius, the sound would have been heard from the Arctic Circle to the equator, from Siberia to mid-Atlantic. Altogether Krakatoa was heard over one-thirteenth of the entire surface of the globe, or over an area of roughly 15 million square miles.

But oscillations of the air too slight to be recorded by human ears were noted on the world's barometers (microbarographs had not been invented in 1883). Ten hours after the explosion which sent the air waves racing across the world the instruments in Central Europe registered the concussion. This was the first air wave arriving via the short route of India and Asia. Several hours later the instruments trembled again under the impact of the second air wave which had already oscillated the barometers in Los Angeles, New York, and on ships in the Atlantic.

Some 34 hours after the first oscillations the barometers trembled again —the air wave had circled the earth and had started its second journey. On

---

[13] The theoretical distance a one-megaton explosion can be heard is 100 miles.

many barometers a total of seven oscillations were recorded, four from Krakatoa and three from its antipodes. The last faint flicker of the needles was noticed nine days after the eruption.

The great mass of volcanic dust injected into the atmosphere at the time of the eruption was carried by jet streams round the world, and eventually settled gently on every sea and country on earth. Some of the dust remained in the atmosphere for years. But while a high proportion of it was in the atmosphere it was the cause of strange optical phenomena and brilliant sunsets.

Blue, green, copper- and silver-colored suns and moons were seen. Owing to the great height to which the dust cloud was carried (some estimates say 100 miles) it reflected sunlight long after darkness had fallen on the earth.

The amazing sunsets were Krakatoa's special glory. The dusty haze produced sunsets of gorgeous hue, and rose-colored twilights that lasted an hour or more after the sun had set. Men realized that the old European chroniclers may not have been drawing on their imaginations overmuch when they wrote of blood-red skies following the earlier eruption of Krakatoa in 1680.

Descriptions by many observers of these sunsets, together with colored drawings, are given in the Royal Society report. Here is a description of sunset at New Caledonia, Southwest Pacific, on January 6, 1884, nearly five months after the eruption:

> As soon as the sun's disc has disappeared, a glow comes up from the west like that of white-hot steel, reddening somewhat as it mounts to the zenith, but changing the while to blue. From the zenith it passes into the most exquisite green, deepening as it loses itself in the east. As the sun sinks lower and lower, the red tints overpower the white-hot steel tints, and the blue of the zenith those of the green.
>
> At 7 P.M., or a little after, nearly the entire western half of the horizon has changed to a fiery crimson: as time goes on, the northern and southern areas lose their glory, and the grays of night contract, from the northern end first, most rapidly; the east is of the normal gray. The south now closes in, and presently, about 8 P.M., there is only a glare in the sky, just over the sun's path, as of a distant conflagration, till the fire in the west dies out. . . .

Thus throughout the world the curtain fell slowly on this mighty spectacle in a literal blaze of glory.

Appendices

Appendix A

Beaufort Scale

(Specifications and Equivalent Speeds[1])

Force	Description	Specifications for use on land	Specifications for use at sea
0	Calm	Calm; smoke rises vertically.	Sea like a mirror.
1	Light air	Direction of wind shown by smoke drift, but not by wind vanes.	Ripples with the appearance of scales are formed, but without foam crests.
2	Light breeze	Wind felt on face; leaves rustle; ordinary vane moved by wind.	Small wavelets, still short but more pronounced. Crests have a glassy appearance and do not break.
3	Gentle breeze	Leaves and small twigs in constant motion; wind extends light flag.	Large wavelets. Crests begin to break. Foam of glassy appearance. Perhaps scattered white horses.
4	Moderate breeze	Raises dust and loose paper; small branches are moved.	Small waves, becoming longer; fairly frequent white horses.
5	Fresh breeze	Small trees in leaf begin to sway; crested wavelets form on inland waters.	Moderate waves, taking a more pronounced long form; many white horses are formed. Chance of some spray.
6	Strong breeze	Large branches in motion; whistling heard in telegraph wires; umbrellas used with difficulty.	Large waves begin to form; the white foam crests are more extensive everywhere. Probably some spray.
7	Moderate gale*	Whole trees in motion; inconvenience felt when walking against wind.	Sea heaps up and white foam from breaking waves begins to be blown in streaks along the direction of the wind.
8	Gale	Breaks twigs off trees; generally impedes progress.	Moderately high waves of greater length; edges of crests begin to break into the spindrift. The foam is blown in well marked streaks along the direction of the wind.
9	Strong gale	Slight structural damage occurs (chimney pots and slates removed).	High waves. Dense streaks of foam along the direction of the wind. Crests of waves begin to topple, tumble and roll over. Spray may affect visibility.
10	Storm	Seldom experienced inland; trees uprooted; considerable structural damage occurs.	Very high waves with long overhanging crests. The resulting foam, in great patches, is blown in dense white streaks along the direction of the wind. On the whole the surface of the sea takes a white appearance. The "tumbling" of the sea becomes heavy and shock-like. Visibility affected.
11	Violent storm	Very rarely experienced; accompanied by widespread damage.	Exceptionally high waves (small and medium-sized ships might be for a time lost to view behind the waves). The sea is completely covered with long white patches of foam lying along the direction of the wind. Everywhere the edges of the wave crests are blown into froth. Visibility affected.
12	Hurricane	—	The air is filled with foam and spray. Sea completely white with driving spray; visibility very seriously affected.

---

* For the purpose of statistical summaries, winds of force 7 are not regarded as gales.
[1] As published in the British *Observer's Handbook* (1962) with modifications later made by the Meteorological Office. Published by permission of Her Majesty's Stationery Office.

Force	Specifications for coastal use	Knots Mean	Knots Limits	Miles per hour Mean	Miles per hour Limits	Metres per second Mean	Metres per second Limits
			Equivalent speed at 10 m. (33 ft.) above ground				
0	Calm.	0	<1	0	<1	0.0	0.0–0.2
1	Fishing smack† just has steerage way.	2	1–3	2	1–3	0.9	0.3–1.5
2	Wind fills the sails of smacks which then travel at about 1–2 kt.	5	4–6	5	4–7	2.4	1.6–3.3
3	Smacks begin to careen and travel at about 3–4 kt.	9	7–10	10	8–12	4.4	3.4–5.4
4	Good working breeze, smacks carry all canvas with good list.	13	11–16	15	13–18	6.7	5.5–7.9
5	Smacks shorten sail.	19	17–21	21	19–24	9.3	8.0–10.7
6	Smacks have double reef in mainsail. Care required when fishing.	24	22–27	28	25–31	12.4	10.8–13.8
7	Smacks remain in harbour and those at sea lie-to.	30	28–33	35	32–38	15.5	13.9–17.1
8	All smacks make for harbour, if near.	37	34–40	42	39–46	18.9	17.2–20.7
9	—	44	41–47	50	47–54	22.6	20.8–24.4
10	—	52	48–55	59	55–63	26.4	24.5–28.4
11	—	60	56–63	68	64–72	30.5	28.5–32.6
12	—	—	≥#64	—	≥#73	—	≥#32.7

---

† The fishing smack in this table may be taken as representing a trawler of average type and trim. For larger or smaller boats and for special circumstances, allowance must be made.

< = less than ≥ = equal to or greater than

The Elements Rage   [272]

Appendix B

Modified Mercalli Earthquake Intensity Scale (Abridged Version)

1. Not felt except by a very few under especially favorable circumstances.
2. Felt only by a few persons at rest, especially on the upper floors of buildings. Delicately suspended objects may swing.
3. Felt quite noticeably indoors, especially on the upper floors of buildings, but many people do not recognize it as an earthquake. Standing motorcars may rock slightly. Vibration like the passing of a truck. Duration estimated.
4. During the day, felt indoors by many, outdoors by few. At night, some awakened. Dishes, windows, doors disturbed; walls make cracking sound. Sensation like heavy truck striking the building. Standing motorcars rocked noticeably.
5. Felt by nearly everyone; many awakened. Some dishes, windows, etc., broken; a few instances of cracked plaster; unstable objects overturned. Disturbance of poles, trees, and other tall objects sometimes noticed. Pendulum clocks may stop.
6. Felt by all; many frightened and run outdoors. Some heavy furniture moved; a few instances of fallen plaster or damaged chimneys. Damage slight.
7. Everybody runs outdoors. Damage negligible in buildings of good design and construction; slight to moderate in well-built ordinary structures (considerable in poorly built or badly designed structures); some chimneys broken. Noticed by persons driving motorcars.
8. Damage slight in specially designed structures; considerable in ordinary substantial buildings with partial collapse; great in poorly built structures. Panel walls thrown out of frame structures. Fall of chimneys, factory stacks, columns, monuments, walls. Heavy furniture overturned. Sand and mud ejected in small amounts. Changes in well water. Disturbs persons driving motorcars.
9. Damage considerable in specially designed structures; well-designed frame structure thrown out of plumb; great in substantial buildings, with partial collapse. Buildings shifted off foundations. Ground cracked conspicuously. Underground pipes broken.
10. Some well-built wooden structures destroyed; most masonry and frame structures destroyed with foundations; ground badly cracked. Rails bent. Land-

[*273*]

slides considerable from river banks and slopes. Shifted sand and mud. Water splashed (slopped) over banks.

11. Few if any (masonry) structures remain standing. Bridges destroyed. Broad fissures in ground. Underground pipelines completely out of service. Earth slumps and landslips in soft ground. Rails bent greatly.

12. Damage total. Waves seen on ground surfaces. Lines of sight and level distorted. Objects thrown upward into the air.

NOTE: Other intensity scales, including one in great detail, are given in William Mansfield Adams' *Earthquakes* (1964).

Appendix C

Energy Scale

BY JOHN HARPUM

The basis of this energy scale is the erg, which is a unit in the centimeter-gram-second system and is widely used by scientists to express the energy released, or work done, in any form of physical activity.

There is no simple way of explaining what an erg is. It represents the work done by a force of one dyne acting through a distance of one centimeter. A dyne is a force which will give a mass of one gram an acceleration of one centimeter per second. The unit is extremely small. The tick of a wrist watch involves an energy expenditure of about 40 ergs, that of an ordinary domestic alarm clock about 250. To lift a weight of one ounce from a floor or table to a height of one foot involves about 850,000 ergs. To hit a home run at baseball involves some 10^{10} (ten thousand million) ergs.

The actual computation of the values on the energy scale involved a great number of calculations, well over 200. Some of these, such as the estimation of kinetic[1] and mass energies, were straightforward but others, such as the estimation of the energies involved in meteorological phenomena, involved a number of approximations. Many of the values given are a direct quotation or a slight reshaping of figures given in scientific journals and texts. It is clear that some of the values are open to dispute, but it is believed that, in general, the actual *order* is near to the real value. Some of the figures are, of course, quite hypothetical; the mass energies of the planets fall into this category.

The lower limit of the scale was taken as 10^{10} ergs, for below this the scale becomes too crowded for clarity. This limit does, unfortunately, exclude such interesting phenomena as the maximum energy detected in cosmic particles (1.6×10^8 ergs) and the value for a single 10^{-3} second energy burst from a ruby laser (10^8 ergs).

The energy values for such meteorological phenomena as thunderstorms, depressions, lightning and tornadoes may seem high. It must be obvious, however, that the potential mechanical energy of a large tropical cumulo-nimbus cloud, capable of precipitating six inches of rain in one hour, is enormous.

The ultimate figure on the scale—the mass energy of the Observable Uni-

---

[1] Kinetic energy is the energy an object has when it is in motion.

verse—is a concept that is open to considerable dispute. It supposedly represents the limit reached in the universe (from any given observer) at which the galaxies recede at the velocity of light and are therefore no longer visible.

Final comment should be made here on man's own efforts with fusion and fission bombs. To some extent the single megaton explosion has become a yardstick for our comparison with the energies of natural phenomena. The scale puts this particular weapon into its correct perspective; it is puny on any scale but man's. Whatever men may do, the elements rage with far greater power and effect.

Energy Scale

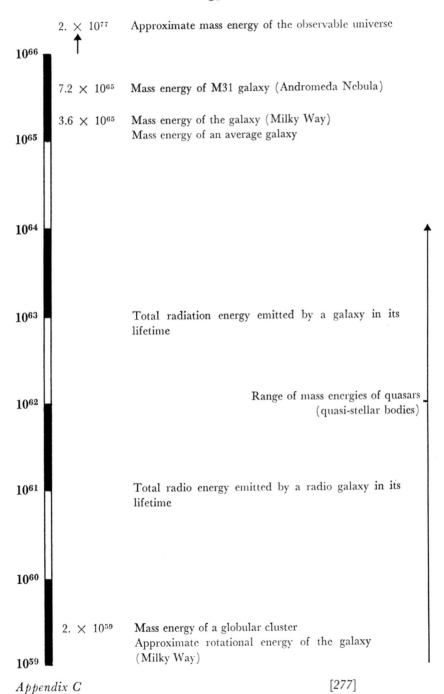

2. × 10⁷⁷   Approximate mass energy of the observable universe

10^{66}

7.2 × 10⁶⁵   Mass energy of M31 galaxy (Andromeda Nebula)

3.6 × 10⁶⁵   Mass energy of the galaxy (Milky Way)
10^{65} Mass energy of an average galaxy

10^{64}

10^{63} Total radiation energy emitted by a galaxy in its lifetime

10^{62} Range of mass energies of quasars (quasi-stellar bodies)

10^{61} Total radio energy emitted by a radio galaxy in its lifetime

10^{60}

2. × 10⁵⁹   Mass energy of a globular cluster
             Approximate rotational energy of the galaxy
10^{59} (Milky Way)

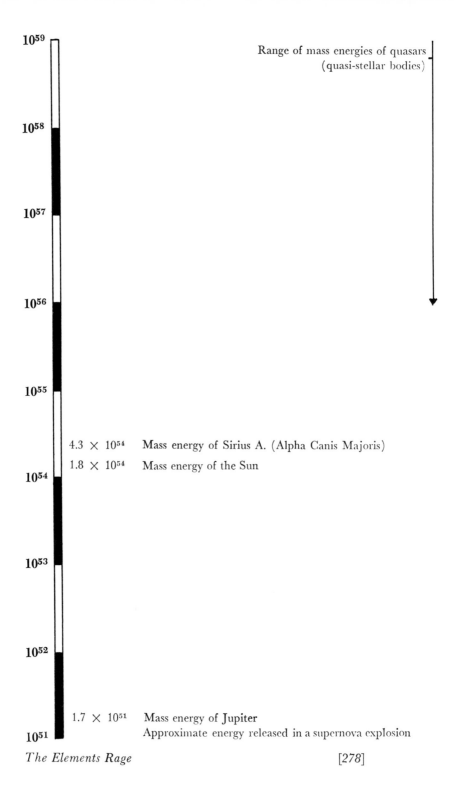

10^{59}

Range of mass energies of quasars
(quasi-stellar bodies)

10^{58}

10^{57}

10^{56}

10^{55}

4.3×10^{54} Mass energy of Sirius A. (Alpha Canis Majoris)

1.8×10^{54} Mass energy of the Sun

10^{54}

10^{53}

10^{52}

1.7×10^{51} Mass energy of **Jupiter**

Approximate energy released in a supernova explosion

10^{51}

The Elements Rage

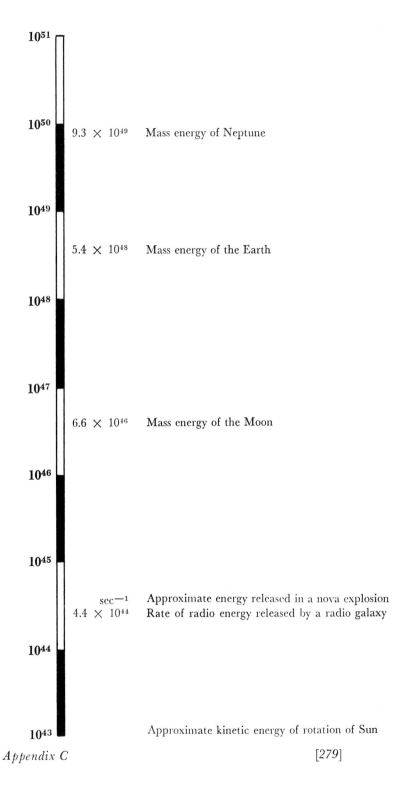

10^{51}

10^{50} 9.3×10^{49} Mass energy of Neptune

10^{49}

   5.4×10^{48} Mass energy of the Earth

10^{48}

10^{47}

   6.6×10^{46} Mass energy of the Moon

10^{46}

10^{45}

   sec^{-1} Approximate energy released in a nova explosion
   4.4×10^{44} Rate of radio energy released by a radio galaxy

10^{44}

10^{43} Approximate kinetic energy of rotation of Sun

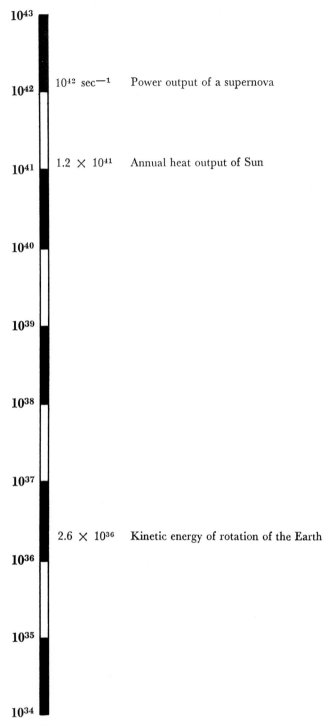

10^{43}

10^{42} 10^{42} $\sec^{-1}$ Power output of a supernova

10^{41} 1.2×10^{41} Annual heat output of Sun

10^{40}

10^{39}

10^{38}

10^{37}

     2.6×10^{36} Kinetic energy of rotation of the Earth

10^{36}

10^{35}

10^{34}

The Elements Rage

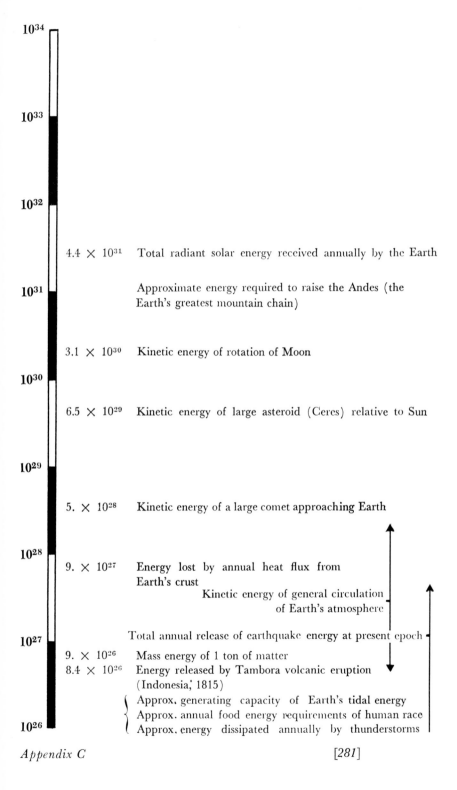

10^{34}

10^{33}

10^{32}

4.4×10^{31} Total radiant solar energy received annually by the Earth

10^{31} Approximate energy required to raise the Andes (the Earth's greatest mountain chain)

3.1×10^{30} Kinetic energy of rotation of Moon

10^{30}

6.5×10^{29} Kinetic energy of large asteroid (Ceres) relative to Sun

10^{29}

$5. \times 10^{28}$ Kinetic energy of a large comet approaching Earth

10^{28}

$9. \times 10^{27}$ Energy lost by annual heat flux from Earth's crust

Kinetic energy of general circulation of Earth's atmosphere

Total annual release of earthquake energy at present epoch

10^{27}

$9. \times 10^{26}$ Mass energy of 1 ton of matter

8.4×10^{26} Energy released by Tambora volcanic eruption (Indonesia, 1815)

Approx. generating capacity of Earth's tidal energy

Approx. annual food energy requirements of human race

10^{26} Approx. energy dissipated annually by thunderstorms

Appendix C   *[281]*

10^{26} — Total annual release of earthquake energy at present epoch ↓

c.2 × 10^{25} { Rotational kinetic energy of a large N. Atlantic depression
Energy released by impact of largest meteorite to hit Earth (S. Africa)

Approximate total energy released by Krakatoa eruptions of 1883

10^{25}

5.6 × 10^{24} Earthquake magnitude 8.9 (among largest recorded)
Approximate energy of 100-megaton fusion bomb

1.5 × 10^{24} Annual potential energy dissipated by Paraña (Guayra) Falls

10^{24}

9. × 10^{23} Mass energy of 1 kilogram of matter

8.8 × 10^{23} Annual potential energy dissipated by Niagara Falls

6. × 10^{23} Measured energy release of a 15-megaton fusion bomb

4.1 × 10^{23} Mass energy of 1 lb. of matter

2.5 × 10^{23} Earthquake magnitude 8

1.8 × 10^{23} Annual potential energy dissipated by Victoria Falls

10^{23} Approximate energy delivered by impact of great Siberian "meteorite" [comet?]

7.1 × 10^{22} Kinetic energy of meteorite that caused Arizona "meteor" crater

10^{22} Approximate energy of 1-megaton fusion bomb

Range of potential mechanical

7.9 × 10^{21} Earthquake magnitude 7   energy of thunderclouds

6.9 × 10^{21} Potential energy of one of largest landslides on record (Gilbert Inlet, July, 1958)

4.7 × 10^{21} Energy of Mt. Pelée eruption, 1902

10^{21} Approximate energy of very large meteorite (1,000 tons) impact on the Earth

9. × 10^{20} Mass energy of 1 gm. of matter

7.3 × 10^{20} Turtle Mountain avalanche, Alberta (April, 1903)

2.5 × 10^{20} Earthquake magnitude 6

10^{20}

Approximate total electrical energy of a thundercloud

4.4 × 10^{19} Earthquake magnitude 5½

2.0 × 10^{19} Annual kinetic energy dissipated by water of R. Amazon at its mouth

10^{19} 1.1 × 10^{19} Western Peru ice avalanche (January 1962)

8. × 10^{18} Kinetic energy of a 1-ton meteorite in space

7.9 × 10^{18} Earthquake magnitude 5 *and* approximate energy of a Hiroshima-type fission bomb

7.2 × 10^{18} Kinetic energy of a one-half-million–ton avalanche

4. × 10^{18} Approximate kinetic energy of rotation of a tornado

10^{18}

The Elements Rage   [282]

10¹⁸

3.7×10^{17} — Thermal energy of combustion of 1 ton of coal
3.0×10^{17} — Kinetic energy of a 1-ton space vehicle in Earth's orbit at 300 km.

2.5×10^{17} — Earthquake magnitude 4

10¹⁷

Approximate energy of a single flash of lightning

5.1×10^{16} — Kinetic energy of a 312,000-lb. jet aircraft flying at 600 mph

10¹⁶

7.9×10^{15} — Earthquake magnitude 3
4.1×10^{15} — Kinetic energy of a 500-ton train moving at 90 mph
3.6×10^{15} — Muzzle kinetic energy of a 16-inch naval shell
and output of a modern electricity generating windmill
1.5×10^{15} — Thermal energy of 1 gallon of fuel oil
1.05×10^{15} — Thermal energy of 1 therm of coal gas

10¹⁵

$5. \times 10^{14}$ — Kinetic energy of rotation of moderate-sized waterspout
2.5×10^{14} — Earthquake magnitude 2
1.6×10^{14} — Thermal energy of combustion of 1 lb. of coal
1.4×10^{14} — Average daily energy consumption and output of adult human male

10¹⁴

Range of potential mechanical energy of thunderclouds

3.6×10^{13} — 1 kilowatt-hour

10¹³

7.9×10^{12} — Earthquake magnitude 1
5.25×10^{12} — Thermal energy of 1 cu. ft. of coal gas
3.6×10^{12} — Kinetic energy of a 1-ton car moving at 60 mph *and* energy used in one hour by 100-watt electric light bulb

10¹²

2.5×10^{11} — Earthquake magnitude 0

10¹¹

4.7×10^{10} — Muzzle kinetic energy of bullet from sporting game rifle
4.2×10^{10} — Chemical energy of 1 gm. of conventional high explosive

10¹⁰

Home run hit at baseball

Appendix [283]

Bibliography

Bibliography

A small proportion of the entries has not been seen personally. In general abbreviations of periodicals follow the *World List of Scientific Periodicals.*

General Works

These references will not always be repeated after the individual chapters but most of them are relevant to all the chapters.

ANDERSON, CHARLES E., editor (1960). *Cumulus dynamics.* London and New York: Pergamon Press.

BRITTON, C. E. (1937). *A meteorological chronology to A.D. 1450.* London: H.M.S.O. (Meteorological Office. Geophysical Memoir—no. 70).

BROOKS, C. E. P. (1949). *Climate through the ages,* rev. ed. New York: McGraw-Hill.

HUSCHKE, RALPH E., editor (1959). *Glossary of meteorology.* Boston: American Meteorological Society.

KHRGIAN, A. K. H., editor (1963). *Cloud physics.* Translated from the Russian. Jerusalem: Israel Programme for Scientific Translations.

McINTOSH, DOUGLAS HAIG, compiler (1963). *Meteorological glossary,* 4th ed. London: H.M.S.O. (M.O. 729, A.P. 827).

MALONE, THOMAS FRANCIS, editor (1951). *Compendium of meteorology.* Boston: American Meteorological Society.

METEOROLOGICAL OFFICE (1963). *The marine observer's handbook,* 8th ed. London: H.M.S.O.

SMITH, DE WITT, editor (1957). Disasters and disaster relief. *Annals of the American Academy of Political and Social Science,* 309.

STRAHLER, ARTHUR N. (1963). *The earth sciences.* New York: Harper.

For a general bibliography, see:

Fassig, Oliver L., editor (1889–91). *Bibliography of meteorology*. A classic catalogue of the printed literature of meteorology from the origin of printing to the close of . . . 1887 . . . Prepared under the direction of A. W. Greely. Washington: War Department. This has been described as the most ambitious and intensive bibliographic project ever undertaken in meteorology.

Malon, Thomas Francis, editor (1951). *Compendium of meteorology*. Boston: American Meteorological Society.

For current references, see:

Meteorological and geoastrophysical abstracts, published by the American Meteorological Society, in particular volume 6, 1955, nos. 1 and 2, a *Bibliography of bibliographies*.

Hurricanes

Ainlay, George (1944). 1944—year for the great hurricane! *Sci. Dig.* May 15: 39–40.

Albright, John Grover (1939). *Physical meteorology*. New York: Prentice-Hall.

Arakawa, H. & Suda, K. (1953). Analysis of winds, wind waves, and swells over the sea to the east of Japan during the typhoon of September 26, 1935. *Mon. Weath. Rev., Wash.* **81:** 31–37.

Arnold, Rudy (1939). After a hurricane. *Pop. Sci. Mon.* **134:** 65–70.

Baldwin, Hanson W. (1951). When the Third Fleet met the great typhoon. *New York Times Magazine,* December 16: 18, 48–49, 51–52.

———— (1955). *Sea fights and shipwrecks*. New York: Hanover House-Doubleday.

Band, Gunther (1955). Bora und Mistral. *Arch. Met. Geophys. Bioklim.* Ser. B. **6:** 225–35.

Bentley, Richard (1907). Weather in war-time. *Quart. J. R. met. Soc.* **33:** 81–138.

Bergeron, T. (1954). The problem of tropical hurricanes. *Quart. J. R. met. Soc.* **80:** 131–64.

Biggs, J. M. (1961). Wind forces on structures. *Trans. Amer. Soc. civil Engrs.* **126:** 124–98.

Bilham, E. G. (1938). *The climate of the British Isles*. London: MacMillan.

Blodget, Lorin (1857). *Climatology of the United States*. Philadelphia: Lippincott.

Bogart, Dean B. (1960). *Floods of August–October 1955, New England to North Carolina*. Washington: U. S. Government Printing Office (U. S. Geological Survey. Water-supply paper 1420). [Floods following hurricanes]

Brooks, C. E. P. (1954). *The English climate*. London: English Universities Press.

Brooks, Charles F. (1935). *Why the weather?* Rev. ed. New York: Harcourt.

———— (1941). Two winter storms encountered by Columbus in 1493 near the Azores. *Bull. Amer. met. Soc.* **22:** 303–309.

BROWN, ANDREW H. (1950). Men against the hurricane. *Nat. geogr. Mag.* **98:** 537–60.

CAIN, ERNEST E. (1932). *Cyclone!* London: Stockwell.

———— (1963). *Cyclone "Hattie," being an illustrated account of the hurricane and tidal wave which destroyed the city of Belize in British Honduras on the 31st day of October, 1961.* Ufracombe: Stockwell.

CARIBBEAN HURRICANE SEMINAR, Ciudad Trujillo, D.N., Dominican Republic, February 16–25, 1955 (1958). *Final Report.* Ciudad Trujillo, D.N. Government of the Dominican Republic. [Seminar held under joint auspices of the Dominican Republic, the U.N. Technical Assistance Administration and the World Meteorological Organization.]

CARSON, RACHEL L. (1951). *The sea around us.* New York: Oxford University Press.

CHANGOPADHYAYA, G., & RIEHL, H. (1958). Exchange of heat, moisture and momentum between *Hurricane Ella* and its environment. *Quart. J. R. met. Soc.* **85:** 278–86.

Chronicon Angliae ad a. 1323 usque ad a. 1388, auctore monacho quodam S. Albani. Ed. E. Maunde Thompson. [Rolls Ser., 64] 1874.

CLINE, ISAAC MUNROE (1926). *Tropical cyclones.* New York: Macmillan.

COLTON, F. BARROWS (1939). The geography of a hurricane [New England hurricane of September 1938]. *Nat. geogr. Mag.* **75:** 529–52.

———— (1943). Weather fights and works for man. *Nat. geogr. Mag.* **84:** 641–70.

COLUMBUS, CHRISTOPHER (1930). *The voyages of Christopher Columbus.* Newly translated and edited by Cecil Jane. London: Argonaut Press.

CONRAD, JOSEPH (1902). *Typhoon.* New York: Putnam's Sons.

COOKE, ALISTAIR (1954). The path of the American hurricane. *Manchester Guardian,* September 2.

DAVIS, ALBERT B., JR. (1961). *Galveston's bulwark against the sea: history of the Galveston sea wall.* Galveston, Texas: U. S. Army Engineer District, Corps of Engineers.

DEFANT, FRIEDRICH (1951). *Wind.* (In *Compendium of meteorology,* edited by Thomas F. Malone. Boston, Mass.: American Meteorological Society.)

DEFOE, DANIEL (1704). *The storm or, A collection of the most remarkable casualties and disasters which happened in the late dreadful tempest, both by sea and land.* London: G. Sawbridge.

DINGLE, AYLWARD EDWARD (1933). *A modern Sinbad: an autobiography.* London: Harrap.

DOBERCK, WILLIAM (1895). *The typhoons in China Seas.* London: Shipmasters' Society (Papers—no. 37).

———— (1896). *How to manage your ship in a typhoon.* London: Shipmasters' Society (Papers—no. 42).

DORLING, H. TAPRELL ["Taffrail"] (1927). *Sea escapes and adventures.* New York: Stokes.

DOUGLAS, MARJORY STONEMAN (1958). *Hurricane.* New York: Rinehart.

DUANE, J. E., JR. (1935). The hurricane of September 2, 1935, at Long Key, Florida. *Bull. Amer. met. Soc.* **16:** 238–39.

DUNN, GORDON E. (1962). The tropical cyclone problem in East Pakistan. *Mon. Weath. Rev., Wash.* **90:** 83–6.

Dunn, Gordon E. & Miller, Banner I. (1960). *Atlantic hurricanes*. Baton Rouge: Louisiana State University Press.

Dunn, Gordon E. & Staff (1962). The hurricane season of 1961. *Mon. Weath. Rev., Wash.* **90:** 107–19.

Durst, C. S. (1926). *The doldrums of the Atlantic.* London: H.M.S.O. (Meteorological Office. Geophysical Memoir—no. 28).

Emeny, Stuart (1942). Tidal wave kills 10,000 people. *News Chronicle,* November 14.

Fassig, O. L. (1929). Discussion of tropical cyclones. *Mon. Weath. Rev., Wash.* **57:** 331.

Fowler, John (1781). *A general account of the calamities occasioned by the late tremendous hurricanes and earthquakes in the West-India Islands.* London: J. Stockdale.

Free, E. E. & Hoke, Travis (1928). *Weather.* New York: McBride.

Freeman, M. H. (1952). *Duststorms of the Anglo-Egyptian Sudan.* London: H.M.S.O. (Meteorological Office. Meteorological reports series—no. 11).

Gaillard, D. D. (1904). *Wave action in relation to engineering structures.* Fort Belvoir, Va.: The Engineer School (U. S. Corps of Engineers Professional Paper—31).

Gentry, R. C. (1955). Wind velocities during hurricanes. *Trans. Amer. Soc. civil Engrs.* **120:** 169.

Halpine, Charles Greham (1941). *A pilot's meteorology.* New York: Van Nostrand.

Harris, D. L. (1963a). *Characteristics of the hurricane storm surge.* Washington, D. C.: U. S. Weather Bureau (Technical paper—no. 48).

——— (1963b). *Coastal flooding by the storm of March 5–7, 1962.* Washington, D. C.: U. S. Weather Bureau [unpublished manuscript].

Horiguti, Yosiki (1925–29). [Series of articles on Far Eastern typhoons in *Memoirs of the Imperial Marine Observatory, Kobe.*]

——— (1932). On the energy of a typhoon. *Geophys. Mag.* **6:** 39–57.

Hubert, L. F. & Berg, O. (1955). A rocket portrait of a tropical storm. *Mon. Weath. Rev., Wash.* **83:** 119–24.

Hughes, Richard Arthur Warren (1938). *In hazard: a sea story.* New York: Harper.

Humphreys, W. J. (1943). *Ways of the weather.* Lancaster, Penna.: Jaques Cattel Press.

Kenney, Nathaniel T. (1962). Our changing Atlantic coastline. *Nat. geogr. Mag.* **122:** 860–87.

Krauss, J. & Stein, W. (1958). *Wetter- und Meereskunde für Seefahrer.* Berlin: Springer Verlag.

Lackner, Peter R. (1945). Tropical cyclones throughout the world. *Proc. U. S. nav. Inst.* **71:** 1059–81.

Lapham, I. A. (1872). List of the great storms, hurricanes and tornadoes of the United States. *J. Franklin Inst.* 3rd series **64** 1: 210–16.

Laughton, L. G. Carr & Heddon, V. (1931). *Great storms,* 2nd ed. New York: W. F. Payson.

The Elements Rage

LEET, LEWIS DON (1948). *Causes of catastrophe.* New York & London: McGraw-Hill.

LUDLUM, DAVID M. (1963). *Early American hurricanes, 1492–1870.* Boston, Mass.: American Meteorological Society (The history of American weather—no. 1).

McWHIRTER, NORRIS & McWHIRTER, ROSS (1964). *The Guinness book of records,* 11th ed. London: Guinness Superlatives Ltd.

MALKIN, W. & GALWAY, J. G. (1953). Tornadoes associated with hurricanes. *Mon. Weath. Rev., Wash.* **81:** 299–303.

MARTYR, WESTON (1937). I am frightened for the men in *Enkaba. News Chronicle,* September 21.

MARVIN, CHARLES F., *et al.* (1934). The great wind of April 11–12, 1934, on Mount Washington, N. H., and its measurement. *Mon. Weath. Rev., Wash.* **62:** 186–95.

MILES, M. K. (1948). The structure of the tropical atmosphere: analytical and prediction methods. *Sci. Progr.* **36:** 86–101.

MILHAM, WILLIS I. (1912). *Meteorology.* New York: Macmillan.

MILLÁS, JOSÉ CARLOS (1962). *The hurricanes of the Caribbean Sea and adjacent regions at the end of the fifteenth century.* Miami, Fla.: Institute of Marine Science, University of Miami (Preliminary report, contract CWB-10279).

———— (1963). *The hurricanes of the Caribbean Sea and adjacent regions during the sixteenth century.* Miami, Fla.: Marine Laboratory, University of Miami (Preliminary report, contract CWB-10467).

———— (1964). *The hurricanes of the Caribbean Sea and adjacent regions during the seventeenth century.* Miami, Fla.: Institute of Marine Science, University of Miami (Final report, contract CWB-10739).

MINIKIN, R. R. (1963). *Winds, waves and maritime structures,* 2nd rev. ed. London: Griffin.

MOORE, WILLIS LUTHER (1927). I am thinking of hurricanes. *American Mercury* **12** September: 81–6.

MORISON, SAMUEL ELIOT (1959). *The liberation of the Philippines: Luzon, Mindanao, the Visayas, 1944–1945.* Boston, Mass.: Little, Brown. (History of United States Naval Operations in World War II—vol. XIII.)

NEWBERRY, C. W. & WISE, A. F. E. (1963). How wind shapes buildings. *Discovery* **24:** 28–34.

NIMITZ, C. W. (1956). [Letter on lessons of damage in typhoon.] *Proc. U. S. nav. Inst.* **82:** 83–88.

PALMEN, E. (1948). On the formation and structure of tropical hurricanes. *Geophysica* **3:** 26–38.

PAULHUS, J. L. H. (1965). Indian Ocean and Taiwan rainfalls set new records. *Mon. Weath. Rev., Wash.* **93:** 331–5.

PAULSEN, CARL G., *et al.* (1940). *Hurricane floods of September 1938.* Washington, D. C.: U. S. Government Printing Office (Water-supply paper—no. 867).

PFEFFER, RICHARD L. (1964). The global atmospheric circulation. *Trans. N. Y. Acad. Sci.* Ser. 2 **26:** 984–97.

PIDDINGTON, HENRY (1876). *The sailor's horn-book for the law of storms,* 6th ed. London: Norgate.

PISTON, DONALD S. (1941). *Meteorology.* 2nd ed. Philadelphia: Blakiston.

Bibliography   [*291*]

PROCEEDINGS OF THE CONFERENCE HELD AT THE NATIONAL PHYSICAL LABORATORY, Teddington Middlesex, 26–28 June, 1963. *Wind effects on buildings and structures* (in press). London: H.M.S.O.

RAETHJEN, P. (1953). *Dynamik der Zyklonen.* Leipzig: Akademische Verlag.

RECLUS, ÉLISÉE (1873). *The ocean, atmosphere, and life.* New York: Harper.

Record of Proceedings of a Court of Inquiry convened on board U.S.S. *Cascade* . . . to inquire into all the circumstances connected with the loss of the U.S.S. *Hull,* etc., December 26, 1944. [Ms in office of Judge Advocate General of the Navy, Washington.]

REDFIELD, ALFRED C. & MILLER, A. R. (1957). Water levels accompanying Atlantic coast hurricanes. *Met. Monogr.* 2 10: 1–23.

REEDS, CHESTER A. (1928). Storms and storm tracks. *Nat. Hist., N. Y.* 28: 589–604.

REID, W. (1846). *An attempt to develop the law of storms by means of facts, arranged according to place and time* . . . , 2nd ed. London: John Weale.

REITER, EIMAR R. (1963). *Jet-stream meteorology.* Chicago, Ill.: Chicago University Press.

RIEHL, HERBERT (1954). *Tropical meteorology.* New York & London: McGraw-Hill.

——— (1958). *On the production of kinetic energy from condensation heating.* Miami, Fla.: National Hurricane Research Project (Report—no. 22).

——— (1962). Jet streams of the atmosphere. *Colorado State University. Technical Paper No. 32:* 117, 188.

——— (1963). On the origin and possible modification of hurricanes. *Science* 141: 1001–10.

——— (1964). Tropical storm. *Encyclopaedia Britannica* 22: 497–500.

RODNEY, LORD GEORGE (1932). Letter-books and order-books of George, Lord Rodney, 1780–1782. *Coll. N. Y. Hist. Soc.* 65 1: 91–92.

SCRUTON, CHRISTOPHER & NEWBERRY, CYRIL WILLIAM (1963). On the estimation of wind loads for building and structural design. *Min. Proc. Inst. civ. Engrs.* 25: 97–126.

SHAW, SIR WILLIAM NAPIER & AUSTIN, ELAINE (1936). *Manual of meteorology,* vol. 2: Comparative meteorology, 2nd ed. Cambridge: Cambridge University Press.

SIMPSON, R. H. (1954). Hurricanes. *Sci. Amer.* 190 6: 32–36.

SMITH, HENRY (1962). A high wind in Sheffield. *The Guardian,* July 4.

STEARUS, ROBERT D. (1960). Dot: Hawaii's third hurricane. *Weatherwise* 13: 146–9.

STEVENSON, THOMAS (1886). *The design and construction of harbours.* Edinburgh: Black.

STOCKING, HOBART E. (1943). Nine-day wonders. *Nat. Hist., N. Y.* 52: 72–77.

STODDART, D. R. (1962). Catastrophic storm effects on the British Honduras reefs and cays. *Nature* 196: 512–15.

SUMNER, H. C. (1944). The North Atlantic hurricane of September 8–16, 1944. *Mon. Weath. Rev., Wash.* 72: 187–89.

SUTTON, SIR GRAHAM (1965). The energy of the atmosphere. *Science J.* 11: 76–81.

TAKAHASHI, K. (1954). On the relationship between typhoon energy and damage amount. *Proceedings of the Unesco Symposium on Typhoons:* 23–30.

The Elements Rage   [292]

——— (1962). Analysis of typhoon disasters in Japan. *Proceedings of the Interregional Seminar on Tropical Cyclones in Tokyo:* 279–87.

TALMAN, CHARLES F. (1931). *The realm of the air.* Indianapolis, Ind.: Bobbs-Merrill.

TANNEHILL, IVAN RAY (1942). *Hurricanes: their nature and history,* 2nd ed. Princeton, N. J.: Princeton University Press.

——— (1954). *Hurricane hunters.* New York: Dodd, Mead & Co.

——— (1956a). *The hurricane.* Washington, D. C.: U. S. Weather Bureau.

——— (1956b). *Hurricanes: their nature and history.* Princeton, N. J.: Princeton University Press.

TOWNSEND, C. H. (1936). Two giant tortoises were swept twenty miles by hurricane. *Bull. N. Y. zool. Soc.* **39:** 119–20.

TREVELYAN, GEORGE MACAULAY (1930). *England under Queen Anne: Blenheim.* New York: Longmans.

TROPICAL CYCLONE CONFERENCE, Brisbane, 13–16 September, 1955 (1955). *Report.* Brisbane: Bureau of Meteorology.

UNDT, W. (1958). Meteorologie des Föhns. *Med.-met. Hefte* No. 13: 97–111.

UNESCO (1955). *Proceedings of the Unesco symposium on typhoons.* Tokyo: Japanese National Commission for Unesco.

UNITED STATES WEATHER BUREAU (1962). *Notes on the naming of hurricanes.* Washington, D. C.: U. S. Weather Bureau.

VARIOUS AUTHORS (1890). Disaster at Apia, Samoa. *Report of the Secretary of the [U.S.] Navy, 1889:* 95–123.

VISHER, STEPHEN S. & HODGE, D. (1925). *Australian hurricanes and related storms.* Melbourne: Commonwealth Bureau of Meteorology Bulletin—no. 16.

WEEMS, JOHN EDWARD (1957). *A weekend in September* [account of the Galveston, Texas, hurricane of September 8–9, 1900]. New York: Holt.

WENSTROM, WILLIAM H. (1942). *Weather and the ocean of air.* Boston, Mass.: Houghton.

WHITBREAD, R. E. (1963). Wind effects on buildings and structures. *Nature* **199:** 1049–50.

WILSON, JUNE (1955). The worst storm in English history. *Country Life* **118:** 1194–95.

WINTERICH, JOHN T. (1938). Hurricane [New England hurricane of September 1938]. *New Yorker,* December 17.

For bibliographies, see:

HUTCHINGS, J. W., editor (1964). *Proceedings of the Symposium on Tropical Meteorology.* Wellington, N. Z.: New Zealand Meteorological Service.

INTER-REGIONAL SEMINAR ON TROPICAL CYCLONES in Tokyo, January 18–31, 1962 (1963). *Proceedings.* Tokyo: Japan Meteorological Agency (Technical report—no. 21).

KRAMER, MOLLIE P. (1955). Annotated bibliography on storm surges. *Met. Abstr.* **6:** 370–92.

NUPEN, WILHELM & RIGBY, MALCOLM (1956). Annotated bibliography on tropical cyclones, hurricanes and typhoons. *Met. Abstr.* **7:** 1115–63.

Bibliography   [*293*]

STEPANOVA, NINA A. (1951). Selective annotated bibliography on special winds. *Met. Abstr.* **2:** 586–629.

Tornadoes

ALBRIGHT, JOHN GROVER (1939). *Physical meteorology.* New York: Prentice-Hall.

ANON. (1925). Engineers study tornado forces. *Illinois Central Magazine* **14:** 14–16.

———— (1944). Many killed in U. S. tornado: damage in three states. *The Times, June 26.*

———— (1959). Waterspouts and tornadoes. *Weather* **14:** 103–104.

BARNABY, RALPH S. (1941). *This Week Magazine,* December 28.

BATES, F. C. (1962). Tornadoes in the central United States. *Trans. Kans. Acad. Sci.* **65:** 215–46.

———— (1963). An aerial observation of a tornado and its parent cloud. *Weather* **18:** 12–18.

BATHURST, G. B. (1964). The earliest recorded tornado. *Weather* **19:** 202–204.

BATTAN, LOUIS J. (1959). Duration of tornadoes. *Bull. Amer. met. Soc.* **40:** 340–42.

———— (1961). *The nature of violent storms.* New York: Doubleday & Co.

BIGELOW, FRANK H. (1908). The truncated dumb-bell vortex illustrated by the St. Louis, Mo., tornado of May 27, 1846. *Mon. Weath. Rev., Wash.* **36:** 245–50.

BILLET, H. (1914). *The South Wales tornado of October 27, 1913.* London: H.M.S.O. (Meteorological Office. Geophysical Memoir—no. 11).

BLAIR, THOMAS ARTHUR (1942). *Weather elements.* New York: Prentice-Hall.

BLEEKER, W. & DELVER, A. (1951). Some new ideas on the formation of windspouts and tornadoes. *Arch. Met., Wien,* Serie A: 220–36.

BLODGET, LORIN (1857). *Climatology of the United States.* Philadelphia: Lippincott.

BONACINA, L. C. W. (1946). The Widecombe calamity of 1638. *Weather* **1:** 123–25.

———— & SIMMONDS, J. (1950). Tornadoes across England. *Weather* **5:** 254–57..

BOTLEY, C. M. (1940). *The air and its mysteries.* New York: D. Appleton-Century.

BROOKS, C. E. P. (1954). *The English climate.* London: English Universities Press.

BROOKS, CHARLES F. (1935). *Why the weather?* rev. ed. New York: Harcourt.

BROOKS, EDWARD M. (1951). *Tornadoes and related phenomena.* In Malone, Thomas Francis, editor (1951). *Compendium of meteorology.* Boston, Mass.: American Meteorological Society.

BUCK, ROBERT N. (1959). "What about the weather, Captain?" *Air Facts* **22** 5: 11–18.

BURR, MALCOLM (1939). *The insect legion.* London: Nisbet.

BUSCH, NOEL FAIRCHILD (1963). *Two minutes to noon.* New York: Simon & Schuster.

BUXTON, P. A. (1923). *Animal life in deserts.* London: Arnold.

BYERS, HORACE ROBERT (1937). *Synoptic and aeronautical meteorology.* New York & London: McGraw-Hill.

CROZIER, W. D. (1964). The electric field of a New Mexico dust devil. *J. Geophys. Res.* **69:** 5427–29.

DAVIS, WILLIAM MORRIS (1884). *Whirlwinds, cyclones and tornadoes.* Boston, Mass.: Lee & Shepard.

DELMER, SEFTON (1961). Did bombing break the Germans? *The Sunday Telegraph,* London, September 24.

DELVER, A. (1955). *Hozen en Hozentheorieën,* The Hague: Staatsdrukkerij–en nitgeverij bedrijf (Koninklijk Nederlands Meteorologisch Instituut. Verspreide Opstellen—2).

DESSENS, JEAN (1962). Man-made tornadoes. *Nature* **193:** 13–14.

ESPY, JAMES POLLAND (1841). *The philosophy of storms.* Boston, Mass.: Little, Brown.

FINLEY, JOHN PARK (1887). *Tornadoes.* New York: Insurance Monitor.

FLAMMARION, CAMILLE (1873). *The atmosphere.* Translated by C. B. Pitman. Edited by J. Glaisher. New York: Harper.

FLORA, SNOWDEN D. (1929). What a tornado looks like. *Mon. Weath. Rev., Wash.* **57:** 337–38.

———— (1953). *Tornadoes of the United States.* Norman, Okla.: Oklahoma University Press.

FLORENTIUS, WIGORNIENSIS [John of Worcester] (1854). *The Chronicle of Florence of Worcester, with the two continuations.* Translated from the Latin by T. Forester. London: Bohn.

FREE, E. E. & HOKE, TRAVIS (1928). *Weather.* New York: McBride.

FUJITA, TETSUYA (1960). *A detailed analysis of the Fargo tornadoes of June 20, 1957.* Washington, D. C.: U. S. Weather Bureau (Research paper—no. 42).

GORDON, A. N. (1959). [Comments quoted in feature entitled "Waterspouts and tornadoes"]. *Weather* **14:** 103–104.

GRAHAM, HOWARD E. (1952). A fire-whirlwind of tornadic violence. *Weatherwise* **5:** 59, 62.

GREELY, A. W. (1888). *American weather.* New York: Dodd, Mead & Co.

HALL, FERGUSON & BREWER, ROBERT D. (1959): A sequence of tornado damage patterns. *Mon. Weath. Rev., Wash.* **87:** 207–16.

HARRIS, SIR ARTHUR (1947). *Bomber offensive.* New York: Macmillan.

HARRISON, H. T. (1952). *Certain tornado and squall line features.* Denver, Colo.: United Air Lines (Meteorology circular—no. 36).

HARVEY, J. B. (1951). An historic storm. *Weather* **6:** 159–60.

HAWKE, E. L. (1938). The tornado of July 7, 1938, in the Chiltern Hills. *Quart. J. R. met. Soc.* **64:** 616–18.

HAZEN, HENRY ALLEN (1890). *The tornado.* New York: N. D. C. Hodges.

HENINGER, S. K., JR. (1960). *A handbook of renaissance meteorology.* Durham, N. C.: Duke University Press.

HERSEY, JOHN (1946). *Hiroshima.* New York: Knopf.

HISSONG, J. E. (1926). Whirlwinds at oil-tank fire, San Luis Obispo, Calif. *Mon. Weath. Rev., Wash.* **54:** 161–63.

HOECKER, WALTER H., JR., *et al.* (1960). *The tornadoes at Dallas, Texas, April 2, 1957.* Washington, D. C.: U. S. Weather Bureau (Research paper—no. 41).

HOUSE, DONALD C. (1963). Forecasting tornadoes and severe thunderstorms. *Met. Monogr.* 5 27: 141–55.

HUMPHREYS, W. J. (1937). *Weather rambles*. Baltimore, Md.: Williams & Wilkins.
—— (1940). *Physics of the air*, 3rd ed. New York & London: McGraw-Hill.
IRVING, DAVID (1963). *The destruction of Dresden*. London: Kimber.
IVES, R. L. (1947). Behavior of dust devils. *Bull. Amer. met. Soc.* **28:** 168–74.
JUSTICE, ALONZO A. (1930). Seeing the inside of a tornado. *Mon. Weath. Rev., Wash.* **58:** 205–206.
KNEBEL, FLETCHER & BAILEY, CHARLES (1960). *No high ground*. New York: Harper.
KOLOBKOV, N. (1962). *Our atmospheric ocean*. Moscow: Foreign Languages Publishing House.
LAMB, H. H. (1957). *Tornadoes in England May 21, 1950*. London: H.M.S.O. (Geophysical memoirs—no. 99).
LAPHAM, I. A. (1872). List of the great storms, hurricanes and tornadoes of the United States. *J. Franklin Institute*. 3rd series **64** 1: 210–16.
LEMONS, HOYT (1938). Some meteorological aspects of Nebraska tornadoes. *Mon. Weath. Rev., Wash.* **66:** 205–208.
LINEHAN, URBAN J. (1957). *Tornado deaths in the United States*. Washington, D. C. U. S. Weather Bureau (Technical paper—no. 30).
LOOMIS, ELIAS (1842). On a tornado which passed over Mayfield, Ohio, February 4, 1842. *American Journal of Science and Arts* **43:** 278–300.
LOWE, A. B. & MCKAY, G. A. (1962). *The tornadoes of Western Canada*. Ottawa: Meteorological Branch, Dept. of Transport.
LUDLUM, DAVID M. *Early American tornadoes and storm theory to 1870* [in preparation].
LYELL, SIR CHARLES (1875). *Principles of geology*, 12th ed. Edited by L. Lyell. London: John Murray.
MARTIN, ROBERT J. (1940). *Tornadoes in the United States, 1916–1937*. Washington, D. C.: U. S. Weather Bureau.
MATTSSON, JAN O. (1963). Några iakttagelser av en tromb i Lundatrakten. *Svensk geogr. Årsb.* **39:** 166–72.
MILHAM, WILLIS I. (1912). *Meteorology*. New York: Macmillan.
MILLIGEN-JOHNSTON, GEORGE (1770). *A short description of the Province of South Carolina*. London: John Hinton [Reprinted in *Colonial South Carolina*. Columbia, S. C.: University of South Carolina Press, 1951].
MOORE, ELY (1908). A buffalo hunt with the Miamis in 1854. *Kansas Hist. Coll.* **10:** 402.
MOORE, WILLIS L. (1922). *The new air world*. Boston, Mass.: Little, Brown.
MORTON, B. R. (1963). Model experiments for vortex columns in the atmosphere. *Nature, Lond.* **197:** 840–42.
MURPHY, J. J. (1935). Meteorological features and history of tornado at Norfolk, Virginia. *Bull. Amer. met. Soc.* **16:** 252–55.
NEWTON, CHESTER W. (1963). Dynamics of severe convective storms. *Met. Monogr.* **5** 27: 33–58.
OUTRAM, T. S. (1904). Storm of August 20, 1904, in Minnesota. *Mon. Weath. Rev., Wash.* **32:** 365–66.
PISTON, DONALD S. (1941). *Meteorology*, 2nd ed. Philadelphia, Pa.: Blakiston.
POPE, L. G. (1928). The wind's whirligig of death. *Pop. Sci. Mon.* **112** May: 31–32.

Pough, Frederick H. (1943). Parícutin is born. *Nat. Hist., N. Y.* **52**: 134–42.

Reeds, Chester A. (1928). *Storms and storm tracks. Nat. Hist., N. Y.* **28**: 589–604.

Reid, W. (1846). *An attempt to develop the law of storms by means of facts, arranged according to place and time,* 2nd ed. London: John Weale.

Reynolds, George W. (1958). Venting and other building practices as practical means of reducing damage from tornado low pressures. *Bull. Amer. met. Soc.* **39**: 14–20.

Roger, de Hoveden (1853). *The annals of Roger de Hoveden.* Translated from the Latin by H. T. Riley. London: Bohn 2 vols.

Ross, J. T. (1816). Narrative of the effects of the eruption from the Tambora Mountain, in the Island of Sumbawa, on the 11th and 12th of April 1815. *Verhandelingen van her Bataviaasch Genootschap van Kunsten en Wetenschappen* **8.**

Rossman, Fritz O. (1958). Differences in the physical behaviour of tornadoes and waterspouts. *Weather* **13**: 259–63.

——— (1959). Some further remarks on waterspouts. *Weather* **14**: 104–105.

[Rowe, J. B.] (1905). *The two Widecombe tracts, 1638 giving a contemporary account of the great storm, reprinted with an introduction.* Exeter: Commin.

Russell, Henry Chamberlaine (1898). Water spouts on the coast of New South Wales. *J. roy. Soc. N. S. W.* **32**: 132–49.

Seelye, C. J. (1945). Tornadoes in New Zealand. *N. Z. J. Sci. Tech.* **27** 2B: 164–74.

——— (1946). Tornadoes in New Zealand. *Met. Off. Note, N. Z.* **28**: 166–74.

Shaw, Sir William Napier (1923). *The air and its ways.* Cambridge: Cambridge University Press.

——— & Austin, Elaine (1936). *Manual of meteorology.* vol. 2: Comparative Meteorology, 2nd ed. Cambridge: Cambridge University Press.

Showalter, A. K. & Fulks, J. R. (1943). *Preliminary report on tornados.* Washington, D. C.: U. S. Weather Bureau.

Smith, Robert L. & Holmes, David W. (1961). Use of Doppler radar in meteorological observations. *Mon. Weath. Rev., Wash.* **89**: 1–7.

Sutton, Sir Graham (1959). *Tornadoes. New Scient.* **5**: 400–401.

——— (1962). *The challenge of the atmosphere.* London: Hutchinson.

Talman, Charles F. (1931). *The realm of the air.* Indianapolis, Ind.: Bobbs-Merrill.

Taylor, George F. (1941). *Aeronautical meteorology.* Revised and enlarged edition. New York: Pitman.

Tepper, Morris (1958). *Tornadoes. Sci. Amer.* **198** 5: 31–37.

United States Weather Bureau (1960). *Community tornado safety.* Washington, D. C.: U. S. Weather Bureau.

Van Everdingen, E. (1925). The cyclone-like whirlwinds of August 10, 1925. *Proc. Sect. Sci. K. ned. Akad. Wet.* **28**: 871–99.

Van Tassel, Edgar L. (1955). The North Platte Valley tornado outbreak of June 27, 1955. *Mon. Weath. Rev., Wash.* **83**: 255–64.

Vonnegut, Bernard (1960). Electrical theory of tornadoes. *J. Geophys. Res.,* **65**: 203–12.

————— & Moore, Charles B. (1958). *Giant electrical storms* (in Smith, L. G., editor (1958): *Recent advances in atmospheric electricity*. London: Pergamon Press).

————— *et al.* (1960). Stabilization of a high-voltage discharge by a vortex. *J. Met.* **174:** 468–71.

Walker, Gilbert T. (1930). On the mechanism of tornadoes. *Quart. J. R. met. Soc.* **54:** 59–66.

Wallace, Anthony F. C. (1956). *Tornado in Worcester*. Washington, D. C.: National Academy of Sciences—National Research Council (Disaster study—no. 3).

Ward, Robert de C. (1917). The tornadoes of the United States as climatic phenomena. *Quart. J. R. met. Soc.* **43:** 317–29.

Wegener, Alfred (1917). *Wind- und Wasserhosen in Europa*. Braunschweig: Vieweg.

Wenstrom, William H. (1942). *Weather and the ocean of air*. Boston, Mass.: Houghton.

Wilkins, E. M. (1964). The role of electrical phenomena associated with tornadoes. *J. geophys. Res.* **69:** 2435–37 [Comments on this paper by N. R. Williams, pp. 5425–26].

Williams, N. R. (1948). Development of dust whirls and similar small-scale vortices. *Bull. Amer. met. Soc.* **29:** 106–17.

Winston, Jay S. (1956). *Forecasting tornadoes and severe thunderstorms*. Washington, D. C.: United States Department of Commerce.

Wolford, Laura V. (1960). *Tornado occurrences in the United States*, rev. ed. Washington, D. C.: U. S. Weather Bureau (Technical paper—no. 20).

Wood, Eliott Colpoys (1962). *A guide to the parish church at Widecombe-in-the-Moor*. Exeter: James Townsend.

Wurtzburg, Charles Edward (1954). *Raffles of the eastern isles*. Toronto: Musson Book Co.

For bibliographies, see:

Kramer, H. P. (1950). Selective annotated bibliography on tornadoes. *Met. Abstr.* **1:** 307–32.

Thuronyi, Geza (1959). Annotated bibliography on tornado analysis and forecasting. *Met. Abstr.* **10:** 270–307.

Waterspouts

Allingham, William (1900). *A manual of marine meteorology*. London: Griffin.

Anon. (1929). Waterspouts. *Bull. Amer. met. Soc.* **10:** 167–69.

————— (1937). Vagaries of the waterspout. *Illustrated London News* **191:** 1100–1101.

————— (1939). A shower of frogs. *The Times*, June 17 [and subsequent correspondence to July 11].

————— (1959). Waterspouts and tornadoes. *Weather* **14:** 103–104.

BIGELOW, FRANK H. (1906). Studies on the thermodynamics of the atmosphere. VI: The waterspout seen off Cottage City, Mass., in Vineyard Sound, on August 19, 1896. *Mon. Weath. Rev., Wash.* **34**: 307–315. [Bigelow wrote several other papers on this waterspout in later issues of the *Monthly Weather Review*.]

BLEEKER, W. & DELVER, A. (1951). Some new ideas on the formation of windspouts and tornadoes. *Arch. Met., Wien,* serie A. 220–36.

DELVER, A. (1955). *Hozen en Hozentheorieën.* The Hague: Staatsdrukkerij-en nitgeverijbedrijf (Koninklijk Nederlands Meteorologisch Instituut. Verspreide Opstellen—2).

DINWIDDIE, F. B. (1959). Waterspout-tornado structure and behavior at Nags Head, N. C., August 12, 1952. *Mon. Weath. Rev., Wash.* **87**: 239–50.

DONN, WILLIAM L. (1946). *Meteorology with marine applications.* New York & London: McGraw-Hill.

EVANS, BERGEN (1946). Concerning rains of fishes. *Science* **103**: 713.

——— (1947). *The natural history of nonsense.* London: Joseph.

FERREL, WILLIAM (1889). *A popular treatise on the winds.* New York & London: Wiley.

FLETCHER, L. F. (1932). Waterspouts. *Mar. Obs.* **9**: 153–55.

FORT, CHARLES (1941). *Book of the Damned.* In *Books of Charles Fort,* New York: Holt.

GORDON, A. H. (1948). Waterspouts and their danger to aircraft. *Met. Mag., Lond.* **77**: 253–54.

——— (1951). Waterspouts. *Mar. Obs.* **21**: 47–60, 87–93.

GUDGER, E. W. (1921). Rains of fishes. *Nat. Hist., N. Y.* **21**: 607–19.

——— (1922). Rains of fishes and of frogs. *Nat. Hist., N. Y.* **22**: 84.

——— (1929). Do fishes fall from the sky with rain? *Sci. Mon., N. Y.* **29**: 523–27.

——— (1929). More rains of fishes. *Ann. Mag. nat. Hist.* Ser. 10, **3**: 1–26.

——— (1946). Rains of fishes—myth or fact? *Science* **103**: 693–94.

HAYDEN, EVERETT (1888). *Waterspouts off the Atlantic coast of the United States, January and February, 1888.* [Supplement to the U. S. Navy Hydrographic Office Pilot Chart of the North Atlantic Ocean for March, 1888.]

HELLMAN, GUSTAV (1925). Wasserhosen auf dem Atlantischen Ocean. *Sber. Preuss. Akad. Wiss.* Phys.-Math. Kl 539.

HERSEY, JOHN (1962). *Here to stay.* New York: Knopf.

HOLDER, CHARLES F. (1887). *Living lights.* London: Sampson Low.

HOWARD, M. & SCHUYLER, E. (1887). Waterspouts. *Science* **10**: 32–33.

HUMPHREYS, W. J. (1940). *Physics of the air,* 3rd ed. New York & London: McGraw-Hill.

HURD, WILLIS EDWIN (1928). Waterspouts. *Mon. Weath. Rev., Wash.* **56**: 207–11.

——— (1948). Waterspouts. *H. O. Pilot Chart Central American Waters,* No. 3500.

JOHNSON, SIR NELSON (1944). The structure of a waterspout. *Quart. J. R. Met. Soc.* **70**: 127.

LOWE, A. B. & MCKAY, G. A. (1962). *The tornadoes of Western Canada.* Ottawa: Meteorological Branch, Department of Transport.

LUCRETIUS (1937). *De rerum natura.* With an English translation by W. H. D.

Rouse. 3rd ed. rev. Cambridge, Mass.: Harvard University Press (Loeb Classical Library).

McAtee, Waldo L. (1917). Showers of organic matter. *Mon. Weath. Rev.* **45:** 217–24.

Martin, Robert E. (1932). It does rain fish! *Pop. Sci. Mon.* **121:** 24–25.

Mitchell, Charles L. (1920). Papers on tornadoes. The thirteen tornadoes of March 28, 1920. *Mon. Weath. Rev., Wash.* **48:** 191–98.

Murphy, J. J. (1935). Meteorological features and history of tornado at Norfolk, Virginia. *Bull. Amer. met. Soc.* **16:** 252–55.

Oersted, H. C. (1839). On waterspouts. *Amer. J. Sci. Arts.* **37:** 250–67.

Phillips, P. E. (1952). Triple-walled waterspout. *Met. Mag., Lond.* **81:** 88–89.

Piddington, Henry (1876). *The sailor's horn-book for the law of storms,* 6th ed. London: Norgate.

Reeds, Chester A. (1928). Storm and storm tracks. *Nat. Hist., N. Y.* **28:** 589–604.

Reid, W. (1846). *An attempt to develop the law of storms by means of facts, arranged according to place and time,* 2nd ed. London: John Weale.

Rossman, Fritz O. (1958). Differences in the physical behaviour of tornadoes and waterspouts. *Weather* **13:** 259–63.

——— (1959). Some further remarks on waterspouts. *Weather* **14:** 104–105.

Russell, Henry Chamberlaine (1898). Water spouts on the coast of New South Wales. *J. Roy. Soc. N. S. W.* **32:** 132–49.

Speight, W. L. (1940). Mirages, red seas and waterspouts. *Naut. Mag.* **143:** 9–11.

Talman, Charles F. (1931). *The realm of the air.* Indianapolis, Ind.: Bobbs-Merrill.

Teale, Edwin (1935). Strange pranks of the wind. *Pop. Sci. Mon.* **127** July: 38–9.

Wegener, Alfred (1917). *Wind- und Wasserhosen in Europa.* Braunschweig: Vieweg.

Wenstrom, William H. (1942). *Weather and the ocean of air.* Boston, Mass.: Houghton.

White, Gilbert (1789). *The natural history of Selborne.* London: B. White.

For bibliographies, see under Tornadoes.

Hail

[Abbe, Cleveland] (1907). Hail shooting in Italy, *Mon. Weath. Rev., Wash.* **35:** 358.

Allix, Andre (1939). L'étude de la grêle par avion et le système de défense du Beaujolais. *Rev. Etud. Calam.,* **2:** No. 5 [Abstract in *Geogr. J.* **94:** 509].

Anon. (1877). Large hailstones. *Mon. Weath. Rev.; Wash.,* May: 5.

——— (1907). The thunderstorms of July 21st and 22nd, 1907. *British Rainf.* **1907:** 20–35.

——— (1935). The great Northamptonshire hailstorm of 22nd September, 1935. *British Rainf.* **1935:** 281–85.

——— (1959). Hail, yes! *The Mats Flyer* **6:** 11–12.

ARAGO, FRANÇOIS (1855). *Meteorological essays*. Edition translated by Col. Sabine. London: Longmans.

ARENBERG, DAVID L. (1938). The formation of irregularly shaped hailstones. *Mon. Weath. Rev., Wash.* **66:** 275–76.

ATLAS, DAVID et al. (1960). Radar scatter by large hail. *Quart. J. R. met. Soc.* **86:** 468–82.

ATLAS, DAVID, editor (1963). *Severe local storms*. Boston, Mass., American Meteorological Society (Meteorological monographs—vol. 5, no. 27).

BEEBE, WILLIAM (1918). A Kashmir barrage of hail. *Bull. N. Y. zool. Soc.* **21:** 1616–19.

BILHAM, E. G. (1938). *The climate of the British Isles*. London: Macmillan.

—— & RELF, E. F. (1937). The dynamics of large hailstones. *Quart. J. R. met. Soc.* **63:** 149–62.

BLAIR, THOMAS A. (1928). Hailstorms of great size at Potter, Nebraska. *Mon. Weath. Rev., Wash.* **56:** 313.

BOTLEY, C. M. (1940). *The air and its mysteries*. New York: D. Appleton-Century.

BRACHET, CHARLES (1938). Pourlutter contre les chutes de grêle utilisez l'avion. *Sci. et Vie* **53:** 101–108.

BROOKS, CHARLES F. (1935). *Why the weather?* rev. New York: Harcourt.

BROWN, W. G. (1912). Explosive hail. *Nature, Lond.* **88:** 350.

BROWNING, K. A. & LUDLAM, F. H. (1960). *Radar analysis of a hailstorm*. London: Department of Meteorology, Imperial College (Technical note—5).

—— —— (1962). Air flow in convective storms. *Quart. J. R. met. Soc.* **89:** 75–84.

—— et al. (1963). The density and structure of hailstones. *Quart. J. R. met. Soc.* **89:** 75–84.

BUCK, ROBERT N. (1959). "What about the weather, Captain?" *Air Facts* **22** 5: 11–18.

BUIST, GEORGE (1856). Remarkable hailstorms in India, from March 1851 to May 1855. *Rep. Brit. Ass.,* 1855.

CROSSLEY, A. F. (1961). Hail in relation to the risk of encounters in flight. *Met. Mag., Lond.* **90:** 101–10.

DONALDSON, R. J. (1958). Analysis of severe convective storms observed by radar. *J. Met.* **15:** 44–50.

DOUGLAS, R. H. & HITSCHFELD, W. (1959). Patterns of hailstorms in Alberta. *Quart. J. R. met. Soc.* **85:** 105–19.

DUFF, D. V. (1936). *Palestine picture*. London: Hodder & Stoughton.

ELIOT, J. (1899). Hailstorms in India during the period 1883–97. *Indian met. Mem.* **6:** 237–315.

EMERSON, JOSEPH B. & SOUTER, ROBERT K. (1952). *Summary of available hail literature and the effect of hail on aircraft in flight*. Washington, D. C.: National Advisory Committee for Aeronautics (Technical note—2734).

FASSIG, OLIVER L. (1915). A remarkable fall of hail in Maryland. *Mon. Weath. Rev., Wash.* **43:** 446–48.

FAWBUSH, ERNEST J. & MILLER, ROBERT C. (1953). A method for forecasting hailstorm size at the earth's surface. *Bull. Amer. met. Soc.* **34:** 235–44.

Bibliography

Flora, Snowden D. (1956). *Hailstorms of the United States*. Norman, Oklahoma: University of Oklahoma Press.

Fort, Charles (1941). *Book of the Damned*. (In *Books of Charles Fort*. New York: Holt.)

Foster, Donald S. (1961). *Aviation hail problem*. Geneva: World Meteorological Organization (Technical note—no. 37).

Frazer, Colin (1929). Hailstorms more destructive than tornadoes. *Literary Digest* **102** 12: 21–22.

Free, E. E. (1929). World's largest hailstone in Nebraska. *Literary Digest* **100**: 7–21.

Froissart, Sir John (1847). *The chronicles of England, France, Spain, etc.* Translated by H. P. Dunster. London: James Burns.

——— (1876). *Chroniques de J. Froissart*. Edition Siméon Luce. Paris: Jules Renouard. Vol. 6, pp. 4–5.

Gaviola, E. & Fuertes, F. Alsina (1947). Hail formation, vertical currents, and icing of aircraft. *J. Met.* **4**: 116–20.

Genève, R. (1961). *La grêle*. Paris: Météorologie Nationale (Mémorial—no. 48).

Gissing, Alwin (1936). Hailstorm that battered trees. *Radio Times*, July 24.

Greely, A. W. (1888). *American Weather*. New York: Dodd, Mead & Co.

Grimminger, G. (1933). The upward speed of an air current necessary to sustain a hailstone. *Mon. Weath. Rev., Wash.* **61**: 198–200.

Harries, Henry (1895). The frequency, size and distribution of hail at sea. *Quart. J. R. met. Soc.* **21**: 230–44.

Humphreys, W. J. (1926). *Rain making and other weather vagaries*. Baltimore, Maryland: Williams & Wilkins.

——— (1928). The uprush of air necessary to sustain the hailstone. *Mon. Weath. Rev., Wash.* **56**: 314.

——— (1940). *Physics of the air*, 3rd ed. New York & London: McGraw-Hill.

Kendrew, W. G. (1957). *Climatology*, 2nd ed. Oxford: Clarendon Press.

Kuhk, Rudolf (1956). Hagelnnwetter als Verlustursache bei Störchen und anderen Vögeln. *Vogelwarte* **18**: 180–82.

Langewiesche, Wolfgang (1945). Winds that blow straight up. *Harper's Magazine*, **191**: 107–16.

Langmuir, Irving (1962). *The collected works of Irving Langmuir*. New York: Pergamon Press, 12 vols.

Lapie, P. O. (1943). *My travels through Chad*. London: John Murray.

Latouche, J. D. (1874). Notes regarding a remarkable . . . hailstorm which occurred in the neighborhood of Pietermaritzburg . . . on the 17th of April 1874. *Quart. J. R. met. Soc.* **2**: 235–36.

Laurie, J. A. P. (1960). *Hail and its effects on buildings*. Pretoria: Council for Scientific and Industrial Research (C. S. I. R. research report—176. National Building Research Institute bulletin—21).

List, Roland (1960). New developments in hail research. *Science* **132**: 1091–98.

Long, Ian F. (1963). Fossil hail prints. *Weather* **18**: 115.

Loveland, George A. (1917). Nebraska hailstorm of August 8, 1917. *Mon. Weath. Rev., Wash.* **45**: 540–42.

LUDLAM, F. H. (1958). Hail and its prevention. *New Scient.* **4:** 105–108.

——— (1961). The hailstorm. *Weather* **16:** 152–62.

——— (1963). Severe local storms: a review. *Met.* Monogr. **5,** 27: 1–30.

——— & MACKLIN, W. C. (1960). The Horsham hailstorm of 5 September 1958. *Met. Mag., Lond.* **89:** 245–51.

——— ——— (1961). The fallspeeds of hailstones. *Quart. J. R. met. Soc.* **87:** 72–81.

MASON, B. J. & MAYBANK, J. (1958). Ice-nucleating properties of some natural mineral dusts. *Quart. J. R. met. Soc.* **84:** 235–41.

MILHAM, WILLIS I. (1912). *Meteorology.* New York: Macmillan.

MINISTRY OF AVIATION (1964). *Detection and avoidance of mountain wave systems —safety heights over high ground.* London: H.M.S.O. (Civil aviation information circular—92/1964).

MOORE, WILLIS L. (1922). *The new air world.* Boston, Mass.: Little, Brown.

MULLS, S. & KULSHRESTHA, S. M. (1962). The severe hailstorm of 27 May 1959 near Sikar (Rajasthan): a synoptic and radar study. *Indian J. Met. Geophys.* **13** Special No. March: 81–94.

NORMAN, JOHN ROXBOROUGH (1963). *A history of fishes.* 2nd ed. by P. H. Greenwood. New York: Hill & Wang.

ODDIE, B. C. V. (1965). The hail cannon. *Weather* **20:** 154–56.

PERNTER, J. M. (1900). The prevention of hailstorms by the use of cannon. *Nat. geogr. Mag.* **11:** 239–41 [an abstract of an article from the *Wiener Abendpost*].

PISTON, DONALD S. (1941). *Meteorology,* 2nd ed. Philadelphia: Blakiston.

ROBB, A. D. (1959). Severe hail, Selden, Kansas, June 3, 1959. *Mon. Weath. Rev., Wash.* **87:** 301–303.

ROTH, RICHARD J. (1949). Crop-hail insurance in the United States. *Bull. Amer. met. Soc.* **30:** 56–58.

——— (1952). Hailstones and hailstorms. *Weatherwise* **5:** 51–54.

RUSSELL, ROLLO (1893). *On hail.* London: E. Stanford.

SCHAEFER, VINCENT J. (1950). Experimental meteorology. *Z. Angew. Math. Phys.,* **1:** 153–84, 217–36.

SCHLEUSENER, RICHARD A. (1962). The 1959 hail suppression effort in Colorado, and evidence of its effectiveness. *Nubila* **5,** 1:31–59.

SCHONLAND, SIR BASIL (1964). *The flight of thunderbolts,* 2nd ed. London: Oxford University Press.

SCHOVE, D. JUSTIN (1951). Hail in history, A.D. 1630–1680. *Weather* **6:** 17–21.

SCHUMANN, T. E. W. (1938). The theory of hailstone formation. *Quart. J. R. met. Soc.* **64:** 3–21.

SELGA, MIGUEL (1929). *Hail in the Philippines.* Manila: Weather Bureau.

SHARP, P. J. (1960). Protecting aircraft against ice. *New Scient.* **8:** 300–302.

SMITH, ALLEN G. (1960). Hail, great destroyer of wildlife. *Audubon Mag.* **62:** 170–71, 189.

——— & WEBSTER, H. R. (1955). Effects of hailstorms on waterfowl population in Alberta, Canada—1953. *J. Wildlife Mgmt.* **19:** 368–74.

SMYTHE, P. H. (1921). Hailstorm in Alabama, November 14, 1921. *Mon. Weath. Rev., Wash.* **49:** 659–60.

Souter, R. K. & Emerson, J. B. (1952). Summary of available hail literature and the effect of hail on aircraft in flight. *Tech. Notes nat. adv. Comm. Aero., Wash., No. 2734.*

Steyn, Keeve (1950). The Pretoria hailstorm. *Public Works of South Africa* **10:** 75: February. [A subsequent reprint corrected inaccuracies.]

Street, A. G. (1937): *Farmer's glory.* London: Faber.

Supf, Peter (1933). *Airman's world.* New York: W. Morrow.

Sutcliffe, R. C. (1940). *Meteorology for aviators.* New York: Chemical Publishing Company.

Talman, Charles F. (1931). *The realm of the air.* Indianapolis, Ind.: Bobbs-Merrill.

——— (1936): Ice from the thunderclouds. *Nat. Hist. N. Y.* **38:** 109–19.

Thompson, Philip D. & O'Brien, Robert (1965). *Weather.* New York: Time.

Vittori, Ottavio (1960). Preliminary note on the effects of pressure waves upon hailstones. *Nubila* **3,** 1:34–52.

Vosburgh, Frederick G. (1938). Men-birds soar on boiling air. *Nat. geogr. Mag.* **74:** 123–40.

For bibliographies, see:

Douglas, R. H. (1963). Recent hail research: a review. Met. Monogr. **5,** 27: 157–67.

Emerson, Joseph B. & Souter, Robert K. (1952) *above,* and Rice, Mary L. & Rigby, Malcolm (1950). Selective annotated bibliography on hail. *Met. Abstr.* **1:** 244–69.

Avalanches

Albright, John Grover (1939). *Physical meteorology.* New York: Prentice-Hall.

Alter, J. Cecil (1926). Avalanche at Bingham, Utah. *Mon. Weath. Rev., Wash.* **54:** 60.

Bentley, Wilson A. (1904). Work on snow crystals. *Nat. geogr. Mag.* **15:** 30–37.

——— (1923). The magic beauty of snow and dew. *Nat. geogr. Mag.* **43:** 103–12.

——— & Humphreys, W. J. (1931). *Snow crystals.* New York & London: McGraw-Hill.

Bilham, E. G. (1938). *The climate of the British Isles.* London: Macmillan.

Botley, C. M. (1940). *The air and its mysteries.* New York: D. Appleton-Century.

Bragg, Sir William Henry (1925). *Concerning the nature of things.* London: Bell.

Breton, Henry Hugh (1928). *The great blizzard of Christmas, 1927.* Plymouth: Hoyten & Cole.

Brooks, Charles F. (1935). *Why the weather?* Rev. ed. New York: Harcourt.

Brown, T. Graham & De Beer, Sir Gavin (1957). *The first ascent of Mont Blanc.* London: Oxford University Press.

Buss, Ernst & Heim, Albert (1881). *Der Bergsturz von Elm don 11 September 1881.* Denkschrift. Zürich: J. Wurster.

COLTON, F. B. (1943). Weather fights and works for man. *Nat. geogr. Mag.* **84:** 641–70.

CONWAY, SIR WILLIAM MARTIN (1895). *The Alps from end to end.* Westminster: Archibald Constable.

DOLLFUS, OLIVIER & DEL AGUILA, CARLOS PENAHERRERA (1962). Informe de la Comisión Peruana de Geomorfología sobre la Castástrofe ocurrida en el Callejón de Huaylas, el 10 de Enero de 1962. *Bol. Soc. Geogr. Lima* **79:** 3–18.

FLAIG, WALTHER (1955). *Lawinen.* Wiesbaden: F. A. Brockhaus.

FREE, E. E. & HOKE, TRAVIS (1928). *Weather.* New York: McBride.

GIBLETT, M. A. (1921). The terminal velocity of snowflakes. *Met. Mag. Lond.* **56** New series 2: 95–6.

GOLD, L. W. & POWER, B. A. (1952). Correlation of snow-crystal type with estimated temperature of formation. *J. Met.* **9:** 447.

GREELY, A. W. (1888). *American Weather.* New York: Dodd, Mead & Co.

THE GUARDIAN (1963). *The long winter, 1962–63.* Manchester: Manchester Guardian and Evening News Ltd.

HEIM, ALBERT (1932). Bergsturz und Menschenleben. Beiblatt zur *Vjschr. naturf. Ges. Zürich* **77** 20 Geologische Nachlese Nr. 30.

HIRZEL, HEINRICH (1809). *Eugenias Briefe an ihre Mutter. Geschrieben auf einer Reise nach den Bädern von Lenk im Sommer 1806.* Zürich: Orell Füssli.

HUMPHREYS, W. J. (1937). *Weather rambles.* Baltimore, Md.: Williams & Wilkins.

LLIBOUTRY, L. (1964). *Traité de glaciologie.* Tome I: Glace, neige, hydrologie nivali. Paris: Masson.

LUDLUM, DAVID M. (1962). Extremes of snowfall in the United States. *Weatherwise,* **15** 6: 246–62.

McDOWELL, BART (1962). Avalanche! *Nat. geogr. Mag.* **121:** 855–80.

MORRISON, C. F., *et al.* (1960). *The collapse of the Listowel arena.* Ottawa: National Research Council, Division of Building Research (Technical paper—no. 97).

NAKAYA, UKICHIRO (1954). *Snow crystals, natural and artificial.* Cambridge, Mass.: Harvard University Press.

NEEDHAM, JOSEPH & LU GWEI-DJEN (1961). The earliest snow crystal observations. *Weather* **16:** 319–26.

PAULCKE, WILHELM (1938). *Praktischen Schnee- und Lawinenkunde.* Berlin: Springer Verlag.

PÉGUY, CHARLES-PIERRE (1952). *La neige.* Paris: Presses Universitaires de France (Que sais-je?—no. 538).

PETER, B. G., *et al.* (1963). Variations of snow loads. *Trans. Engng. Inst. Can.* **6:** 3–11.

PRESSER, HELMUT (1956). Vom Berge verschlungen—in Büchern bewahrt. *Schweiz. Gutenbergmus.* **4:** 185–207.

QUERVAIN, M. R. DE (1957). Avalanche classification. *International Association of Scientific Hydrology. General Assembly of Toronto* **4:** 387–92.

——— & ZINGG, TH. (1951). Die aussergewöhnlichen Schneefälle vom Januar und Februar 1951 in den Schweizer Alpen und ihr Folgen. *Wass—u. Energ Wirt.* **43:** 205–19.

Roch, A. (1960/1). *Mesure de la force des avalanches.* Davos: Swiss Institute for Snow and Avalanche Research (Report no. 25).

—— (1964). Possibilités de protection en déviant ou en freinant l'avalanche. *Strasse und Verkehr* **50**: 19–22.

Schaefer, Vincent J. (1942). Fossilizing snowflakes as a hobby. *Sci. Dig.* **11** March: 43–45.

—— (1943). How to fingerprint a snowstorm. *Nat. Hist., N. Y.* **51**: 20–27.

Schaerer, P. (1962). *Avalanche defences for the Trans-Canada Highway at Rogers Pass.* Ottawa: National Research Council (Division of Building Research. Technical paper—no. 141).

Seligman, Gerald (1936). *Snow structure and ski fields.* New York: Macmillan.

—— (1937a). The nature of snow. *Nature, Lond.* **139**: 1090–94.

—— (1937b). Physical investigations on falling snow. *Nature, Lond.* **140**: 345–48.

—— (1947). Snow avalanches. *Geographical Mag.* **19**: 467–68.

Spink, P. C. (1947). Famous snowstorms, 1878–1945. *Weather* **2**: 50–54.

Talman, Charles F. (1931). *The realm of the air.* Indianapolis, Ind.: Bobbs-Merrill.

Tuckett, F. F. (1920). *A pioneer in the high Alps.* London: Arnold.

Voellmy, A. (1955). Uber die Zerstorungskraft von Lawinen. *Schweiz. Bauztge* **73**: 159–65, 212–17, 246–49, 280–85 [An English translation by the U. S. Department of Agriculture, Forest Service, Alta Avalanche Study Centre, Wasatch National Forest was published in 1964].

Vokes, H. E. (1942). Landslide. *Nat. Hist., N. Y.* **49**: 32–37.

Wechsberg, Joseph (1958). *Avalanche.* New York: Knopf.

Whitlock, Herbert P. (1919). Art motives in snow crystals. *Nat. Hist., N. Y.* **19**: 437–40.

Worden, William L. (1955). The deadly mountain that walks [Turtle Mountain]. *Saturday Evening Post,* January 1 [pp. 20–21, 54–55; **227**, No. 27].

Zdarsky, M. (1930). *Beiträge zur Lawinenkunde.* Vienna: Alpen-Skiverein.

For bibliographies, see:

Department of Agriculture. U. S. Forest Service. Wasatch National Forest (1956). *Bibliography of avalanche literature* [typescript].

Lliboutry, above.

For current references, see:

Berichte über die Tätigkeit des Eidg. *Institutes für Schnee- und Lawinenforschung,* published annually by the Schweiz. Zeitschrift fur Fürstwesen.

Lightning

Albright, John Grover (1939). *Physical meteorology.* New York: Prentice-Hall.

Anon. (1962). Fireballs for defense? *Christian Science Monitor.* July.

Anon. (1892). Singular freaks of lightning. *Chambers's Journal* **9**: 463–64.

———— (1945). Photographs of lightning: it strikes downward—also upward. *Current Science and Aviation* **30:** 197–99.

ARAGO, FRANÇOIS (1854). *Oeuvres complètes.* Tome 1: Notices scientifiques. Paris: Legrand, Pomey et Crouzet.

———— (1855). *Meteorological essays.* Edition translated by Col. Sabine. London: Longmans.

ATLAS, DAVID, editor (1963). *Severe local storms.* Boston, Mass.: American Meteorological Society (Meteorological monographs—vol. 5, no. 27).

BATTAN, LOUIS J. (1964). *The thunderstorm.* New York: New American Library (Signet P2473).

BELL, T. H. (1960). *Thunderstorm.* New York: Viking Press.

BERGER, K. & VOGELSANGER, E. (1965). Messungen und Resultate der Blitzforschung der Jahre 1955–1963 auf dem Monte San Salvatore. *Bull. Schweiz. elektrotech. Ver.* **56** 1: 2–22.

BOTLEY, C. M. (1940). *The air and its mysteries.* New York: D. Appleton-Century.

BRAGG, SIR WILLIAM LAWRENCE (1936). *Electricity.* New York: Macmillan.

BRAHAM, ROSCOE R. (1952). The Water and energy budgets of the thunderstorm and their relation to thunderstorm development. *J. Met.* **9:** 227–42.

BRAND, WALTHER (1923). *Der Kugelblitz.* Hamburg: H. Grand (Probleme der Kosmischen Physik 2/3).

BRITISH STANDARDS INSTITUTION (1948). *Protection of structures against lightning.* London: British Standards Institution (CP 326.101). [Revised code in preparation.]

BROOK, M. & VONNEGUT, BERNARD (1960). Visual confirmation of the junction process in lightning discharges. *J. geophys. Res.* **65:** 1302–1303.

BROOKS, C. E. P. (1925). *The distribution of thunderstorms over the globe.* London: H.M.S.O. (Meteorological Office. Geophysical memoir—no. 24).

BROOKS, CHARLES F. (1935). *Why the weather?* rev. ed. New York: Harcourt.

BRUCE, C. E. R. (1944). *A new approach in astrophysics and cosmogony.* London, Woking: Unwin Brothers.

———— (1958). *Terrestrial and cosmical lightning discharges.* Leatherhead: British Electrical and Allied Industries Research Association (Technical report—Z/T119).

———— (1960). An all-electric universe. *Elect. Rev. Lond.,* **167:** 1070–75.

———— (1963). Ball lightning, "stellar rotation" and radio galaxies. *Engineer, London,* **216:** 1047–48.

———— (1964). Ball lightning. *Nature, Lond.* **202:** 996–97.

BUCK, ROBERT N. (1959). "What about the weather, Captain?" *Air Facts* **22** 5: 11:18.

BYERS, HORACE R. (1949). Structure and dynamics of the thunderstorm. *Weather* **4:** 220–22, 244–50.

———— (1953). *Thunderstorm electricity.* Chicago, Ill.: Chicago University Press.

———— & BRAHAM, ROSCOE, JR., editors (1949). *The thunderstorm: report of the Thunderstorm Project.* (A joint project of four U. S. Government Agencies: Air Force, Navy, National Advisory Committee for Aeronautics, and Weather Bureau.) Washington, D. C.: U. S. Weather Bureau.

CADE, C. MAXWELL (1962). Thunderbolts as the X-weapon. *Discovery* **23** 11: 23–28.

CHALMERS, J. ALAN (1957). *Atmospheric electricity.* New York & London: Pergamon Press.

CHARCOT, JEAN-MARTIN (1890). Wirkungen des Blitzschlages auf das Nervensystem, *Wien. med. Wschr.* **40:** 9–12, 57–59, 104–106.

CIVIL AERONAUTICS BOARD (1965). *Aircraft accident report: Boeing 707–121, N709PA, Pan American World Airways, Inc., near Elkton, Maryland, December 8, 1963.* Washington, D. C.: Civil Aeronautics Board (File no. 1-0015).

CIVIL AERONAUTICS BOARD (1965). *Aircraft accident report: Northwest Airlines, Inc., Boeing 720B, N724US near Miami, Florida, February 12, 1963.* Washington, D. C. Civil Aeronautics Board (SA–372).

COLTON, F. BARROWS (1943). Weather fights and works for man. *Nat. geogr. Mag.* **84:** 641–70.

CRITCHLEY, MacDONALD (1932). The effects of lightning: with especial reference to the nervous system. *Bristol med.-chir. J.* **49:** 285–300.

DAUVILLIER, ALEXANDRE (1965). Sur la nature de la foudre globulaire. *C. r. hebd. Séanc. Acad. Sci., Paris* **260:** 1707–1708.

DAVIS, DELPHINE & CADE, C. MAXWELL (in press). *Flame of the heavens: an anthology of ball lightning.* London: Hale.

DEWAN, EDMOND M. (1964). *Attempted explanations of ball lightning.* Hanscom Field, Mass. Air Force Cambridge Research Laboratories (Physical sciences research papers—no. 67).

——— (1964). *Eyewitness accounts of Kugelblitz.* Hanscom Field, Mass. Air Force Cambridge Research Laboratories.

FINKELSTEIN, DAVID & RUBINSTEIN, JULIO (1964). Ball lightning. *Phys. Rev.* **135:** No. 2A: A 391–96.

FLAMMARION, CAMILLE (1873). *L'atmosphère.* Paris: Hachette.

——— (1905). *Thunder and lightning.* Translated by W. Mostyn. London: Chatto and Windus.

FLETCHER, COLIN (1963). Ordeal by lightning on glacier mountain. *Reader's Digest,* July [English edition].

FORT, CHARLES (1941). *Book of the damned.* (In *Books of Charles Fort.* New York: Holt.)

FOX, SIDNEY W. (1965). A theory of macromolecular and cellular origins. *Nature* **205:** 328–39.

———, editor (1965). *The origins of prebiological systems.* New York: Academic Press.

GAMBELL, ARLO W. & FISHER, DONALD W. (1964). Occurrence of sulfate and nitrate in rainfall. *J. geophys. Res.* **69:** 4203–10.

GOLD, E. (1952). Thunderbolts. The electric phenomena of thunderstorms. *Nature, Lond.* **169:** 561–63.

GOLDE, R. H. (1945). Frequency of occurrence of lightning flashes to earth. *Quart. J. R. met. Soc.* **71:** 89–109.

GOODLET, B. L. (1937). Lightning. *J. Instn. elect. Engrs.* **81:** 1–56.

GOYER, GUY G. (1965). Mechanical effects of a simulated lightning discharge on the water droplets of 'Old Faithful' geyser. *Nature, Lond.* **206:** 1302–4.

DER GROSSE HERDER (1953–6). Nachschlagewerk für Wissen und Leben. 5. neu-
bearb . . . Freiburg: Herder 10 vols.

HAGENGUTH, J. H. (1961). *Memorandum on ball lightning.* Pittsfield, Mass.: General Electric Company [typescript].

HARRIS, SIR WILLIAM SNOW (1847). *Remarkable instances of the protection of certain ships . . . from the destructive effects of lightning . . .* London.

—— (1854). *Shipwrecks by lightning: copies of papers relative to shipwrecks by
lightning, as prepared by Sir Snow Harris, and presented by him to the admiralty.* Parliamentary Papers, 1854 (453) Vol. XLII, p. 553.

HAWKE, E. L. (1945). This amazing weather. *Daily Mail,* July 16.

HENINGER, S. K., JR. (1960). *A handbook of Renaissance meteorology.* Durham,
N. C.: Duke University Press.

HILL, E. L. (1960). Ball lightning as a physical phenomenon. *J. geophys. Res.* **65:**
1947–1952.

HISSONG, J. E. (1926). Whirlwinds at oil-tank fire, San Luis Obispo, Calif. *Mon.
Weath. Rev., Wash.* **54:** 161–63.

HOLBROOK, STEWART (1945). *Burning an empire.* New York: Macmillan.

HOLZER, R. E. & WORKMAN, E. J. (1939). Photographs of unusual discharges occurring during thunderstorms. *J. appl. Phys.* **10:** 659–62.

HUMPHREYS, W. J. (1936). Ball lightning. *Proc. Amer. phil. Soc.* **76:** 613–26.

—— (1937). *Weather rambles.* Baltimore, Md.: Williams & Wilkins.

—— (1940). *Physics of the air,* 3rd ed. New York & London: McGraw-Hill.

—— (1943). *Ways of the weather.* Lancaster, Pa.: Jaques Cattel Press.

ISRAEL, H. (1957–61). *Atmosphärische Elektrizität.* Leipzig: Akademisch Verlag
2 vols.

—— (1963). [Ball lightning]. *Bericht der 7. Internationalen Blitzschutzkonferenz,
Arnhem, Holland, 11–13 September:* 207–12.

JENSEN, J. C. (1933). Ball lightning. *Physics* **4:** 372–4.

—— (1933). Ball lightning. *Sci. Mon., N. Y.* **37:** 190–2.

JONES, R. F. (1954). Radar echoes from lightning. *Quart. J. R. met. Soc.* **80:**
579–82.

KAPITSA, P. L. (1961). *The nature of ball lightning.* (In Ritchie, Donald J., editor
(1961): *Ball lightning: a collection of Soviet research in English translation.*
New York: Consultants Bureau.)

KLEINWÄCHTER, H. & GEERK, J. (1961). Die Erzeugung einer frei im Raume bren-
nenden Gasent-ladung im 3 entrum einer Stehenden e. m. kugelwelle. (In *Proceedings,* Fifth International Conference on Ionization Phenomena in Gases,
Munich 1961. Amsterdam: North-Holland Publishing Company.)

KOGAN-BELETSKI, G. I. (1957). [The nature of ball lightning.] *Priroda, Mosk.* No.
4: 71–73.

KUDRYAVTSEV, B. B. (1954). *The life and work of M. V. Lomonosov.* Moscow:
Foreign Languages Publishing House.

KUETTNER, JOACHIM (1950). The electrical and meteorological conditions inside
thunderclouds. *J. Met.* **7:** 322–32.

KUHN, ERICH (1951). Ein Kugelblitz auf einer Moment-Aufnahme? *Naturwissen-
schaften* **38:** 518–19.

Lewis, Harold W. (1963). Ball lightning. *Sci. Amer.* **208:** 107–16.

Ligda, Myron G. H. (1956). The radar observation of lightning. *J. atmos. terr. Phys.* **9:** 329–46.

Loeb, Leonard B. (1961). *Thunderstorms and lightning: a summary.* Berkeley, Calif.: University of California, Department of Physics [typescript].

——— (1964). Discussion of paper by M. A. Uman, "The diameter of lightning." *J. geophys. Res.* **69:** 587–88.

Lucretius (1851). *The nature of things.* Translated by J. S. Watson. London: Henry G. Bohn.

Lynch, M. J. G. & Shorthouse, P. H. (1949). Injuries and death from lightning. *Lancet* **256:** 473–78.

McAdie, Alexander George (1926). *Man and weather.* Cambridge, Mass.: Harvard University Press.

MacCready, Paul B., Jr. (1958). *Equipment for forecasting lightning danger.* (In Smith, L. G., editor [1958]: *Recent advances in atmospheric electricity* . . . London: Pergamon Press.)

McEachron, Karl B. (1938). Lightning to the Empire State Building. *Elect. Engng. N. Y.* **57:** 493–505, 507.

——— (1942a). Phenomena of lightning. *J. west. Soc. Engrs.* **47** 2: 43–58.

——— (1942). *The story of lightning.* Schenectady: General Electric Company.

——— & Patrick, K. G. (1940). *Playing with lightning.* New York: Random House.

McNally, J. R., Jr. (1960). *Preliminary report on ball lightning.* Second Annual Meeting, Division of Plasma, American Physical Society, Gatlinburg, Tennessee, November 2–5, 1960. Ithaca, N. Y.: American Physical Society.

Malan, D. J. (1959). Lightning. *Endeavour* **18** 70: 61–69.

——— (1961). Unusual types of lightning discharges. *Annls. Géophys.* **17:** 388–94.

——— (1964). *Physics of lightning.* London: English Universities Press.

Mallinson, A. B. (1937). [A floating fireball.] *J. Instn. elect. Engrs.* **81:** 487 July: 46.

Mason, B. J. (1953). A critical examination of theories of charge generation in thunderstorms. *Tellus* **5:** 446–60.

——— (1957). *The physics of clouds.* London: Oxford University Press.

——— (1962a). Charge generation in thunderstorms. *Endeavour* **21:** 83–84, 156–63.

——— (1962b). *Clouds, rain and rainmaking.* Cambridge: Cambridge University Press.

Mason, D. (1964). Lightning strikes on aircraft—II. *Weather* **19:** 248, 253–55.

Matthias, B. T. & Buchsbaum, S. J. (1962). Pinched lightning. *Nature, Lond.* **194:** 327.

Menzel, Donald Howard & Boyd, L. G. (1963). *The world of flying saucers* . . . New York: Doubleday.

Milham, Willis I. (1912). *Meteorology.* New York: Macmillan.

Miller, Stanley L. (1953). A production of amino acids under possible primitive earth conditions. *Science* **117:** 528–29.

Ministry of Transport and Civil Aviation (1957). *The effect of thunderstorms on aircraft operations.* London: Ministry of Transport and Civil Aviation (Civil aviation information circular—no. 21).

NATIONAL FIRE PROTECTION ASSOCIATION (1963). *Lightning code, 1963.* Boston, Mass.: National Fire Protection Association (NFPA—no. 78. ASAC5.1) [revised code in preparation].

NAUER, HERBERT (1953). Modellversuche zum Kugelblitz. *Z. Angew Phys.* **5:** 441–50.

OGLE, GEORGE M. (1924). Nature's super-power plant. *Pop. Sci. Mon.* **105** August: 24–25, 120.

PEDGLEY, D. E. (1962). *A meso-synoptic analysis of the thunderstorms on 28 August 1958.* London: H.M.S.O. (Meteorological Office. Geophysical memoirs—no. 106).

PISTON, DONALD S. (1941). *Meteorology,* 2nd ed. Philadelphia, Pa.: Blakiston.

PONNAMPERUMA, CYRIL (1965). The chemical origin of life. *Science J.* **1** 3:39–45.

PRIESTLEY, JOSEPH (1767). *The history and present state of electricity.* London: J. Dodsley.

PRUEITT, MELVIN L. (1963). The excitation temperature of lightning. *J. geophys. Res.* **68:** 803–11.

REITER, R. (1965). Precipitation and cloud electricity. *Quart. J. R. met. Soc.* **91:** 60–72.

REMILLARD, WILFRED J. (1960). *The acoustics of thunder.* Cambridge, Mass.: Acoustics Research Laboratory, Division of Engineering and Applied Science, Harvard University (Technical memorandum—no. 44).

——— (1961). The history of thunder research. *Weather* **16:** 245–53.

RIETH, ADOLF (1953). *Der Blitz in der bildenden Kunst* [Lightning in art]. Munich: Heimeran.

RITCHIE, DONALD J. (1959). Red lightning. *Bendix Research Data Sheet* August-September: 7–9, 12–15.

——— (1959). Reds may use lightning as weapon. *Missiles Rockets* **7** August 24: 117–18.

——— (1963). Ball lightning in nature and in the laboratory. *J. Inst. elect. Engrs* **9** May: 202–06.

———, editor (1961). *Ball lightning: a collection of Soviet research in English translation.* New York: Consultants Bureau.

RUSSELL, SPENCER C. (1958). Observations on the colour of lightning made at Epsom, 1903 to 1907. *Quart. J. R. met. Soc.* **34:** 271–76.

RÜST, E. & BERGER, K. (1945). Geschichte einer merkwürdigen Blitzaufnahme. *Bull. Schweiz. Elektrotech. Ver.* **11:** 1483.

SCHONLAND, SIR BASIL (1938). *The lightning discharge.* Being the Halley Lecture delivered on 28 May 1937. Oxford: Clarendon Press.

——— (1953). *Atmospheric electricity.* 2nd ed. revised and reset. New York & London: Wiley.

——— (1962). Lightning and the long electric spark. *Advmt. Sci., Lond.* **19:** 306–13.

——— (1964). *The flight of thunderbolts,* 2nd ed. London: Oxford University Press.

SCIENTIFIC AMERICAN (1903). Various letters on thunder.

SHIPLEY, JOHN F. (1941). Lightning and its symbols. *Quart. J. R. met. Soc.* **67:** 135–51.

———— (1946). Lightning and trees. *Weather* **1**: 206–10.

SINGER, STANLEY (1963). The unsolved problem of ball lightning. *Nature, Lond.* **198**: 745–47.

SMITH, L. G. (1957). Intracloud lightning discharges. *Quart. J. R. met. Soc.* **83**: 103–11.

————, editor (1958). *Recent advances in atmosphere electricity:* proceedings of the second Conference on Atmospheric Electricity, held at Portsmouth, New Hampshire, May 20–23, 1958. London: Pergamon Press.

SPENCER, HENRY ALEXANDER (1932). *Lightning, lightning strike and its treatment.* London: Ballière & Company (Minor monograph series).

TALJAARD, J. J. (1952). How far can thunder be heard? *Weather* **7**: 245–46.

TALMAGE, STERLING B. (1929). The spoor of a thunderbolt. *Scientific Monthly,* April.

THOMPSON, D. (1945). Explosion of a "fire-ball" at Kamaran Island, Red Sea. *Quart. J. R. met. Soc.* **71**: 39–40.

UMAN, MARTIN A. (1964). The diameter of lightning. *J. geophys. Res.* **69**: 583–85.

VAN DORN, CARL CLINTON (1938). *Benjamin Franklin.* New York: Viking Press.

VEENEMA, L. C. (1917 & 1918). Series of articles in *Das Wetter.*

VIEMEISTER, PETER E. (1961). *The lightning book.* New York: Doubleday & Co.

VOKES, HAROLD E. (1939). When the earth is electrocuted. *Nat. Hist., N. Y.* **44**: 158–59.

———— (1944). Clouds, rain and picnics. *Nat. Hist., N. Y.* **53**: 272–73, 287.

VONNEGUT, BERNARD (1960). Electrical theory of tornadoes. *J. geophys. Res.* **65**: 203–12.

———— (1963). Some facts and speculations concerning the origin and role of thunderstorm electricity. *Met. Monogr.* **5** 27: 224–41.

———— & MOORE, CHARLES B. (1958). *Giant electrical storms.* (In Smith, L. G., editor (1958): *Recent advances in atmospheric electricity* . . . London: Pergamon Press).

WALLINGTON, C. E. (1964). Lightning strikes on aircraft—I. *Weather* **19**: 206–08.

WASSON, R. GORDON (1956). Lightning-bolt and mushrooms: an essay in early cultural exploration. (In *For Roman Jakobson.* The Hague: Mouton.)

WENSTROM, WILLIAM H. (1942). *Weather and the ocean of air.* Boston, Mass.: Houghton.

WILSON, C. T. R. (1920). Investigations on lightning discharges and on the electrical field of thunderstorms. *Phil. Trans. R. Soc.* A 221: 73.

WINSTON, JAY S. (1956). *Forecasting tornadoes and severe thunderstorms.* Washington, D. C.: United States Department of Commerce.

WORLD METEOROLOGICAL ORGANIZATION (1953). *World distribution of thunderstorm days.* Geneva: World Meteorological Organization (Publication—no. 21, TP6).

YOUNG, GEORGE A. (1962). *A lightning strike of an underwater explosion plume.* White Oak, Md.: U. S. Naval Ordnance Laboratory, Explosions Research Department (NOLTR 61-43).

YOUNG, WARREN R. (1965). Turbulence—hidden giant in the sky. *Life International,* January 11: 36–41.

For bibliographies, see:

BAKER, RONALD & KISS, ELEMÉR (1963): Annotated bibliography on the physics of the lightning Flash. *Met. Abstr.* **14**: 2923–88.

KRAMER, HARRIS P. (1950). Selective annotated bibliography on thunderstorms. *Met. Abstr. 1:* 517–55; and RITCHIE, DONALD J., editor (1961), above.

Floods

ALLEY, REWI (1956). *Man against flood: a story of the 1954 flood on the Yangtse and of the reconstruction that followed it.* Peking: New World Press.

ANON. (1952). *Kansas-Missouri floods of June–July 1951.* Washington, D. C.: Hydrologic Services Division, U. S. Weather Bureau (Technical paper—no. 17).

——— (1953). *The battle of the floods: Holland in February 1953.* Amsterdam: Netherlands Booksellers and Publishers Association; London: Newman Neame.

——— (1962). *1962 floods in East Pakistan: the story of an unprecedented calamity.* Dacca: East Pakistan Government Press.

——— (1964). *Flood control in the Lower Mississippi River Valley.* Vicksburg, Miss.: Mississippi River Commission and U. S. Army Engineer Division.

BARROWS, H. K. (1948). *Floods: their hydrology and control.* New York & London: McGraw-Hill.

BLEASDALE, A. (1959). The measurement of rainfall. *Weather* **14**: 12–18.

——— & DOUGLAS, C. K. M. (1952). Storm over Exmoor on August 15, 1952. *Met. Mag., Lond.* **81**: 353–67.

BOGART, DEAN B. (1960). *Floods of August–October 1955, New England to North Carolina.* Washington, D. C.: U. S. Government Printing Office (U. S. Geological Survey. Water-supply paper—no. 1420).

BONACINA, L. C. W. (1952). The Exmoor cataclysm. *Weather* **7**: 336–37.

BROOKS, C. E. P. & GLASSPOOLE, J. (1928). *British floods and droughts.* London: Benn.

BURTON, S. H. (1952). The 'Chains' of Exmoor. *Weather* **7**: 334–36.

CHANTER, JOHN FREDERICK (1907). *The history of the parishes of Lynton and Countisbury* . . . Exeter: J. G. Commin.

COLTON, F. BARROWS (1939). The geography of a hurricane [New England hurricane of September 1938]. *Nat. geogr. Mag.* **75**: 529–52.

CONFERENCE ON THE NORTH SEA FLOODS OF 31 JANUARY/1 FEBRUARY, 1953 (1954). *A collection of papers presented to the Institute in December 1953.* London: Institution of Civil Engineers.

DELDERFIELD, ERIC R. (1958). *The Lynmouth flood disaster,* 3rd ed. Exmouth: Raleigh Press.

DOBBIE, CHARLES HERBERT & WOLF, PETER OTTO (1953). The Lynmouth flood of August 1952. *Min. Proc. Instn. civ. Engrs.* **2** 3: 522–88.

ECKART, ALLAN (1965). *A time of terror.* Boston: Little, Brown.

FARB, PETER (1956). A flood prevention plan that works. *National Municipal Review,* May.

FERINGA, P. A. & SCHWEIZER, CHARLES W. (1953). One hundred years of improvement on Lower Mississippi River. *Trans. Amer. Soc. civil Engrs* **CT:** 1100–24.

FRYE, RALPH (1955). The great molasses flood. *Reader's Digest,* September [English edition].

GIFFORD, JOYCE (1953). Landslides on Exmoor caused by the storm of 15th August, 1952. *Geography* **38** 1: 9–17.

GRIEVE, HILDA (1959). *The great tide: the story of the 1953 flood disaster in Essex.* Chelmsford: County Council of Essex.

GROSVENOR, GILBERT M. & NEAVE, CHARLES (1954). Helping Holland rebuild her land. *Nat. Geogr. Mag.* **106:** 365–413.

GROVER, NATHAN C. (1938). *Floods of the Ohio and Mississippi rivers January–February 1937.* Washington, D. C.: U. S. Government Printing Office (U. S. Geological Survey. Water-supply paper—no. 838).

[HARRISON, ROBERT] (1962). *A strange relation of the suddain and violent tempest, which happened at Oxford May 31. Anno Domini 1682 . . .* Oxford: Richard Sherlock.

HARRISON, SAMUEL (1864). *A complete history of the great flood of Sheffield on March 11 and 12, 1964.* Sheffield: Harrison.

HAWKE, E. L. (1952). Rainfall in a 'cloudburst.' *Nature, Lond.* **165:** 204.

HENRY, ALFRED J. (1919). The distribution of maximum floods. *Mon. Weath. Rev., Wash.* **47:** 861–67.

HERSEY, JOHN (1963). *Here to stay.* New York: Knopf.

HOOD, J. DENNIS (1892). *Waterspouts on the Yorkshire Wolds: cataclysm at Langtoft and Driffield.* Driffield: Frank Fawcett.

HOYT, WILLIAM G. & LANGBEIN, WALTER B. (1955). *Floods.* Princeton, N. J.: Princeton University Press.

INSTITUUT VOOR SOCIAAL ONDERZOEK VAN HET NEDERLANDSE VOLK (1955). *Studies in Holland flood disaster 1953.* Amsterdam.

JANES, R. W. (1942). *The collective action involved in the removal and relocation of Shawneetown, Illinois.* Urbana, Ill.: University of Illinois [unpublished Ph.D. dissertation].

JARVIS, CLARENCE S. (1936). *Floods in the United States.* Washington, D. C.: U. S. Government Printing Office (U. S. Geological Survey. Water-supply paper—no. 771).

KENYON, FREDERIC (1940). *The Bible and archaeology.* New York: Harper.

KIDSON, C. (1953). The Exmoor storm and the Lynmouth floods. *Geography* **38** 1: 1–9.

KOLOBKOV, N. (1962). *Our atmospheric ocean.* Moscow: Foreign Languages Publishing House.

LAUDER, SIR THOMAS DICK (1873). *An account of the great floods of August 1829, in the Province of Moray, and adjoining districts,* 3rd ed. Elgin: Forsyth & Young.

LENNON, G. W. (1963). The identification of weather conditions associated with the generation of major storm surges along the west coast of the British Isles. *Quart. J. R. met. Soc.* **89:** 381–94.

Lovel, John (1893). Thunderstorm, cloudburst and flood at Langtoft, East Yorkshire, July 3rd, 1892. *Quart. J. R. met. Soc.* **19:** 1–15.

McGonagall, William (1934). *Poetic gems, selected from the works of William McGonagall.* Dundee: David Winter; London: Duckworth.

McMaster, John Bach (1933). The Johnstown Flood. *Pennsylvania Magazine of History and Biography* **57:** 209–43, 316–54.

Marschall, W. A. L. (1952). The Lynmouth floods. *Weather* **7:** 338–42.

Mason, B. J. (1959). Recent developments in the physics of rain and rainmaking. *Weather* **14:** 81–97.

O'Connor, Richard (1957). *Johnstown: the day the dam broke.* Philadelphia, Pa.: Lippincott.

Overman, Edwin S. (1957). The flood peril and the Federal Flood Insurance Act of 1956. *Annals of the American Academy of Political and Social Science* **309:** 98–106.

Pardé, Maurice (1964). Quelques données sur des crues remarquables en diverses contrées et sur les bilans de leurs écoulements. *Revue de l'Union internationale de secours,* September 2: 6–39.

Paulhus, J. L. H. (1965). Indian Ocean and Taiwan rainfalls set new records. *Mon. Weath. Rov., Wash.* **93:** 331–5.

Paulsen, Carl G., et al. (1940). *Hurricane floods of September 1938.* Washington, D. C.: U. S. Government Printing Office (U. S. Geological Survey. Water-supply paper—no. 867).

Report of the Committee on the Cause of the Failure of the South Fork Dam [Johnstown Flood] (1891). *Trans. Amer. Soc. civil Engrs.* **24** June: 431–69.

Schove, D. Justin (1949). Chinese "raininess" through the centuries. *Met. Mag., Lond.* **78:** 11–16.

Simpich, Frederick (1927). The great Mississippi flood of 1927. *Nat. Geogr. Mag.* **52:** 243–89.

——— (1937). Men against the rivers. *Nat. geogr. Mag.* **71:** 767–94.

Steers, J. A. (1953). The East coast floods. *Geogr. J.* **119:** 280–98.

Stiles, William W. (1957). How a community met a disaster: Yuba City flood, December 1955. *Annals of the American Academy of Political and Social Science* **309:** 160–69.

Sturgis, Samuel Davis, Jr. (1957). Floods. *Annals of the American Academy of Political and Social Science* **309:** 15–22.

Thomas, Lowell (1937). *Hungry waters: the story of the great flood.* [January 1937, southeast U. S. A.] Philadelphia, Pa.: John C. Winston.

Todd, Oliver J. (1942). Taming "Flood Dragons" along China's Hwang Ho. *Nat. geogr. Mag.* **81:** 205–34.

Ufford, H. A. Quarles V. (1953). The disastrous storm surge of 1 February. *Weather* **8:** 116–20.

Waverley, John Anderson (1954). Report [of the Departmental Committee on Coastal Flooding]. London: H.M.S.O. (Cmd. 9165) [East Coast floods of 1953, etc.].

Weikinn, Curt (1958–). *Quellentexte 3ur Witterungsgeschichte Europas von der Zeitwende bis zum Jahre 1850.* Berlin: Akademie-Verlag [in progress].

Bibliography

WHITE, GILBERT F. & COOK, HOWARD L. (1962). *Making wise use of flood plains.* Washington: U. S. Government Printing Office [typescript].

WOOLLEY, SIR LEONARD (1954). *Excavations at Ur.* New York: Crowell.

For bibliographies, see:

HOYT, WILLIAM G. & LANGBEIN, WALTER B. (1955) above, and

TENNESSEE VALLEY AUTHORITY. Technical library (1964). *Flood damage prevention: an indexed bibliography.* Knoxville, Tenn.: T.V.A.

For current references, see:

Bibliography on irrigation, drainage, river training and flood control, published annually by the International Committee on Irrigation and Drainage, New Delhi, and the United Nations *Flood Control Series,* 1950 to date.

Meteoroids

ASTAPOWITSCH, I. S. (1934). Air waves caused by the fall of the meteorite on 30th June, 1908, in Central Siberia. *Quart. J. R. met. Soc.* **60:** 493–504.

BAKER, ROBERT H. (1964). *Astronomy,* 8th ed. Princeton, N. J.; London: Van Nostrand.

BALDWIN, RALPH B. (1949). *The face of the moon.* Chicago, Ill.: University of Chicago Press.

——— (1963). *The measure of the moon.* Chicago, Ill.: University of Chicago Press.

BALL, SIR ROBERT (1904). *The story of the heavens.* London: Cassell.

BARRINGER, DANIEL MOREAU (1905). Coon Mountain and its crater. *Proc. Acad. nat. Sci. Phila.* **57:** 861–86.

——— (1964). The meteorite search. *Nat. Hist., N. Y.* **73:** 56–59.

BATES, DAVID ROBERT, editor (1957). *The planet earth.* New York & London: Pergamon Press.

BERNHARD, HUBERT J. (1936). Stardust. *Nat. Hist., N. Y.* **38:** 300–303.

BIOT, J. B. (1803). *Relation d'un voyage fait dans le départment de l'Orne, pour constater la réalité d'un météore observé à l'Aigle le 26 floréal an 11.* Paris.

BOTLEY, C. M. (1940). *The air and its mysteries.* New York: D. Appleton-Century.

BOUTWELL, WILLIAM D. (1928). The mysterious tomb of a giant meteorite. *Nat. geogr. Mag.* **53:** 721–30.

BREZINA, A. (1904). The arrangement of collections of meteorites. *Proc. Amer. phil. Soc.* **43:** 211–47.

BROOKS, CHARLES F. (1935). *Why the weather?* rev. ed. New York: Harcourt.

BUCHER, WALTER H. (1963). Are cryptovolcanic structures due to meteorite impact? *Nature, Lond.* **197:** 1241–45.

——— (1963). Cryptoexplosion structures caused from without or from within the earth? ("Astroblemes" or "Geoblemes"?) *Am. J. Sci.* **261:** 597–649.

BUDDHUE, JOHN D. (1957). Are there ice meteorites? *Mineralogist* **25:** 294–95.

——— (1960). Partial list of ice falls: reward $500. *Mineralogist* **28:** 14–18.

CADE, C. MAXWELL (1961). The prospects and consequences of a major stellar explosion. *Discovery* **22**: 357–63.

CEPLECHA, Z. D. (1960). Experimental data on the final mass of the body landed on the earth after penetrating the atmosphere at cosmical velocity. *Bulletin of the Astronomical Institutes of Czechoslovakia* **11**: 9–13.

CHALDNI, ERNST FLORENS FRIEDRICH (1794). *Ueber den Ursprung der von Pallas gefundenen und anderer ihr ähnlicher Eisenmassen, und über einige damit in Berbindung stehende Naturerschlinungen.* Riga: Hartknoch.

CLARK, NEIL M. (1927). Treasures from the sky. *Pop. Sci. Mon.* **111** October: 27–28, 176.

CLAUS, GEORGE & NAGY, BARTHOLOMEW (1961). A microbiological examination of some carbonaceous Chondrites. *Nature, Lond.* **192**: 594–96.

COLE, DANDRIDGE (1963). The asteroids. *Discovery* **24**: 24–28.

COWAN, CLYDE (1965). Possible anti-matter content of the Tunguska meteor of 1908. *Nature, Lond.* **206**: 861–5.

DACHILLE, FRANK (1962). Interactions of the earth with very large meteorites. *Bulletin of South Carolina Academy of Science* **24**.

DAVIDSON, MARTIN (1943). *An easy outline of astronomy.* London: Watts (Thinker's Library—no. 95).

DAVIS, J. (1963). The design and performance of three meniscus Schmidt meteor cameras. *Quart. J. R. astron. Soc.* **4**: 74–84.

DEGENS, EGON T. (1964). Genetic relationships between the organic matter in meteorites and sediments. *Nature, Lond.* **202**: 1092–95.

DIETZ, ROBERT S. (1961). Vredefort Ring structure: meteorite impact scar? *J. Geol.* **69**: 499–516.

DRAPER, ARTHUR L. & LOCKWOOD, MARION (1939). *The story of astronomy.* New York: Dial Press.

ELLISON, M. A. (1963). Energy release in solar flares. *Quart. J. R. astr. Soc.* **4**: 62–73.

FESENKOV, V. G. (1961). The nature of the Tunguska meteorite. *Meteoritika* **20**: 27–31.

FINCH, B. E. (1960). Visitors to earth. Letter, *Sunday Times* November 6.

FISHER, CLYDE (1934). When a comet struck the earth. *Nat. Hist., N. Y.* **34**: 754–62.

——— (1936). The meteor craters in Estonia. *Nat. Hist., N. Y.* **38**: 292–99.

FLORENSKY, K. P., *et al.* (1960). [The great Siberian meteorite of 1908] *Meteoritika* **19**: 103–34.

FOOTE, WARREN M. (1912). Preliminary note on the shower of meteoric stones near Holbrook, Navajo County, Arizona, July 19th, 1912, including a reference to the Perseid swarm of meteors visible from July 11th to August 22nd. *Am. J. Sci.* **34** 4th ser.: 437–56.

GALLANT, R. (1964). *Bombarded earth.* London: John Baker.

GOULD, RUPERT T. (1943). *The stargazer talks.* London: Bles.

HAAS, WALTER H. (1947). A report on searches for possible lunar meteoric phenomena. *Pop. Astron.* **55**: 266–73.

HALLIDAY, IAN (1957). The orbit and spectrum of a bright sporadic meteor. *Jl. R. astr. Soc. Can.* **51**: 287–97.

HÉDERVÁRI, PÉTER (1963). Volcanological considerations in the calculations of the energy necessary to produce the craters of the moon. *Bull. volcan.* **25**: 387–90.

HEIDE, FRITZ (1964). *Meteorites.* Translated by Edward Anders. Chicago, Ill.: University of Chicago Press.

HEY, M. H. (1963). *Meteorites and life.* (In Porter, J. G. and Moore, Patrick, editors (1963): *Yearbook of astronomy, 1963.* New York: Norton).

HOFFMEISTER, C. (1948). *Meteorströme.* Leipzig: Weimar.

HOWARD, EDWARD (1802). *Experiments and observations on certain stony and metalline substances, which at different times are said to have fallen on the earth; also on various kinds of native iron.* (From the *Philosophical Transactions*) London: W. Bulmer.

IMOTO, SUSUMU & HASEGAWA, ICHIRO (1958). Historical records of meteor showers in China, Korea, and Japan. *Smithsonian Contributions to Astrophysics,* **2** 6: 131–44.

JOHNSON, DOUGLAS WILSON (1942). *The origin of the Carolina bays.* New York: Columbia University Press.

JONES, R. V. (1962). Sub-acoustic waves from large explosions. *Nature, Lond.* **193**: 229–32.

KAISER, T. R., editor (1955). *Meteors.* London & New York: Pergamon Press.

KING, EDWARD (1796). *Remarks concerning stones said to have fallen from the clouds, both in these days, and in antient times.* London: G. Nicol.

KRINOV, E. L. (1960). *Principles of meteorites.* Translated from the Russian by Irene Vidzinnas. New York: Pergamon Press.

KUIPER, G. P., *et al.* (1958). Survey of asteroids. *Astrophys. J.* Supplement Series no. 32 **3**: 289–428.

LAPAZ, LINCOLN (1951). Injuries from falling meteorites. *Pop. Astr.* **59**: 433–39.

——— (1952). *Meteoroids, meteorites, and hyperbolic meteoritic velocities.* (In White, Clayton S. & Benson, Otis O., Jr., editors (1952): *Physics and medicine of the upper atmosphere.* Albuquerque, N. M.: University of New Mexico Press.)

——— (1958). The effects of meteorites upon the earth (including its inhabitants, atmosphere and satellites). *Adv. Geophys.* **4**: 217–350.

——— (1959). Some aspects of meteoritics. *New Mexico Quarterly* **29** 2: 169–208.

——— & LAPAZ, JEAN (1961). *Space nomads: meteorites in sky, field, & laboratory.* New York: Holiday House.

LEY, WILLY (1937). How the moon got its craters. *Nat. Hist., N. Y.* **39**: 275–79.

——— (1963). *Watchers of the sky.* New York: Viking Press.

LINDEMANN, F. A. & DOBSON, G. M. B. (1923). A theory of meteors, and the density of temperatures of the outer atmosphere to which it leads. *Proc. R. Soc.* Ser. A **102**: 411–37.

LIVY [Livius, Titus] (1935). *History of Rome.* Translated by James Brodie. Book I, Section 3. London: James Brodie.

LOVELL, A. C. B. (1954). *Meteor astronomy.* Oxford: Clarendon Press.

MASON, BRIAN (1962). *Meteorites.* New York & London: Wiley.

——— (1963). Organic matter from space. *Sci. Amer.* **208** 3: 43–49.

The Elements Rage

MEEN, V. BEN (1952). Solving the riddle of Chubb Crater. *Nat. geogr. Mag.* **101:** 1–32.

MEHL, ROBERT F. (1938). Iron from heaven. *Carnegie Magazine* **11** January: 241–46.

MENZEL, D. N. & BOYD, L. G. (1963). *World of the flying saucer.* New York: Doubleday and Co.

MERRILL, GEORGE P. (1958). The Meteor Crater of Canyon Diablo, Arizona: its history, origin, and associated meteoric irons. *Smithsonian Miscellaneous Collections* **50:** 461–98.

MIDDLEHURST, BARBARA M. & KUIPER, GERARD P., editors (1963). *The moon, meteorites and comets.* Chicago, Ill.: University of Chicago Press (The solar system—vol. 4).

MILLMAN, PETER M. (1959). The Meanook-Newbrook meteor observatories. *Jl. R. astr. Soc. Can.* **53:** 15–38.

———— (1962). Sous-commission pour normaliser la terminologie et les notations concernant les meteors. *Transactions Institute Astronomy University XIA—* Reports: 228–30.

MOORE, CARLETON B. (1962). *Researches on meteorites.* New York & London: Wiley.

MOORE, PATRICK (1963). *Survey of the moon.* New York: Norton.

NININGER, H. H. (1933). *Our stone-pelted planet.* Boston, Mass.: Houghton.

———— (1940). Some practical aspects of meteorites. *Pop. Astron.* **48:** 381–83.

———— (1943). The Eaton, Colorado, meteorite: introducing a new type. *Pop. Astron.* **51:** 273–80.

———— (1947). *Chips from the blasted moon.* El Centro, Calif.: Desert Press.

———— (1956). *Arizona's meteorite crater, past—present—future.* Sedona, Arizona: American Meteorite Museum.

———— (1959). *Out of the sky.* New York: Dover.

———— (1961). *Ask a question about meteorites.* Denver, Colo.: American Meteorite Laboratory.

———— (1963). *Meteorite distribution on the earth.* (In Middlehurst, Barbara M. & Kuiper, Gerard P., editors (1963): *The moon, meteorites and comets.* Chicago, Ill.: University of Chicago Press (The solar system—vol. 4).

O'CONNELL, EDNA (1965). *A catalog of meteorite craters and related features with a guide to the literature.* Santa Monica, Calif.: The Rand Corporation [typescript].

O'KEEFE, J. A., editor (1964). *Tektites.* Chicago, Ill.: University of Chicago Press.

OLIVIER, CHARLES P. (1925). *Meteors.* Baltimore, Md.: Williams & Wilkins.

OPIK, E. J. (1958). *Physics of meteor flight in the atmosphere.* New York: Interscience.

PALMER, H. P. (1965). The enigmatic quasars. *New Scient.* **25:** 16–19.

PANETH, FRITZ A. (1940). *The origin of meteorites.* Being the Halley Lecture delivered on 16 May 1940. Oxford: Clarendon Press.

———— (1964). Meteorites. *Encyclopaedia Britannica* **15:** 336–41.

PRESTON, F. W., *et al.* (1941). The Chicora (Butler County, Pa.) meteorite. *Proc. U. S. Natn. Mus.* **90:** 3111.

Prior, G. T. (1953). *Catalogue of meteorites* . . . 2nd ed. revised and enlarged by Max H. Hey. London: British Museum (Natural History).

Proctor, Mary (1926). *The romance of comets.* New York: Harper.

Reeds, Chester A. (1933). Comets, meteors, and meteorites. *Nat. Hist. N. Y.* **33:** 311–24.

Richter, Nikolaus B. (1963). *The nature of comets.* Translated and revised ed. by Arthur Beer. London: Methuen.

Rickard, T. A. (1941). The use of meteoric iron. *Jl. R. anthrop. Inst.* **71:** 55–66.

Robey, Donald H. (1960). An hypothesis on the slow moving green fireballs. *J. Br. interplanet. Soc.* **17:** 398–411.

Romig, Mary F. (1965). [History of meteoritics]. *Meteoritics* **2:** 5.

―――― (1965). *The scientific study of meteors in the 19th century.* Santa Monica, Calif.: The Rand Corporation [typescript].

―――― & Lamar, Donald L. (1963). *Anomalous sounds and electromagnetic effects associated with fireball entry.* Santa Monica, Calif.: The Rand Corporation. (Memorandum RM-3724-ARPA).

Roth, Günter D. (1962). *The system of minor planets.* London: Faber.

Salmon, W. H. (1939). Comets: history and science. *Chambers's Journal* **8:** 425–28.

Schmidt, J. F. J. (1878). *Charte der Gebirge des Mondes.* Berlin: Dietrich Reimer.

Sciama, D. W. (1964). Quasi-stellar objects. *Listener* **72:** 266–67.

Sears, Paul M. (1949). The man who grabbed a shooting star. *Nat. Hist., N. Y.* **58:** 166–67, 191.

Shand, S. J. (1947). *Eruptive rocks,* 3rd ed. New York & London: Wiley.

Shoemaker, Eugene M. (1960). *Penetration mechanics of high velocity meteorites, illustrated by Meteor Crater, Arizona.* Copenhagen: International Geological Congress (Report, XXI Session. Part XVIII).

―――― (1964). The moon close up. *Nat. geogr. Mag.* **126:** 690–707.

Spencer, L. J. (1932). Hoba (South-West Africa), the largest known meteorite. *Mineral Mag.* **23:** 1–18.

―――― (1933). Meteorite craters as topographical features on the earth's surface. *Geogr. J.* **81:** 227–48.

Stocking, Hobart E. (1944). Bombs from interstellar space. *Nat. Hist., N. Y.* **53:** 28–32.

Symposium on the Astronomy and Physics of Meteors at Smithsonian Astrophysics Observatory, 1961 (1963). *Proceedings.* Washington, D. C.: Smithsonian Institute (Smithsonian Contributions to Astrophysics—vol. 7).

Thornton, Francis H. (1947). Things do happen on the moon. *J. Brit. astron. Soc.* **57:** 143–44.

Thorpe, A. N., *et al.* (1963). Magnetic and chemical investigations of iron in tektites. *Nature, Lond.* **197:** 836–84.

Urey, Harold C. (1962). Origin of life-like forms in carbonaceous Chondrites. *Nature, Lond.* **193:** 1119–23 [and other articles on life-forms in meteorites in same issue].

Voas, Robert B. (1962). John Glenn's three orbits in *Friendship 7. Nat. geogr. Mag.* **121:** 792–827.

The Elements Rage   [*320*]

WATSON, FLETCHER G. (1956). *Between the planets,* rev. ed. Cambridge, Massachusetts: Harvard University Press.

WHIPPLE, F. J. W. (1930). The great Siberian meteor and the waves, seismic and aerial, which it produced. *Quart. J. R. met. Soc.* **56:** 287–304.

———— (1934). On phenomena related to the great Siberian meteor. *Quart. J. R. met. Soc.* **60:** 505–13.

WHIPPLE, FRED L. (1951). *Meteors as probes of the upper atmosphere* (in Malone, Thomas Francis, editor (1951): *Compendium of meteorology.* Boston, Mass.: American Meteorological Society).

———— (1952). *Meteoritic phenomena and meteorites* (in White, Clayton S. & Benson, Otis O. Jr., editors (1952): *Physics and medicine of the upper atmosphere.* Albuquerque, N. M.: University of New Mexico Press).

———— (1963). On meteoroids and penetration. *J. geophy. Res.* **68:** 4929–39.

WOOD, J. A. (1963). *Physics and chemistry of meteorites* (in Middlehurst, Barbara M. & Kuiper, Gerard P., editors (1963): *The moon, meteorites and comets.* Chicago, Ill.: University of Chicago Press (The solar system—vol. 4).

ZIMMER, G. F. (1916). The use of meteoritic iron by primitive man. *J. Iron & Steel Inst.* **94** (2): 306–56.

For bibliographies, see:

BROWN, HARRISON, editor (1953). *A bibliography of meteorites.* Chicago, Ill.: University of Chicago Press. And MOORE, CARLETON B. (1962), and O'CONNELL, EDNA (1965), above.

For current references, see:

Mineralogical Abstracts, published jointly by The Mineralogical Society of Great Britain, London, and The Meteorological Society of America, Ann Arbor, Michigan.

Earthquakes

ALDEN, WILLIAM C. (1928). Landslide and flood at Gros Ventre, Wyoming. *Trans. Amer. Inst. min. (metall.) Engrs* **76:** 347–61.

ANON. (1959). Building in earthquake areas. *Overseas Bldg Notes October.* No. 63: 1–22.

ANON. (1962). *The Agadir, Morocco earthquake February 29, 1960.* New York: Committee of Structural Steel Producers of American Iron and Steel Institute.

BERG, GLEN V. & STRATTA, JAMES L. (1964). *Anchorage and the Alaska earthquake of March 27, 1964.* New York: American Iron and Steel Institute.

BERKMAN, S. C. & SYMONS, J. M. (1964). *The tsunami of May 22, 1960 as recorded at tide stations.* Washington, D. C.: U. S. Depart. of Commerce (Coast and Geodetic Survey).

BESTERMAN, THEODORE (1962). *Voltaire essays and another.* London: Oxford University Press.

BILLINGS, L. G. (1915). Some personal experiences with earthquakes. *Nat. geogr. Mag.* **27:** 57–71.

Bibliography

BIRD, ROLAND T. (1943). Recording earthquakes. *Nat. Hist., N. Y.* **52:** 24–29, 42–43.

BOESEN, VICTOR HUGO (1941). America's greatest earthquake. *Coronet* **9:** 75–80.

BOONE, ANDREW R. (1933). Scientists unite in greatest war on earthquakes. *Pop. Sci. Mon.* **122** May: 11–13, 104.

BRETT, WILLIAM BAILLIE (1935). *A report on the Bihar Earthquake and on the measures taken in consequences thereof up to the 31st December 1934.* Patna.

BULLEN, K. E. (1963). *An introduction to the theory of seismology,* 3rd ed. Cambridge: Cambridge University Press.

BUSCH, NOEL FAIRCHILD (1963). *Two minutes to noon.* New York: Simon & Schuster.

BYERLY, PERRY (1942). *Seismology.* New York: Prentice-Hall.

CALIFORNIA STATE EARTHQUAKE INVESTIGATION COMMISSION (1908–1910). *The California earthquake of April 18, 1906.* Report . . . Washington, D. C.: Carnegie Institution of Washington 2 vols.

CHAPIN, HENRY & SMITH, F. G. WALTON (1953). *The ocean river.* Philadelphia: Saunders.

CONFERENCE OF EXPERTS TO STUDY THE METHODS OF DETECTING VIOLATIONS OF A POSSIBLE AGREEMENT ON THE SUSPENSION OF NUCLEAR TESTS, GENEVA, JULY 1 TO AUGUST 21, 1958 (1958). *Report.* London: H.M.S.O.

DAILY NEWS-MINER, March 27, 1964. *Alaska earthquake disaster* [report and photographic survey].

DALY, REGINALD ALWORTH (1926). *Our mobile earth.* New York: Scribner.

———— (1938). *Architecture of the earth.* New York: D. Appleton-Century.

DAVIS, T. NEIL & SANDERS, NORMAN K. (1960). Alaska earthquake of July 10, 1958: intensity distribution and field investigation of northern epicentral region. *Bull. seismol. Soc. Amer.* **50:** 221–52.

DAVISON, CHARLES (1921). *A manual of seismology.* Cambridge: Cambridge University Press.

———— (1924). *A history of British earthquakes.* Cambridge: Cambridge University Press.

———— (1931). *The Japanese earthquake of 1923.* London: Thomas Murby.

———— (1936). *Great earthquakes.* London: Thomas Murby.

———— (1937). Luminous phenomena of earthquakes. *Discovery* **18:** 278–79.

———— (1938). The effects of earthquakes on animals. *Chambers's Journal* **7:** 263–65.

ECKEL, EDWIN B., editor (1958). *Landslides and engineering practice, by the Committee on Landslide Investigations.* Washington, D. C.: Highway Research Board (Special report—29).

EIBY, G. A. (1957). *About earthquakes.* New York: Harper.

ENOCK, C. R. (1950). Structural earthquake-proof principles for buildings. *J. Trans. Soc. Engrs.* **41:** 23–4.

FREEMAN, J. R. (1932). *Earthquake damage and earthquake insurance.* New York & London: McGraw-Hill.

GALANOPOULOS, A. G. (1960). Tsunamis observed on the coasts of Greece from antiquity to present time. *Annali di Geofisica* **13:** 369–86.

GEIKE, ARCHIBALD (1897). *Ancient volcanoes of Great Britain.* London: Macmillan 2 vols.

GRANTZ, ARTHUR, et al. (1964). *Alaska's Good Friday earthquake, March 27, 1964: a preliminary geologic evaluation.* Washington, D. C.: U. S. Dept. of the Interior (Geological Survey Circular—491).

GRAVES, WILLIAM P. E. (1964). Alaska earthquake: horror strikes on Good Friday. *Nat. geogr. Mag.* **126:** 112–39.

GREGORY, JOHN WALTER (1929). *Earthquakes and volcanoes.* London: Benn.

GUTENBERG, B. (1939). Tsunamis and earthquakes. *Bull. seismol. Soc. Amer.* **29:** 517–26.

—— & RICHTER, C. F. (1942). Earthquake magnitude, intensity, energy and acceleration. *Bull. seismol. Soc. Amer.* **32:** 163–91.

—— —— (1954). *Seismicity of the earth and associated phenomena,* 2nd ed. Princeton, N. J.: Princeton University Press.

HECK, NICHOLAS HUNTER (1936). *Earthquakes.* Princeton, N. J.: Princeton University Press.

—— (1947). List of seismic sea waves. *Bull. seismol. Soc. Amer.* **37:** 269–86.

—— (1958). Earthquake history of the United States. Part 1: *Continental United States and Alaska* (exclusive of California and Western Nevada). Revised ed. (through 1956) by R. A. Eppley. Washington, D. C.: U. S. Government Printing Office (No. 41–1).

HILL, M. N., editor (1962). *The sea.* Vol. 3: The earth beneath the sea: history. New York & London: Interscience.

HODGSON, JOHN (1964). *Earthquakes and earth structure.* Englewood Cliffs, N. J.: Prentice-Hall.

HOLMES, ARTHUR (1965). *Principles of physical geology,* 2nd rev. ed. London: Nelson.

HOLMSEN, GUNNAR (1936). De siste bergskred i Tafjord og Loen, Norge. *Svensk geogr. Arsb.* **12:** 171–90.

HOLMSEN, PER (1953). Landslips in Norwegian quick-clays. *Géotechnique* **3:** 187–200.

HOVEY, EDMUND OTIS (1923). *Earthquakes. Nat. Hist., N. Y.* **23:** 457–62.

HOWELLS, D. A. (1959). Structures to withstand earthquakes. *Engineering, Lond.* **187:** 346–49.

IACOPI, ROBERT (1964). *Earthquake country.* Menlo Park, Calif.: Lane Book Co. (Sunset book).

IMAMURA, A. (1937). *Theoretical and applied seismology.* Tokyo: Maruzen.

JACKSON, ROBERT (1960). *Thirty seconds at Quetta: the story of an earthquake.* London: Evans Brothers.

JAKOBSON, B. (1952). The land slide at Surte on the Göta River, September 29, 1950. *Proc. R. Swed. Geotech. Inst.* 5.

JAMES, WILLIAM (1906). On some mental effects of the earthquake. *Youth's Companion* **80:** 283–84.

JEFFREYS, SIR HAROLD (1950). *Earthquakes and mountains,* 2nd ed. rev. London: Methuen.

—— (1962). *The earth: its origin, history and physical constitution,* 4th ed. repr. with additions. Cambridge: Cambridge University Press.

JOHNSON, DOUGLAS WILSON (1919). *Shore processes and shoreline development.* New York & London: Wiley.

KENDRICK, SIR THOMAS D. (1956). *The Lisbon earthquake.* London: Methuen.

KERR, PAUL F. (1963). Quick clay. *Sci. Amer.* **209:** 132–42.

——— & LIEBLING, RICHARD S. (1963). *Glacial and post glacial quick clays.* Bedford, Mass.: Air Force Cambridge Research Laboratories (AFCRL—63—253).

KINGDON-WARD, F. (1951). Notes on the Assam earthquake. *Nature, Lond.* **167:** 130–31.

——— (1952). Caught in the Assam-Tibet earthquake. *Nat. geogr. Mag.* **101:** 402–16.

KINGDON-WARD, JEAN (1952). *My hill so strong.* London: Cape.

LANDES, KENNETH K. (1959). *Petroleum geology.* 2nd ed. New York & London: Wiley.

LEET, L. DON (1948). *Causes of catastrophe: earthquakes, volcanoes, tidal waves and hurricanes.* New York & London: McGraw-Hill.

LOVE, A. E. H. (1927). *A treatise on the mathematical theory of elasticity,* 4th ed. Cambridge: Cambridge University Press.

LUTTMAN-JOHNSON, H. (1898). The earthquake in Assam. *Journal of the Society of Arts* **46:** 473–95.

LYELL, SIR CHARLES (1875). *Principles of geology,* 12th ed. Edited by L. Lyell. London: John Murray 2 vols.

LYNCH, JOSEPH (1940). *Our trembling earth.* New York: Dodd, Mead and Company.

MACELWANE, JAMES BERNARD (1947). *When the earth quakes.* Milwaukee, Wisc.: Bruce Pub. Co.

MALLET, ROBERT (1853–1855). Catalogue of recorded earthquakes from 1606 B.C. to A.D. 1850. *Rep. Brit. Ass.* 1852–1854.

MATTHEWS, SAMUEL W. (1960). The night the mountains moved. *Nat. geogr. Mag.* **117:** 329–59.

MATUZAWA, TAKEO (1964). *Study of earthquakes.* Tokyo: Uno Shoten.

MELDOLA, RAPHAEL & WHITE, WILLIAM (1885). Report on the East Anglian earthquake of April 22nd, 1884. *Essex Field Club special memoirs* **1:** 223 p.

MERCALLI, GIUSEPPE (1902). Sulle modificazioni proposte alla scala sismica De Rossi-Forel. *Società Sismologica Italiana* **8:** 184–91.

MILLER, DON J. (1960). *Giant waves in Lituya Bay, Alaska.* Washington, D. C.: U. S. Government Printing Office (Geological Survey professional paper—354-C).

MILNE, JOHN (1911). A catalogue of destructive earthquakes. *Rep. Brit. Ass.* 1911.

——— (1939). *Earthquakes and other earth movements,* 7th ed. Revised by A. W. Lee. London: Kegan Paul.

MINTROP, L. (1930). *On the history of the seismic method for the investigation of underground formations and mineral deposits.* Hanover: Seismos G.m.b.H.

MOHOROVIČIĆ, A. (1909). Das Beben vom 8. x. 1909. *Godis. Izv. Kr. zem. Zav. Met. Geodin.* **9:** 1–63.

MOREIRA DE MENDONÇA, JOACHIM JOSEPH (1758). Historia universal dos terremotos . . . Lisbon.

MORSE, PHILIP M. (1938). This ball of clay—how old? *Technol. Rev.*

MUSYA, KINKITI (1934). On the luminous phenomena that accompanied the great

Sannku tsunami in 1933. *Bulletin Earthquake Research Institute, Tokyo.* Supplementary vol. **1:** 87–111.

NIDDRIE, DAVID (1962). When the earth shook. New York: Devin-Adair.

OLDHAM, R. D., *et al.* (1899). Report on the great earthquake of 12th June 1897. *Memoirs of the Geological Survey of India* **29.** [Entire issue devoted to this earthquake]

OLIVER, JACK (1959). Long earthquake waves. *Sci. Amer.* **200** 3: 131–43.

REEDS, CHESTER A. (1923). The Japanese earthquake explained. *Nat. Hist., N. Y.* **23:** 462–69.

——— (1934). Earthquakes. *Nat. Hist. N. Y.* **34:** 733–47.

REID, HARRY FIELDING (1911). The elastic rebound theory of earthquakes. *Bull. Dep. Geol. Univ. Calif.* **6:** 413–43.

——— (1914). The Lisbon earthquake of November 1, 1755. *Bull. seismol. Soc. Amer.* **4:** 53.

REUSCH, H. (1901). Nogle Optegnelser fra Vaerdalen. *Norg. geol. Unders.* **32:** 1–7, 218–23.

RICHTER, CHARLES F. (1935). An instrumental earthquake magnitude scale. *Bull. Seismol. Soc. Amer.* **25:** 1–32.

——— (1958). *Elementary seismology.* San Francisco, Calif.: W. H. Freeman.

ROBERTS, ELLIOTT B. (1961). History of a tsunami: [Alaskan tsunami of July 9, 1958]. *Rep. Smithson. Instn* 1960: 237–40.

ROSENQVIST, I. TH. (1953). Considerations on the sensitivity of Norwegian quickclays. *Géotechnique* **3:** 195–200.

SHARPE, C. F. STEWART (1938). *Landslides and related phenomena.* New York: Columbia University Press.

SHEPARD, FRANCIS P. (1963). *Submarine geology.* New York: Harper.

SKEMPTON, A. W. & NORTHEY, R. D. (1952). The sensitivity of clays. *Géotechnique* **3:** 30–53.

STEADMAN, EVAN (1963). *Earthquake: the story of Skopje.* London: Pictorial Charts Unit.

STEFFENS, R. J. (1957). *Earthquake-proof design in theory and practice: a selected bibliography.* Garston: Building Research Station (Library bibliography—no. 172).

STRONG, S. W. S. (1933). The Sponge Bay uplift, Gisborne, and the Hangaroa mud blowout. *N. Z. J. Sci. Tech.* **15:** 76–78.

STUBBS, PETER (1965). The new seismology. *New Scient.* **25:** 269–71.

TAZIEFF, HAROUN (1964). *When the earth trembles.* Tr. from the French by Patrick O'Brian. New York: Harcourt.

TERADA, TORAHIKO (1934). Luminous phenomena accompanying destructive seawaves. *Bulletin Earthquake Research Institute, Tokyo.* Supplementary vol. 1: 25–35.

——— (1931). On the luminous phenomena accompanying earthquakes. *Bulletin Earthquake Research Institute, Tokyo* 9: 225–55.

TILLOTSON, ERNEST (1940). Earthquakes. *Geogr. Mag., Lond.* **10:** 328–35.

——— (1951). The great Assam earthquake of August 15, 1950. *Nature, Lond.* **167:** 128–30.

Tsuboi, C., et al. (1962). *Prediction of earthquakes: progress to date and plans for future development*. Tokyo: Earthquake Research Institute, University of Tokyo.

Tsuya, H., editor (1950). *The Fukui earthquake of June 28, 1948*. Report of the Special Committee for the Study of the Fukui Earthquake. Tokyo: The Committee.

U. S. Geological Survey (1964). *The Hebgen Lake, Montana, earthquake of August 17, 1959*. Washington, D. C.: U. S. Government Printing Office (Geological Survey professional paper—435).

Vening Meinesz, Felix Andries (1964). *The earth's crust and mantle*. New York: Elzevier (Developments in solid earth geophysics—no. 1).

Wall, A. E. P. (1960). *The Big Wave, May 23, 1960*. Hilo, Hawaii: Hilo Tribune-Herald.

Wartnaby, J. (1957). *Seismology: a brief historical survey and catalogue of exhibits in the Seismological Section of the Science Museum*. London: H.M.S.O. (Geophysics handbooks no. 1).

Wellington, George (1933). Earthquake! *Chambers's Journal* **2**: 122–26.

Wood, H. O. & Heck, Nicholas Hunter (1961). Earthquake history of the United States. Part 2: *Stronger earthquakes of California and Western Nevada*. Revised ed. (through 1960) by R. A. Eppley. Washington, D. C.: United States Government Printing Office (No. 41-1).

———— & Neumann, F. (1931). Modified Mercalli intensity scale of 1931. *Bull. Seismol. Soc. Amer.* **21**: 277–83.

World Conference on Earthquake Engineering, Berkeley, California, June 1956 (1956). *Proceedings*. San Francisco, Calif.: Earthquake Engineering Research Institute.

Wright, Frank Lloyd (1932). *An autobiography*. New York: Longmans.

For bibliographies, see:

Ambraseys, N. N. (1963). *Earthquake engineering reference index*. London: Cementation Co.

Gutenberg & Richter (1954), above.

Tompkin, J. M. & Britt, S. H. (1951). *Landslides: a selected annotated bibliography*. Washington, D. C.: Highway Research Board (Bibliography—10).

For current references, see:

Publications of the Dominion Observatory, Ottawa, and *Geological Abstracts*, published by the Geological Society of America.

Volcanoes

Anderson, Robert, et al. (1965). Electricity in volcanic clouds. *Science*, Washington, D. C. **148**: 1179–89.

Barth, Tom. F. W. (1950). *Volcanic geology, hot springs, and geysers of Iceland*. Washington, D. C.: Carnegie Institution of Washington (Publication—no. 587).

BENNETT, J. G. (1963). Geophysics and human history. *Systematics* **1**: 127–56.

BENSON, WILLIAM E. (1961). Drilling beneath the deep sea. *Rep. Smithson. Instn:* 397–403.

BOEHM, GEORGE A. W. (1964). The alchemy of ultrahigh pressure. *Fortune* October.

BORDET, P., *et al.* (1963). Contribution à l'étude volcanologique du Katmai et de la Vallée des Dix Mille Fumées (Alaska). *Mem. Soc. belge Géol. Ser. 8° 7.*

BROOKS, CHARLES F. (1935). *Why the weather?* rev. ed. New York: Harcourt.

BULLARD, FRED MASON (1962). *Volcanoes, in history, in theory, in eruption.* Austin, Texas: University of Texas Press.

BULLEN, K. E. (1963). *An introduction to the theory of seismology,* 3rd ed. Cambridge: Cambridge University Press.

CARRINGTON, R. C. (1936). *Pompeii.* Oxford: Clarendon Press.

COLEMAN, SATIS NARRONA (1946). *Volcanoes old and new.* Toronto: Longmans, Green.

COLTON, F. BURROWS (1952). Our home-town planet, earth. *Nat. geogr. Mag.* **101**: 116–39.

DAMMERMAN, K. W. (1929). *Krakatan's new fauna (In Krakatan* (1929). Batavia-Bandoeng).

DANA, J. D. (1890). *Characteristics of volcanoes, with contributions of facts and principles from the Hawaiian Islands.* New York: Dodd, Mead & Co.

DAY, A. L. & ALLEN, E. T. (1925). *The volcanic activity and hot springs of Lassen Peak.* Washington, D. C.: Carnegie Institution of Washington (Publication— no. 360).

DIETZ, ROBERT S. (1954). The explosive birth of Myojin Island. *Nat. geogr. Mag.* **105**: 117–28.

DOWNEY, FAIRFAX (1938). *Disaster fighters.* New York: Putnam's Sons.

ERSKINE, WILSON FISKE (1962). *Katmai.* New York: Abelard-Schuman.

FLORES, TEODORO (1948). *El Parícutin.* Mexico: Imprenta Universitaria (Estudios Volcanologicos).

FOSHAG, WILLIAM F. (1954). The life and death of a volcano [Parícutin]. *Geogr. Mag., Lond.* **27**: 159–68.

FOX, SIDNEY W. (1965). A theory of macromolecular and cellular origins. *Nature, Lond.* **205**: 328–39.

FURNEAUX, RUPERT (1964). *Krakatoa.* Englewood Cliffs, N. J.: Prentice-Hall.

GALANOPOULOS, ANGELOS G. (1963). Die Deukalionische Flut aus geologischer Sicht. *Das Altertum* **9** 1: 3–7.

———— (1964). Die ägyptischen Plagen und der Auszug Israels aus geologischer Sicht. *Das Altertum* **10** 3: 131–38.

GEIKIE, SIR ARCHIBALD (1897). *Ancient volcanoes of Great Britain . . .* London: Macmillan 2 vols.

GONZÁLEZ, R., *et al.* (1947). The Birth of Parícutin. *Rep. Smithson. Instn* 1946: 223–24.

GORSHKOV, G. S. (1959). Gigantic eruption of the Bezymianny volcano. *Bull. volcan.* **20**: 77–109.

GREEN, JAMES A. (1944). Parícutin: the cornfield that grew a volcano. *Nat. geogr. Mag.* **84**: 129–64.

GREGORY, J. W. (1929). *Earthquakes and volcanoes.* London: Benn.

GRIGGS, ROBERT FISKE (1922). *The valley of ten thousand smokes.* Washington, D. C.: National Geographic Society.

GRUENING, ERNEST (1963). Lonely wonders of Katmai. *Nat. geogr. Mag.* **123:** 800–31.

GUTENBERG, B. & RICHTER, C. F. (1954). *Seismicity of the earth and associated phenomena,* 2nd ed. Princeton, N. J.: Princeton University Press.

HÉDERVÁRI, PÉTER (1963). On the energy and magnitude of volcanic eruptions. *Bull. volcan.* **25:** 373–85.

HEDWORTH, W. A. (1936). Exploiting the volcano. *Chambers's Journal* **5:** 662–64.

HEILPRIN, ANGELO (1904). *The tower of Pelée.* Philadelphia: Lippincott.

———— (1906). The shattered obelisk of Mount Pelée. *Nat. geogr. Mag.* **17:** 465–74.

———— (1908). *The eruption of Pelée: a summary and discussion of the phenomena and their sequels.* Philadelphia: Geographical Society of Philadelphia.

HILL, ROBERT T. (1902). Report . . . on the volcanic disturbances in the West Indies. *Nat. geogr. Mag.* **13:** 223–67.

HOLMES, ARTHUR (1965). *Principles of physical geology,* 2nd revised ed. London: Nelson.

HOVEY, EDMUND OTIS (1902). The eruptions of La Sonfrière, St. Vincent, in May, 1902. *Nat. geogr. Mag.* **13:** 444–59.

INTERNATIONAL VOLCANOLOGICAL ASSOCIATION (1951–). *Catalogue of the active volcanoes of the world including solfatara fields.* Naples: International Volcanological Association.

JAGGAR, THOMAS AUGUSTUS (1921). Experiences in a volcano observatory. *Nat. Hist., N. Y.* **21:** 337–55.

———— (1945). *Volcanoes declare war.* Honolulu: Paradise of the Pacific Ltd.

———— (1949). Steam blast volcanic eruptions. *Hawaiian Volcano Observatory,* 4th Special Report.

JEFFREYS, SIR HAROLD (1962). *The earth: its origin, history and physical constitution.* 4th ed. repr. with additions. Cambridge: Cambridge University Press.

JUDD, JOHN W. (1893). *Volcanoes: what they are and what they teach,* 5th ed. London: Kegan Paul.

KAEMPFFERT, WALDEMAR (1943). Volcano bombing: block-busters might set off craters in Italy and Japan. *New York Times,* June 20.

KENNAN, GEORGE (1902). *The tragedy of Pelée.* New York: Outlook Company.

KOSTER, A. L. (1956). City of the dead. *Nat. Hist., N. Y.* **65:** 412–15.

LEET, L. DON (1948). *Causes of catastrophe: earthquakes, volcanoes, tidal waves and hurricanes.* New York & London: McGraw-Hill.

LEY, WILLY (1941). *Days of creation.* New York: Viking Press.

LONGWELL, CHESTER R. (1937). *Outlines of geology.* New York & London: Wiley.

LYELL, SIR CHARLES (1875). *Principles of geology,* 12th ed. Edited by L. Lyell. London: John Murray 2 vols.

MCBIRNEY, ALEXANDER R. (1963). Factors governing the nature of submarine volcanism. *Bull. volcan.* **26:** 455–69.

MACKAY, MARGARET (1964). *Angry island: the story of Tristan da Cunha (1506–1963).* Chicago, Ill.: Rand McNally.

MILLER, LOIS MATTOX (1943). *Pan-American Magazine,* October.

MOHOROVIČIĆ, A. (1909). Das Beben vom. 8. x. 1909. *Godis. Izv. Kr. zem. Zav. Met. Geodin.* **9:** 1–63.

NOE-NYGAARD, ARNE a1940). *Sub-glacial volcanic activity in ancient and recent times.* Translated by W. E. Calvert. Copenhagen: I Kommission Hos. H. Hagerups Forlag (Folia Geographica Danica—Tom. 1, no. 2).

PADANG, MAUR NEUMANN VAN (1951). *Catalogue of the active volcanoes of Indonesia.* Naples: International Volcanological Association (Catalogue of the active volcanoes of the world—part 1) [Krakatoa].

PARSONS, WILLARD HALL (1940). Volcanoes in the making. *Sci. Dig.* **8** July: 35–38.

PAUL, WILLIAM, & WARSCHAUER, DOUGLAS M. (1963). *Solids under pressure.* New York: McGraw-Hill.

PERRET, FRANK A. (1924). *The Vesuvius eruption of 1906: study of a volcanic cycle.* Washington, D. C.: Carnegie Institution of Washington (Publication—no. 339).

——— (1935). *The eruption of Mount Pelée 1929–1932.* Washington, D. C.: Carnegie Institution of Washington (Publication—no. 458).

——— (1937). What to expect of a volcano. *Nat. Hist., N. Y.* **39:** 99–105.

PLINY THE YOUNGER (1915). *Letters.* With an English translation by William Melmoth, revised by W. M. L. Hutchinson. London: Heinemann (The Loeb classical library.)

POUGH, FREDERICK H. (1943). Parícutin is born. *Nat. Hist., N. Y.* **52:** 134–42.

——— (1944). Parícutin comes of age. *Nat. Hist., N. Y.* **53:** 342–49.

——— (1948). Parícutin has a birthday. *Nat. Hist., N. Y.* **57:** 206–08.

REEDS, CHESTER A. (1928). Volcanoes in action. *Nat. Hist., N. Y.* **28:** 302–17.

——— (1933). The volcano museum on Mont Pelée. *Nat. Hist., N. Y.* **33:** 31–40.

REES, T. IFOR (1943). Birth of a volcano [Parícutin]. *Geogr. Mag., Lond.* **9:** 147–51.

RICHARDS, ADRIAN F. & WALKER, LEWIS WAYNE (1954). Operation cremation: a personal account of the dramatic first landing on a new volcano [El Bonquerón] in the Pacific . . . *Nat. Hist., N. Y.* **63:** 56–65.

RITTMANN, A. (1963). *Les volcans et leur activité.* Edition française à partir de l'originale, établie et introduite par Haroun Tazieff. Paris: Masson.

——— (1962). *Volcanoes and their activity.* Translated from the second German edition by E. A. Vincent. New York: Interscience.

ROSS, J. T. (1816). Narrative of the effects of the eruption from the Tambora Mountain in the island of Sumbawa, on the 11th and 12th of April 1815. *Verhandelingen van her Bataviaasch Genootschap van Kunsten en Wetenschappen* **8.**

RUSSELL, ISRAEL C. (1902). The recent volcanic eruptions in the West Indies. *Nat. geogr. Mag.* **13:** 267–85.

——— (1902). Volcanic eruptions on Martinique and St. Vincent. *Nat. geogr. Mag.* **13:** 415–36 bibliog.

SAPPER, KARL (1931). Volcanoes, their activity and their causes. *Bull. natn. Res. Coun., Wash.* February. No. 77: 1–33.

SCHMIDT, JOHANN F. J. (1874). *Vulkanstudien, Santorin 1866 bis 1872.* Leipzig.

SCHULZ, PAUL E. (1952). *Geology of Lassen's landscape.* Mineral, Calif.: Lassen Volcanic National Park.

Bibliography [*329*]

Serviços Geológicos de Portugal (1959). *Le volcanisme de l'Ile de Faial et l'éruption du volcan de Capelinhos.* Lisbon: Serviços Geológicos de Portugal (Memória no. 4—nova série).

Shand, Samuel James (1947). *Eruptive rocks* . . . Revised 3rd ed. New York & London: Wiley.

Simpich, Frederick, Jr. (1960). Fountain of fire in Hawaii. *Nat. geogr. Mag.* **117:** 303–27.

Stehn, Ch. E. (1929). *The geology and volcanism of the Krakatan group* (In Krakatan (1929): Batavia-Bandoeng).

Stocking, Hobart E. (1943). The greatest explosion of all time. *Nat. Hist., N. Y.* **51:** 236–39, 244.

Symons, G. J., editor (1888). *The eruption of Krakatoa, and subsequent phenomena.* Report of the Krakatoa Committee of the Royal Society. London: Trübner.

Symposium on Prediction of Volcanic Eruption and Relation Between Magmas and Nature of Volcanic Eruptions, Tokyo, May 1962 (1962–3. Proceedings. *Chron. U.G.G.I.* Nos. 43 & 48.

Takashashi, Taro, & Bassett, William A. (1965). The composition of the earth's interior. *Sci. Amer.* **212:** 100–8.

Tazieff, Haroun (1962). *Volcanoes.* Englewood Cliffs, N. J.: Prentice-Hall (Symbol series).

Thorarinsson, Sigurdur (1953). Some new aspects of the Grímsvötn problem. *J. Glaciol.* **2:** 267–74.

——— (1958). *The Öraefajökull eruption of 1362.* Reykjavík: Nátúrugripasafn Íslands (Acta Naturalia Islandica—V. II, no. 2).

——— (1964). *Surtsey: the new island in the North Atlantic.* Reykjavík: Almenna Bókafélagid.

——— (1965). Surtsey: island born of fire. *Nat. geogr. Mag.* **127:** 713–26.

Thoroddsen, Thorvaldr (1925). *Die Geschichte der isländischen Vulkane* . . . Copenhagen. (Mémoires de l'Académie Royale des Sciences et des Lettres de Danemark. Section des Sciences. Sér. 8 tom. 9.)

Trask, Parker D. (1943). The Mexican volcano Parícutin. *Science* **98:** 501–505.

Tyrrell, G. W. (1931). *Volcanoes.* New York: Holt.

Van Leeuwen, W. M. Docters (1929). *Krakatan's new flora (In Krakatan (1929). Batavia-Bandoeng).*

Vening Meinesz, Felix Andries (1964). *The earth's crust and mantle.* New York: Elzevier (Developments in solid earth geophysics—no. 1).

Verbeek, R. W. M. (1885–1886). *Krakatau.* Batavia: Imprimerie de l'état.

Wexler, Harry (1952). Volcanoes and world climate. *Sci. Amer.,* April.

Wurtzburg, Charles Edward (1954). *Raffles of the eastern isles* . . . Toronto Musson Book Company.

For bibliography, see:
Bullard, Fred Mason (1962), above.
Rittman, A. (1962), above.

For current references, see:
Geological Abstracts, Washington (U. S. Geological Survey).

Index

Index

Earthquakes—*Continued*
  recording of, 203–205
  rivers flowing backward in, 212
  safety measures in, 224–225
  sand geysers with, 212
  seaslides with, 228–229
  soil compression with, 212
  tectonic warping with, 217
  tsunami with, 229–234
    See also Tsunami
  types of, 202
  vertical motion in, 208, 213, 217
  warnings of, 221–222
East Indies, tektites in, 185
Eddystone Lighthouse, 11
Egypt, annual rainfall in, 150
Electrical activity, giant storms with, 124
  as lightning, 119
    See also Lightning
  tornadoes with, 67, 124
Energy release, from earthquakes, 206, 217, 220
  from meteoroids, 175, 199
  from quasars, 192
  in thunderstorms, 119, 126
  from volcanoes, 252, 255–256
Energy scale, 275–283
England, annual rainfall in, 150
  avalanches in, 106
  ball lightning in, 135, 136
  British Meteorological Office in, 2, 63, 95, 136
  color of lightning in, 124
  earthquakes in, 217–218
  fatalities from lightning in, 143
  floods in, 146, 147–148
  fulgurites in, 131
  hailstorms in, 88
  inland floods in, 153–155
  lightning damage in, 130, 133
  meteorites in, 172, 181
  multiple-stroke lightning in, 123
  rainfalls in, 150, 151–152, 153
  seismographic records in, 194, 200
  showers of organic matter in, 79
  snowfall in, 98, 99

England—*Continued*
  thunderstorm days in, 123
  thunderstorms in, 123, 126
  tornadoes in, 62–66
  windstorms in, 10–11
Epicenter, of earthquakes, 206
Erg, definition of, 275
Etna volcano, 256

Falcon Island, 253
Falkland Islands, peat flow in, 226
Falls, with hailstorms, 86
  of meteorites, 180
  with waterspouts, 78–81
Fire, with earthquakes, 217, 224
  tornadoes from, 57–59
  with volcanoes, 245
Fireballs, 134–141
  from meteoroids, 174, 176
Fissures, with earthquakes, 207–208
  on volcanoes, 250
Flash floods, 152
Floods, 146–169
  benefits of, 169
  bibliography of, 313–316
  Boston molasses flood, 165
  control of, 158, 167, 168–169
  damage from, 146–150, 155, 157, 158, 162, 163, 166, 167
  from dams bursting, 160, 161, 202, 225
  early records of, 146–148, 165
  fatalities from, 148, 149
  financial loss from, 150, 157, 158, 162, 163, 167
  flash floods, 152
  from glacier burst, 150, 243
  with hurricanes, 22, 155–157
  inland, 146, 150
  inundation, 146
  from rainfall, 150–155
  sporadic, 146
  winds with, 147, 148
Florida, hurricanes in, 6, 8, 18, 19, 22, 27, 37
  National Hurricane Center in, 34
  rainfalls in, 152

Heat—*Continued*
  and thunder formation, 124
  and tornado formation, 57–59
Heat lightning, 126–127
Hermes asteroid, 193
Hilda, hurricane, 2
Hoba West meteorite, 180
Holland, dykes in, 147
  earthquake affecting, 206–207
  floods in, 147, 148–150
  tornadoes in, 64
Hurricanes, 1–38
  affecting history, 11, 12, 16, 37–38
  average life of, 6
  barometric pressure in, 9
  benefits from, 37
  bibliography of, 288–294
  control of, 34–35
  destruction from, 4, 7, 16–21, 33
  early records of, 2–3
  energy released by, 6
  extra-tropical, 5
  eye of, 8–9
  fatalities from, 4, 11–12, 15–16, 19,
    21, 26, 29, 33
  financial loss from, 4, 11, 19, 21, 33
  flights through, 9
  floods with, 22, 155–157
  formation of, 4–5
  Great Hurricane of 1780, 13–14, 27–
    29
  heat released in, 6
  height of waves in, 13
  location of, 4, 12
  movement of, 5–6
  naming of, 33
  National Hurricane Center, 34
  noise of, 12
  rainfall in, 21–22, 37, 151
  safety rules for, 36
  seeding of, 34
  shape of, 6
  ships in, 12–16
  signs of, 6
  storm surges in, 23, 26, 29
  warning services for, 31–33
  waterspouts with, 72

Hurricanes—*Continued*
  wave action in, 22–27
  wind speed in, 2, 7
    See also Typhoons
Hwang-Ho, flooding of, 166–167
Hypernovae, 192

Ice, volcanoes erupting beneath, 150,
    243
Ice avalanches, 102, 106, 111–113
Ice crystals, 119
Ice meteorites, 185
Iceland, volcanic island near, 253, 254,
    264
  volcanoes in, 256
Icelandic volcanic eruptions, 242–243
Ida, hurricane, 9
Ignimbritic eruptions, 250
Illinois, tornadoes in, 50, 61
India, early theories of earthquakes in,
    201
  earthquakes in, 218
  floods in, 166
  hailstorms in, 84, 91, 92
  meteorites in, 172
  showers of organic matter in, 79
  typhoons in, 30
Indian Ocean, rainfall in, 152
Indiana, tornadoes in, 61
Indonesia, tornadoes in, 57
  volcano in, 251
Inundations. *See* Floods
Ione, hurricane, 33
Iowa, hailstorm in, 91
  meteoroid fall in, 182
Ireland, meteorite in, 181
  peat flows in, 226
Iron, meteoritic, 186
Islands, volcanic, 252–253
Italy, avalanches in, 109
  ball lightning in, 134
  earthquakes in, 207, 213, 225
  hail prevention in, 94, 95
  lightning damage in, 130
  meteorites in, 172
  thunderstorm in, 122

Index   .

Lightning—*Continued*
  safety measures for, 132, 144–145
  sheet, 127
  speed of, 121
  streak, 126
  and streamers from earth, 121
  with tornadoes, 43, 56, 65, 124
  types of, 126–128
  with volcanoes, 119, 235, 244, 254, 264, 265
  warning devices for, 144
  wildfire, 127
  zig zag path of, 121
Lights, with earthquakes, 215–217
Lisbon, earthquake in, 206–207, 210
Louisiana, hurricane in, 29–30

Magma in volcanoes, 202, 238, 239
Magnetism, from lightning, 133
Mantle of earth, 237
Mare Imbrium, 191, 192
Marge, hurricane, 9
Martinique, volcano in, 243–250
Maryland, rainfall in, 152
Massachusetts, flood in, 157
  hailstones in, 86
  molasses flood in, 165
  tornadoes in, 52, 53, 60, 61, 124
  waterspouts near, 75
Mauna Loa, eruption of, 240
Mediterranean area, volcanoes in, 261–263
Mercalli earthquake intensity scale, modified, 205, 273–274
Meteor, definition of, 170
Meteor craters, 187–192
Meteorites, damage from, 184
  definition of, 170
  early use of, 186
  fatalities from, 183
  fossils in, 186
  of ice, 185
  kinds of, 184–185
  minerals in, 185–186, 188, 192
  naming of, 181, 184
  seismic sea waves from, 194

Meteorites—*Continued*
  value of, 185
Meteoroids, 170–200
  accounts of falls, 181–184, 196
  angle of fall of, 175
  bibliography of, 316–321
  collisions with, 186
  color of, 176
  cometary origin of, 172–173
  dating of, 173
  disbelief in, 78, 170–172
  dust from, 186–187, 199
  early records of, 170–171, 183, 186
  energy released from, 175, 199
  heat affecting, 177
  heat from, 196
  light from, 175, 176
  noise from, 179, 183, 184, 193, 196
  number of, 173, 175, 178, 179
  origin of, 172–173
  passage through atmosphere, 175, 176–177, 185, 189
  photography of, 174, 176
  possible dangers from, 193
  showers of, 172, 177–179, 180, 183
  size of, 175
  speed of, 175, 176
  sporadic, 172, 173
  types of, 172
  weight of, 180–181, 199
Mexico, hurricanes in, 18
  volcano near, 248
  volcanoes in, 254, 257–261, 262
Minerals, in meteorites, 185, 186, 188, 192
  molten, in earth, 237
  in volcanoes, 255
Minnesota, tornadoes in, 49
Mississippi, tornadoes in, 60, 61
Mississippi River, flooding of, 157–158
  levees on, 168–169
Missouri, earthquakes in, 207, 208, 212, 213
  floods in, 158
  tornadoes in, 43, 46, 47, 48, 53, 61, 67

Shooting stars, 173, 176
Showers, of meteorites, 180
    of meteors, 172, 177–179
    of organic matter, 78–81, 86
Siberia, early theories of earthquakes in, 201
    meteoroid explosion in, 194–200
    tsunami in, 232
Sicily, earthquakes in, 218, 224
    volcanoes near, 241
Siderites, 184
Siderolites, 184
Singapore, annual rainfall in, 150
Slides or flows, 226
Snow, air in, 98, 111
    benefits of, 111
    fatalities from, 99
    formation of, 96
    ice in, 98
    layer of "ball bearings," 106
    record depths of, 98–99
    specific gravity of, 98
    weight of, 99
    See also Avalanches
Snow crystals, 96–98
    artificial, 96
    depth-hoar, 106
    hexagonal, 97
    needle, 97
    number of, in storms, 98
    rate of fall of, 98
    shape of, 97
Snowflakes, aggregates of, 98
    formation of, 98
    rate of fall of, 98
Solano's hurricane, 37
Solfataric eruption, 243
Sound, speed of, 125
South Carolina, earthquake in, 224
    hurricanes in, 27, 29
    tornadoes in, 61
Speed, of avalanches, 102
    of jet stream, 7
    of lightning, 121
    of meteoroids, 175, 176
    of Peléean blasts, 247

Speed—*Continued*
    of quasars, 192
    of raindrops, 98
    of snowfall, 98
    of sound, 125
    of submarine slides, 229
    of tsunami, 229
    of wind. *See* Wind speed
Speedometer, for tornadoes, 46
Stars, shooting, 173, 176
    supernovae, 192
Steam, with volcanoes, 239, 243, 250, 256
Storm surges, in hurricanes, 23, 26, 29
    and sea floods, 146
Storm swell, 6
Streak lightning, 126
Streamers, and lightning formation, 121
Stromboli, volcanoes in, 241, 260
Strombolian eruptions, 259
Submarine slides, 228–229
Sumatra, volcano near, 263–267
Sunda Strait, volcano in, 263–267
Sunsets, after volcanic eruptions, 255–267
Supernovae, 192
Surges, storm, 23, 26, 29, 146
Surtsey, formation of, 253, 254, 264
Swan Island, hurricane in, 8
Sweden, earthquake affecting, 207
    light phenomenon in, 194
    meteorites in, 177
    quick clay slide in, 227
Swell, storm, 6
Swiss Snow and Avalanche Research Institute, 109
Switzerland, avalanches in, 109
    See also Avalanches
    building codes in, 99
    hail experiments in, 83, 95
    lightning studies in, 137
    rockslides in, 113

Tambora volcano, 250–252, 253, 254
Tektites, 184–185
Temperature. *See* Heat

Tennessee, lake formation in, 209
Texas, hailstorm in, 89
  hurricanes in, 7, 18, 22, 26, 31, 33
  meteorites in, 184
  tornadoes in, 41, 49, 50, 60, 61
Thunder, acoustics of, 126
  cause of, 119, 124
  compression waves from, 126
  continuous, 126
  horsepower expended in, 126
  mushrooms linked with, 131
  noise of, 124–125
  studies of, 124–126
Thunderclouds, electricity in, 120–121
  formation of, 119
  recharging in, 122
  simulated, 128
Thunderstorms, aircraft in, 84–85, 144
  energy released by, 119
  formation of, 119
  giant storms, 124
  hail with, 82, 119, 126
  locations of, 123
  noise in, 120, 122, 124–125
  parachutists in, 84, 86, 119–120
  size of, 119
  updrafts in, 78, 82, 84–85, 119, 124
  with volcanoes, 254
  yearly number of, 123
Tidal waves, 22, 229
Tillamook Rock, Oregon, 24
Tonga, as volcanic island, 252
Tornadoes, 39–70
  artificially induced, 57–58
  ascending air current in, 51
  bibliography of, 294–298
  causes of, 39
  characteristics of, 39
  cloud masses with, 42
  color of, 42
  conditions preceding, 41–42
  duration of, 41
  early records of, 60–61
  effects on trees, 55
  electrical activity with, 67, 124
  families of, 41, 63

Tornadoes—*Continued*
  fatalities from, 50–51, 53, 59, 61–63, 65
  financial loss from, 41, 59, 61–63, 65
  fire-induced, 57–59
  flights through, 49, 67
  funnel formation in, 42, 47–54
  hail with, 43, 86, 91
  length of path of, 41
  lightning with, 43, 56, 65, 124
  locations of, 39, 40, 41
  most destructive, 61–62
  movement of, 42
  noise of, 42–43
  non-American records of, 62–66
  number of, in United States, 59
  power in, 45
  pressure with, 46–47
  rending action of, 54–55
  reporting of, 59, 67
  safety rules for, 67–70
  season for, 40
  seeding of, 66
  shelters from, 70
  skipping action of, 42, 54, 55
  types of, 40
  updraft with, 47–51
  vacuum in, 51–54
  velocity of, 45–46
  with volcanoes, 254
  warning services for, 66–67
  water lifted by, 54, 61, 73, 81
  waterspouts with, 61, 73, 81
    See also Waterspouts
  width of, 41
Tristan da Cunha volcano, 239
Troposphere, 1
Tsunami, damage from, 230, 232
  from earthquakes, 217, 229–234
  height of, 232
  ships in, 233–234
  speed of, 229
  from volcanic eruptions, 266
Tycho crater, 191
Typhoons, 2, 30
  damage from, 15–16
  naming of, 34